TABLES

SIMPLIFIED DESIGN OF STRUCTURAL TIMBER

BOOKS BY HARRY PARKER

Simplified Design of Reinforced Concrete
Second Edition

Simplified Design of Roof Trusses for Architects and Builders
Second Edition

Simplified Design of Structural Steel
Second Edition

Simplified Design of Structural Timber
Second Edition

Simplified Engineering for Architects and Builders
Third Edition

Simplified Mechanics and Strength of Materials
Second Edition

Simplified Site Engineering for Architects and Builders
By Harry Parker and John W. MacGuire

Kidder-Parker Architects' and Builders' Handbook
By the late Frank E. Kidder and Harry Parker
Eighteenth Edition

Materials and Methods of Architectural Construction
By Harry Parker, the late Charles Merrick Gay, and John W. MacGuire
Third Edition

New York · London · Sydney

JOHN WILEY & SONS, INC.

SIMPLIFIED DESIGN OF STRUCTURAL TIMBER

SECOND EDITION

HARRY PARKER, M.S.

Emeritus Professor of Architectural Construction

School of Fine Arts

University of Pennsylvania

Second Edition

Third Printing, April, 1967

Library of Congress Catalog Card Number: 63-14074

Printed in the United States of America

To A. K. P.

PREFACE TO SECOND EDITION

The first edition of this book was published in 1948. Since then, numerous changes have been made in recommended allowable working stresses and design specifications for structural timber. In addition, new methods of construction have been introduced. In order to retain its usefulness, it has been necessary to revise and supplement nearly all of the material that appeared in the first edition. The entire book has been reset and many new problems, tables, and figures have been added.

As noted in the preface to the first edition, this is primarily a book for the use of those who are unfamiliar with the design of structural members and whose preparation in mathematics has been limited to high-school arithmetic and algebra. Most important of all, it is intended to be a useful book. Its purpose is not only for use in class rooms but in drafting rooms as well, as an aid in determining the size of timber members to resist loads. There are a number of safe-load tables. Some of the items for which safe-load tables are given are beams, girders, joists, rafters, plank floors and roofs, laminated floors, columns, bolted joints, split-ring connectors, steel rods, and stud walls. In addition to the magnitudes of the safe loads given in these tables, practical examples explain the mathematics and theory involved in computing these loads. The purpose of these examples is to avoid the temptation of using safe-load tables indiscriminately, without a full understanding of their use and limitations.

This book has been used in class rooms and in home study. In order to add to its value in explaining design methods, a great portion of the text is devoted to the solution of practical problems. These illustrative examples are followed by similar problems to be solved by the reader.

Some of the items that have been added to this new edition are conversion factors for beam tables, notched beams, an entirely new chapter on timber columns, eccentric loads on columns, bolted joints, new allowable stresses for split-ring connectors, trussed rafters, Teco-plate-type roof trusses, framing anchors, stud walls, glued laminated beams, and plywood gussets.

As in all books of this character, it is necessary to make use of engineering data and tables that have been established by engineering societies, universities, lumber associations, and testing laboratories. The research and experiments pursued by these bodies have resulted in the valuable knowledge that we now possess. I have drawn freely on this engineering data and I am grateful to the following associations and companies for their cooperation and for the privilege of reproducing their data and tables. They are the National Lumber Manufacturers Association, the Timber Engineering Company, the Forest Products Laboratory of the United States Department of Agriculture, the Southern Pine Association, and the West Coast Lumbermen's Association. These companies have always given freely of their engineering knowledge relating to their products.

Because of the inherent characteristics of wood, there are many factors involved in the design of certain structural timber members; some of the problems are complicated and their solution is tedious. It is the purpose of this book, however, to discuss principally the every-day problems, to present information that will enable the reader to determine properly the size of the usual timber members that occur so frequently in building construction, members whose sizes are established by the loads they support.

HARRY PARKER

High Hollow, Southampton
Bucks County, Pennsylvania
March 1963

PREFACE TO FIRST EDITION

This volume is the fifth of a series of elementary books relating to the design of structural members in buildings. The author has endeavored to explain as simply as possible the methods commonly used in determining proper timber sizes. This book deals primarily with wood members that support loads in buildings.

The material is arranged not only for classroom use but also for the many young architects and builders who desire a guide for home study. With this in mind, a major portion of the book is devoted to the solution of practical problems, which are followed by problems to be solved by the student. In addition to explanations of basic principles of mechanics involved in the design of members, numerous safe load tables have been included. These tables will enable one to select promptly members of proper size to use for given conditions.

Stress tables, properties of sections, and the tabulations of technical information pertinent to timber construction are included, thus making reference books unnecessary.

It is assumed that those who use this book have had no previous training. As in the previous books of the series, the use of advanced mathematics has been avoided, and a knowledge of high school arithmetic and algebra is all that is necessary to understand the mathematics involved.

In preparing material the author has employed the commonly used design procedures. He has drawn freely from recommendations and suggestions advanced by leading authorities on timber construction, namely, the Forest Products Laboratory of the United States Department of Agriculture, the National Lumber

Manufacturers Association, the Timber Engineering Company, the Southern Pine Association, the West Coast Lumbermen's Association, and the American Institute of Steel Construction. Grateful acknowledgment is made to these associations and agencies for their kindness in granting permission to reproduce tables and technical information. Without this cooperation a book of this nature would be impossible.

HARRY PARKER

High Hollow, Southampton
Bucks County, Pennsylvania
1948

CONTENTS

INTRODUCTION

The allowable unit stresses to be used in the design of structural members of any building material are modified from time to time. Structural timber is no exception. The designer must employ the allowable stresses and design procedures that are specified in his governing building code. Many municipal codes are revised infrequently and, in respect to lumber, often are not in agreement with the allowable stresses recommended by the National Lumber Manufacturers Association, as given in Table 3–1. Consequently, the stresses used throughout this book do not conform to any one code; many different stresses are employed.

For those who use this book for home study it is recommended that each chapter in the book be read in the same sequence in which it is presented. Very often the material found in one chapter is based on the subject matter previously given.

In solving problems, it will be found to be helpful first to jot down the given data and then to make diagrams showing the magnitudes and positions of the loads acting on a member. These sketches often indicate the design procedure to be followed.

One of the ways to avoid errors is to form the habit of writing the denomination of each quantity after its magnitude. Do not be content with merely the magnitude. For example, the solution of an equation may be 26,000. But what are the units? Is it 26,000 pounds or is it 26,000 pounds per square inch? Is a computed bending moment 250,000 foot-pounds or is it 250,000 inch-pounds?

If you do not own a slide rule, get one at the first opportunity. It is not necessary to become proficient in the use of all the scales that are given, but you will be amazed to find how indispensable the slide rule becomes for multiplication and division and for extracting the roots of numbers. When you purchase your slide rule, be sure to get a pamphlet of instructions. The use of the slide rule is readily acquired and you will be well paid for your efforts.

An abbreviation is a shortened form of a name or expression. Abbreviations are used in texts and tabulations; they should not be used in equations. They should never be used where the meaning would not be clear. If there is doubt concerning the sense or significance, the name should be spelled out.

Throughout this text abbreviations appear constantly. Those employed are as follows:

Names	*Abbreviations*
cubic foot	cu ft
cubic inch	cu in.
cubic yard	cu yd
foot	ft
foot-pound	ft-lb
inch	in.
inch-pound	in-lb
linear foot	lin ft
pound	lb
pounds per cubic foot	lb per cu ft
pounds per square foot	psf
pounds per square inch	psi
square foot	sq ft
square inch	sq in.
thousand pounds	kip
weight	wt
yard	yd

The same abbreviation is used for both the singular and the plural. Thus "one foot" and "eight feet" are written 1 ft and 8 ft, respectively.

CHAPTER 1

CHARACTERISTICS AND CLASSIFICATIONS OF WOOD

1–1. Timber Used for Structural Members. Unlike many building materials, wood is not a processed material but an organic material generally used in its natural state. The most important of the numerous factors that influence its strength are density, natural defects, and moisture content. Because of the defects and variations inherent in wood, it is impossible to assign working unit stresses with the degree of accuracy employed for steel or concrete. From an engineering point of view wood presents a greater complexity and variety of problems than many other structural materials.

The two groups of trees used for building purposes are the *softwoods* and the *hardwoods.* The softwoods, such as the pines or cypress, are coniferous or cone bearing, whereas the hardwoods, for example, the oaks and maples, have broad leaves. The terms softwood and hardwood are not a true indication of the degree of hardness of the various species of trees. The oaks, for instance, are very hard, whereas the basswood, also classed among the hardwoods, is extremely soft. On the other hand, the Southern yellow pine and Douglas fir, although classified as softwoods, are, in reality, two of our hardest woods. The two species of trees used most extensively in the United States for structural timbers are the southern pines and the Douglas firs, both of which are classified among the softwoods.

1–2. Growth of Trees. The trees used for lumber in this country are exogenous; that is, they increase in size by a growth of new wood on the outer surface under the bark. The cross section of a tree trunk reveals the layers of new wood that are formed annually.

These layers, called *annual rings*, are frequently composed of light and dark layers, the light ring, the springwood, being the wood grown in the spring of the year and the darker ring the summerwood. Thus the number of annual rings at the base of a tree indicates the age of the tree. The band of annual rings at the outer edge of the trunk is known as the *sapwood*. This band is frequently light colored. It contains the living cells and carries the sap from the roots to the leaves. As the tree ages, the sapwood gradually changes to *heartwood* and new sapwood is formed. The heartwood is usually darker in color than the sapwood. It is composed of the inactive cells and constitutes the major portion of the tree trunk. In general, the sapwood is light and more porous than the heartwood. The heartwood is denser and gives strength to the tree trunk. It is stronger and more durable than sapwood, but, if the wood is to be treated with a preservative, sapwood is desirable because of its absorptiveness.

The structure of trees consists of longitudinal bundles of wood fibers or cells. These small hollow fibers vary in shape and arrangement, affecting both appearance and physical properties of the various species. Smaller bands of fibers, called *medullary* or *wood rays*, radiate from the center of the tree trunk and serve to bind the structure together. The medullary rays are not distinctive in some species of trees but are pronounced in others; quarter-sawed oak, for example, shows these wood rays quite clearly.

1–3. Density of Wood. The difference in arrangement and size of the cell cavities and the thickness of the cell walls determine the specific gravity of various species of wood. The strength of wood is closely related to its density. The term *close grained* refers to wood with narrow, closely spaced annual rings. Certain woods, such as Douglas fir and Southern yellow pine, show a distinct contrast between springwood and summerwood, and the proportion of summerwood affords a visual basis for approximating strength and density. The weight of wood substance of all species is about 1.53 times the weight of water, but the wood cells contain air in varying degrees; hence the weights of species vary not only because of their density but also because of the moisture content. For purposes of computation, the average weight of wood is taken as 40 lb per cu ft.

1–4. Defects in Lumber. Any irregularity in wood that affects its strength or durability is a defect. Because of the natural characteristics of the material, there are several common defects inherent in wood which affect its strength, appearance, and durability. The most common defects are described below.

A *check* is a crack or lengthwise separation of the wood *across* the annual rings; it generally arises from the process of seasoning. See Fig. 1–1 (*b*).

A separation along the grain principally between the annual rings is called a *shake*. See Fig. 1–1 (*a*). A check or shake reduces the resistance to shear; hence members subjected to bending are directly affected by their presence. The strength of members in longitudinal compression is not greatly affected by shakes. Shakes produce weakness of bond between annual rings.

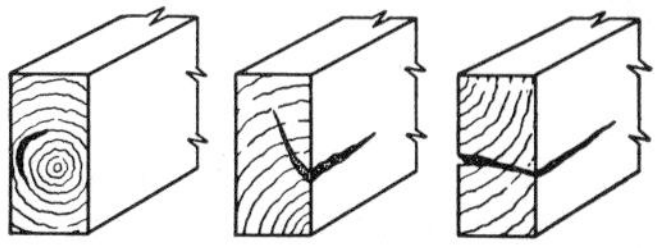

(*a*) Shake (*b*) Check (*c*) Split

FIG. 1–1

Decay is the disintegration of wood substance due to the action of wood-destroying fungi. Decay is easily recognized, for the wood becomes soft, spongy, or crumbly. The growth of fungi is encouraged by air, moisture, and a favorable temperature. If air is excluded, as for instance when wood is constantly submerged, fungi cannot exist. Wood is often impregnated with preservatives such as coal tar and creosote to prevent growth of fungi. The development of fungi is also prevented by the application of paint to the wood when it is dry. The extent of decay is generally difficult to determine: therefore any form of decay is usually prohibited in structural grades of wood.

Wane is the term applied to bark, or absence of wood or bark, on the edge or corner of a piece of sawed wood. The strength of a member may be affected by wane because the member has an inadequate cross-sectional area. In specifying, wane may be avoided by requiring material that is *square edge.*

A *knot* is a portion of a branch or limb incorporated in the body of a tree. There are several types and classifications of knots, and the strength of a member is affected by the size and location of the knots it may contain. The grading rules for structural timber are specific concerning the number and size of knots, and their presence is considered in determining the allowable working stresses.

A *pitch pocket* is an opening parallel to the annual rings containing pitch, either solid or liquid.

1–5. Seasoning of Wood. All green wood contains moisture, and the serviceability of wood is improved by its removal. The process of removing moisture from green wood is known as *seasoning*; it is accomplished by exposing it to the air or by heating it in kilns. Seasoned wood is stiffer, stronger, and more durable than green wood. The removal of moisture results in the shrinkage of the fiber cells; side fiber walls shrink more than end walls and sapwood more than heartwood. The shrinkage of wood fibers causes internal stresses which result in checking and warping, the effect of seasoning varying with the size of the timber. Softwoods generally shrink in seasoning more than hardwoods.

1–6. Classification of Softwood Lumber. *Lumber* is defined as the product of the saw and planing mill not further manufactured than by sawing, resawing, and passing lengthwise through a standard planing machine, crosscut to length and matched. There are three main classes of softwood lumber under the American lumber standards system:

1. Yard lumber.
2. Structural material (often referred to as *timber*).
3. Factory and shop lumber.

Yard lumber comprises the material less than 5 in. thick used for general building purposes. It is the lumber found most commonly in retail lumber yards. It includes boards and siding less than 2 in. thick, flooring, laths, shingles, pickets, finishing material, planks less than 4 in. thick, and joists 4 in. or less in thickness. Studding and the common sizes of joists and rafters are included in this classification.

Structural material includes lumber (except joists and planks) 5 in. or more in thickness and width. Material in this group is generally referred to as *timbers*. In general, structural material is used to support loads and is graded on the basis of strength and on use of the entire piece. Under the classification of structural material are (*a*) joists and planks (2 to 4 in. thick and 4 in. or more wide); (*b*) beams and stringers (5 in. or more thick and 8 in. or more wide); and (*c*) posts and timbers (5 x 5 in. and larger).

Factory and shop lumber includes factory plank graded for door, sash, and other cuttings $1\frac{1}{4}$ in. or more thick and 5 in. or more wide. It is used for general millwork and other industrial commodities.

Table 1–1 gives the classification of softwood lumber and the

TABLE 1–1. CLASSIFICATION OF SOFTWOOD LUMBER

				Grades
SOFTWOOD LUMBER. (This classification applies to rough or dressed lumber sizes given are nominal.)	YARD LUMBER (lumber less than 5 in. thick, intended for general building purposes grading based on use of the entire piece).	Finish (4 in. and under thick and 16 in. and under wide).		A. B. C. D.
		Common boards (less than 2 in. thick and 1 or more in. wide).		No. 1. No. 2. No. 3. No. 4. No. 5.
		Common dimension (2 in. and under 5 in. thick and 2 or more in wide).	Planks (2 in. and under 4 in. thick and 8 or more in. wide).	No. 1. No. 2. No. 3.
			Scantling (2 in. and under 5 in. thick and less than 8 in. wide).	No. 1. No. 2. No. 3.
			Heavy joists (4 in. thick and 8 or more in. wide).	No. 1. No. 2. No. 3.
	STRUCTURAL LUMBER (lumber 5 or more in. thick and wide, except joists and planks grading based on strength and on use of entire piece).	Joists and planks (2 to 4 in. thick and 4 or more in. wide).		
		Beams and stringers (5 or more in. thick and 8 or more in. wide).		
		Posts and timbers (5 x 5 in. and larger.		
	FACTORY AND SHOP LUMBER (grading based on area of piece suitable for cuttings of certain size and quality).	Factory plank graded for door, sash and other cuttings $1\frac{1}{4}$ or more in. thick and 5 or more in. wide.	Association grading rules should be referred to for standard grades and sizes.	
		Shop lumber graded for general cut-up purposes.		

Reproduced by permission of the U. S. Forest Products Laboratory.

grade names used by lumber manufacturers' associations for the various classes of material under the American lumber standards system.

1–7. Dimension Lumber. Dimension lumber is yard lumber 2 in. but less than 5 in. thick and 2 in. or more wide. It includes all yard lumber except boards, strips, and timbers. Planks, scantling, studding, and heavy joists are included under dimension lumber, and their sizes are given in Table 1–1. Dimension lumber is found in all lumber yards but frequently in only one of the general purpose construction woods such as spruce, pine, hemlock, or fir. The grades are No. 1 dimension, No. 2 dimension, and No. 3 dimension, the grading being based on strength, stiffness, and straightness. In general, dimension lumber is used for framing of buildings where common practice determines the size rather than special design in accordance with predetermined allowable stresses.

No. 1 dimension is a sound grade allowing knots limited in size, depending on the size of the piece. This grade is used for joists, rafters, and scaffolding in light framing. For buildings designed for heavy loads, the structural grades of joists, planks, and beams should be used in preference to dimension grades.

No. 2 dimension admits larger and coarser features than No. 1. It is used principally in medium-priced, light-frame construction.

No. 3 dimension includes all pieces falling below the No. 2 grade that are suitable for use in low-priced or temporary construction.

1–8. Structural Material. Structural material is very often referred to as *timbers*. Because the strength of a timber varies with the type of loading to which it is subjected and also because the effect of seasoning varies with the size, grading necessitates classifying timbers according to their *size and use*. Structural material, therefore, is classified as follows:

Beams and stringers. Nominal thickness, 5 in. or more; nominal widths, 8 in. or more; standard sizes, S1S, S1E, S2S, S4S, $\frac{1}{2}$ in. off each way.

Joists and planks. Nominal thicknesses, 2 in. to, but not including, 5 in.; nominal widths, 4 in. or more; standard thicknesses, S1S or S2S, $\frac{3}{8}$ in. off; standard widths, S1E or S2E, 4 in., $\frac{3}{8}$ in. off, and 6 in. or more, $\frac{1}{2}$ in. off.

Posts and timbers. Nominal sizes, 5 x 5 in. and larger; standard sizes, S1S, S1E, S2S, or S4S, $\frac{1}{2}$ in. off each way.

Dressing of rough lumber is specified as surfacing on 1 side (S1S), 2 sides (S2S), 1 edge (S1E), 2 edges (S2E), or both sides and both edges (S4S). By $\frac{1}{2}$ or $\frac{3}{8}$ in. off we mean $\frac{1}{2}$ or $\frac{3}{8}$ in. less than the full nominal dimension.

In general, the standard lengths of all three classes are in multiples of 2 ft except for the following odd lengths which are allowed:

2″ x 4″, 6″ x 8″	9′ and 11′
2″ x 8″	13′
2″ x 10″	13′ and 15′
8″ x 8″, 10″ x 10″, 12″ x 12″, 14″ x 14″, 16″ x 16″, 18″ x 18″	11′ and 13′
6″ x 16″, 6″ x 18″, 8″ x 16″, 8″ x 18″	15′ and 17′

CHAPTER 2

UNIT STRESSES

2–1. Forces. A *force* may be defined as that which changes or tends to change the state of rest or motion or causes a body, on which the force acts, to change its shape if held in place by another force or forces. In the United States the magnitude of a force is expressed in units of pounds. Frequently, in engineering problems, we use the term *kip*, a kip being a unit of 1000 lb (1000 pounds). Some building codes use the term *ton* in connection with the allowable bearing capacity of foundation beds. When so used, a ton is a unit of 2000 lb.

External forces with which we are particularly concerned are vertical downward forces due to gravity. Other forces to be considered result from the action of wind; these forces are not vertical.

2–2. Loads. A *load* is the magnitude of pressure or tension due to a superimposed weight. The two types most common in engineering problems are *concentrated loads* and *uniformly distributed loads.*

A *uniformly distributed load* is a load of uniform magnitude, for each unit of length, that extends over a portion or the entire length of a member. A floor joist that supports board flooring is an example of a beam supporting a uniformly distributed load. It should be noted, in the design of beams, that the load due to the weight of the beam itself constitutes a uniformly distributed load. A load exerted by a beam resting on a girder is an example of a *concentrated load.* In reality, the load from the beam extends over a short length of the girder, actually the breadth of the beam, but for practical purposes we consider that the load from the beam is acting at the midbreadth of the beam—a concentrated load.

The term *dead load* is applied to the weight of the materials of construction, the weight of the beams, flooring, partitions, and columns. The *live load* is composed of the weight of human occupants, furniture, equipment, stored materials, and snow. The *total load* is the sum of all dead and live loads.

Figure 2–1 (*a*) represents the floor framing of a bay in a building in which structural timber is used. The columns are spaced 14 ft 0 in. on centers in one direction and 16 ft 0 in. in the other direction. The girders and beams extend in the short and long dimensions, respectively. The girders have a span of 14 ft 0 in., and at the midpoint of the span the girder supports a beam. The beams in turn

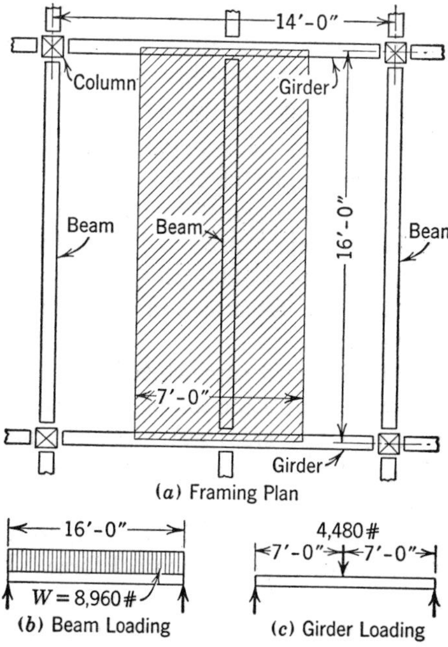

FIG. 2–1

support plank flooring (not shown in the drawing) running parallel to the girders. Let us assume that the total load on the floor, live and dead, is 80 psf (80 pounds per square foot). As the floor area supported by the beam, *in this bay only*, the hatched area, is 7 × 16 or 112 sq ft (112 square feet), the total uniformly distributed load on the beam is 112 × 80 or 8960 lb. Figure 2–1 (*b*) is the conventional diagram representing this beam and load. In this text we use W to represent the total uniformly distributed load and w the uniformly distributed load *per linear foot*. In this instance $W = 8960$ lb, and, since the beam is 16 ft 0 in. in length, $8960 \div 16 = 560$ lb. Therefore $w = 560$ lb.

The total load on the beam is 8960 lb, and, since it is uniformly distributed, it exerts a pressure of 4480 lb at each end on the girders. The concentrated loads on the girders, therefore, are 4480 lb each, as shown in Fig. 2–1 (*c*). We use the letter P to indicate a concentrated load; hence $P = 4480$ lb, the loads on the girders. If this were a problem involving the design of the girder, we should, of course, take into consideration the adjacent bays. In this case the beam load on the girder from the adjoining bay would also be 4480 lb, making a total concentrated load of 8960 lb.

2–3. Unit Stress. In books of this kind we find constant use of technical terms. It is impossible to gain a knowledge of the subject without an understanding of the terms that are employed. Form the habit of using the correct term or name. As an example, in referring to a timber, never speak of it as a beam if in reality it is a column. If a stress is 1200 psi (1200 pounds per square inch), do not say 1200 lb. Exactness in this respect is certain to aid in avoiding errors.

A 6 x 6 in. short timber post supports an axial compressive load of 36,000 lb. The actual cross section of a 6 x 6 in. is 5.5 x 5.5 in. (Table 3–3); therefore the cross-sectional area is 5.5×5.5 or 30.25 sq in. If it is assumed that each square inch of the cross section resists an equal force, each square inch resists $36{,}000 \div 30.25$ or 1190 psi. A *unit stress* may be defined as an internal resistance, per unit area, that results from an external force. It may be described as a distributed internal resisting force. In this illustration the unit compressive stress resulting from the load of 36,000 lb is 1190 psi.

The fundamental principle illustrated in the preceding example, if the stresses are assumed to be equally distributed over the cross section, is expressed by the basic formula

$$f = \frac{P}{A} \quad \text{or} \quad P = fA \quad \text{or} \quad A = \frac{P}{f}$$

in which P = the external load, in pounds
A = the area of the cross section, in square inches
f = the unit stress, in pounds per square inch

2–4. Types of Stresses. The three different types of stresses with which we are principally concerned are *compression*, *tension*, and *shear*.

A *compressive stress* is the stress that results from a force that tends to compress or crush a member. In the example given in Art. 2–3, 1190 psi is a compressive stress.

A *tensile stress* is the stress that results from a force that tends to stretch or elongate a member. A 6 x 8 in. member of a roof truss resists a tensile force of 45,000 lb. The actual cross-sectional dimensions of a 6 x 8 in. are 5.5 x 7.5 in. (Table 3–3). Therefore, the area of the section is 5.5 × 7.5 or 41.25 sq in. To compute the tensile unit stress we use the basic formula

$$f = \frac{P}{A}$$

$$f = \frac{45{,}000}{41.25}$$

$$f = 1090 \text{ psi, the tensile unit stress}$$

A *shearing stress* results from the tendency of two equal and parallel forces, acting in opposite directions, to cause adjoining surfaces of a member to slide one on the other. Figure 2–2 (*a*)

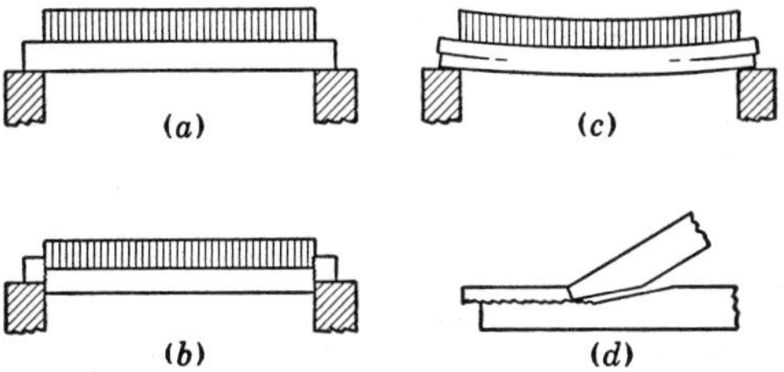

FIG. 2–2

represents a beam with a uniformly distributed load. There is a tendency for the beam to fail by dropping down between the supports as indicated in Fig. 2–2 (*b*). This is an example of *vertical shear*. Figure 2–2 (*c*) shows an exaggerated bending action in a beam and the failure of portions of the beam by sliding horizontally. Figure 2–2 (*d*) illustrates the tendency of the lower chord of a truss to fail by shearing from the action of the upper chord at the end joint. Both Figs. 2–2 (*c*) and (*d*) are illustrations of *horizontal shear.* It is shown later that shearing failures in beams are due to horizontal, not vertical, shear. In timber beams horizontal shear deserves important consideration. It is the resistance to the tendency of the upper half of the beam to slide on the lower half.

The upper chord of a roof truss transfers a compressive force of 25,400 lb to the lower chord. The angle between the two members is 30°, and the breadth of the members is 9.5 in. See Figs. 2–3 (*a*)

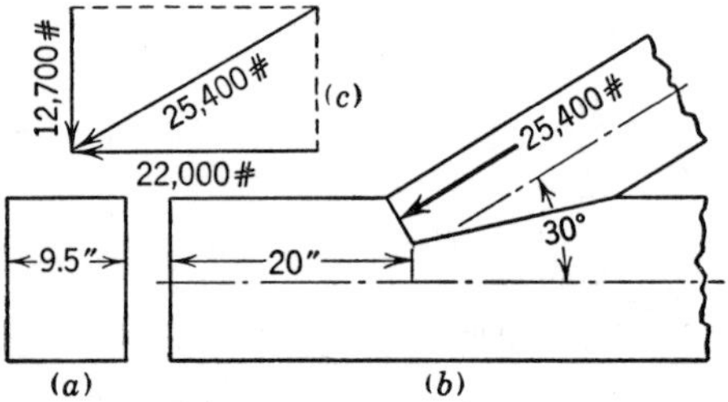

FIG. 2–3

and (*b*). By the use of trigonometry or by drawing a "parallelogram of forces" * we find that the vertical and horizontal components of the force 25,400 lb are 12,700 and 22,000 lb, respectively; see Fig. 2–3 (*c*). The important point in this illustrative example is that the force from the upper chord tends to cause a sliding (shearing) failure in the lower chord and that the magnitude of the force is 22,000 lb. As the breadth of the chord is 9.5 in. and as there is a length of 20 in. to resist this tendency to shear, the area resisting the horizontal shear is 9.5 × 20 or 190 sq in. Then

$$f = \frac{P}{A}$$

$$f = \frac{22{,}000}{190}$$

$f = 115.26$ psi, the horizontal shearing unit stress

* See *Simplified Mechanics and Strength of Materials,* Second Edition, by Harry Parker, John Wiley and Sons, New York, 1961.

A beam with loads that cause *bending* is subjected to a complexity of stresses. This is discussed later; for loaded beams we find tensile, compressive, and shearing stresses.

2–5. Deformation. Whenever a body is subjected to a force, there is a change in its size or shape; this change is called the *deformation.* For axial compressive and tensile forces the deformations are a shortening and lengthening, respectively. When a force acts on a member in such a manner that it tends to cause bending, such as a load on a beam, the deformation is called *deflection.* For beams, the deformation (deflection) should be kept within certain limits.

2–6. Elastic Limit. To explain the terms used in identifying different stresses, consider the following illustration. A short specimen of wood is placed in a testing machine to be tested for compressive stresses. A load resulting in a unit stress of 1000 psi is applied, and the deformation is found to be 0.0006 in. For the load that produces a unit stress of 2000 psi, the deformation is increased 0.0006 in., making a total deformation of 0.0012 in. Twice the load, twice the amount of deformation. As the test is continued, it is found that the deformations increase in direct proportion to the applied load until we reach a unit stress of about 6000 psi. At this point we find that the deformations begin to increase at a more rapid rate than the applied loads. This unit stress is called the *elastic limit* or *proportional limit* of the material.

Elasticity is that property of a material that enables a body to return to its original dimensions when the load is removed. *This occurs, however, only when the unit stress does not exceed the elastic limit.* Beyond this stress a permanent lengthening or shortening, called a *permanent set,* results.

2–7. Ultimate Strength. Assume that the compressive test referred to in the preceding article is continued. It is found that rupture occurs when the unit stress has reached about 8500 psi. This stress is called the *ultimate compressive stress* of the material.

It is to be noted that strength properties for various species of wood are not so clearly defined as they are for other structural materials such as steel. Tests of specimens of the same species and size and in the same condition may give considerably different results.

2–8. Modulus of Elasticity. The *modulus of elasticity* of a material is a measure of its *stiffness*. A specimen of steel deforms a certain amount when subjected to a given load, but a wood specimen of the same dimensions subjected to the same load deforms probably 20 times as much. We say the steel is *stiffer* than the wood. The ratio between the unit stress and the unit deformation, *provided the unit stress does not exceed the elastic limit of the material,* is called the modulus of elasticity of the material. For Douglas fir and Southern pine it is 1,760,000 psi (Table 3–1); for structural steel it is 29,000,000 psi. The modulus of elasticity of timber is used in computing the deflection of beams.

2–9. Allowable Unit Stress. The *allowable unit stress* is variously called *safe working stress, working unit stress,* and *allowable stress.* It is the stress used in design computations and represents the maximum actual unit stress deemed desirable in structural members. Sometimes it is determined by taking a fraction of the ultimate strength or a fractional part of the elastic limit. Since stresses beyond the elastic limit result in a permanent set, obviously the allowable unit stress should be well below the elastic limit.

Formerly, it was the custom to divide the ultimate strength by some arbitrary number to establish the allowable working stress. The number was called the *factor of safety.* If, for example, the ultimate compressive stress of a certain species of timber is 8000 psi and the factor of safety to employ is 8, $8000 \div 8 = 1000$ psi, the allowable compressive unit stress. The term *factor of safety* is frequently misunderstood, the layman believing that a timber with a factor of safety of 6 or 8 will carry six or eight times the load for which it is designed. Actually, a load of such magnitude would result in stresses exceeding the elastic limit and probably in failure.

The designer must conform his computations to the allowable working stresses specified in his building code. For wood, these stresses are given with no reference to the ultimate strength or elastic limit.

CHAPTER 3

WORKING STRESSES FOR STRUCTURAL LUMBER

3–1. Working Stresses for Structural Lumber. There are many factors to be considered in determining the working stresses for lumber. Numerous tests by the Forest Products Laboratory of the U. S. Department of Agriculture made on material free from defects have resulted in a tabulation known as *basic stresses.* To obtain working stresses, the basic stresses are reduced by factors that take into consideration the loss of strength from defects, size and position of knots, slope of grain, size of member, its density, conditions of exposure, and the extent of shakes and checks.

There is no single standard of correlating working stresses with structural grading. Some lumber associations have established a series of working stresses known as *stress grades.* The designations *1450 f* and *1200 c*, etc., by which the various stress grades are identified, represent allowable unit working stresses applicable to material used in locations continuously dry or protected and assure the designer of certain strength values. Other lumber associations adhere to the system of referring to structural grades by name. The stress or structural grades are described in the grading rules of the various lumber associations and can be obtained on application to the respective association.

The designer of structural lumber must, of course, adhere to the requirements and working stresses set down in his local building code. Those who use this book should consult the codes having jurisdiction in their own localities and note the requirements therein. Table 3–1 is a part of a table of working stresses for stress-grade lumber published and recommended by the National Lumber Manufacturers Association. Working stresses in this table are

TABLE 3–1. ALLOWABLE UNIT STRESSES FOR STRESS-GRADE LUMBER
THE ALLOWABLE STRESSES BELOW ARE FOR NORMAL LOADING CONDITIONS

Species and Commercial Grade		Allowable Unit Stresses in Pounds per Square Inch				
		Extreme fiber in Bending, *f*, and Tension Parallel to Grain, *t*	Horizontal Shear, *H*	Compression Perpendicular to Grain, $c\perp$	Compression Parallel to Grain, *c*	Modulus of Elasticity, *E*
CYPRESS, SOUTHERN, INLAND TYPE						
1700 *f* Grade	J.&P.–B.&S.	1700	145	360	1425	1,320,000
1300 *f* Grade	J.&P.–B.&S.	1300	120	360	1125	1,320,000
1450 *c* Grade	P.&T.	....	...	360	1450	1,320,000
1200 *c* Grade	P.&T.	....	...	360	1200	1,320,000
DOUGLAS FIR, COAST REGION						
Dense Select Structural	J.&P.	2050	120	455	1650	1,760,000
Select Structural	J.&P.	1900	120	415	1500	1,760,000
Dense Construction	J.&P.	1750	120	455	1400	1,760,000
Construction	J.&P.	1500	120	390	1200	1,760,000
Standard	J.&P.	1200	95	390	1000	1,760,000
Dense Select Structural	B.&S.	2050	120	455	1500	1,760,000
Select Structural	B.&S.	1900	120	415	1400	1,760,000
Dense Construction	B.&S.	1750	120	455	1200	1,760,000
Construction	B.&S.	1500	120	390	1000	1,760,000
Dense Select Structural	P.&T.	1900	120	455	1650	1,760,000
Select Structural	P.&T.	1750	120	415	1500	1,760,000
Dense Construction	P.&T.	1500	120	455	1400	1,760,000
Construction	P.&T.	1200	120	390	1200	1,760,000
HEMLOCK EASTERN						
Select Structural	J.&P.–B.&S.	1300	85	360	850	1,210,000
Prime Structural	J.&P.	1200	60	360	775	1,210,000
Common Structural	J.&P.	1100	60	360	650	1,210,000
Utility Structural	J.&P.	950	60	360	600	1,210,000
Select Structural	P.&T.	....	...	360	850	1,210,000
PINE SOUTHERN						
Dense Structural 86	3″ & 4″ thick	2900	150	455	2200	1,760,000
Dense Structural 72	"	2350	135	455	1800	1,760,000
Dense Structural 65	"	2050	120	455	1600	1,760,000
Dense Structural 58	"	1750	105	455	1450	1,760,000
No. 1 Dense SR	"	1750	120	455	1750	1,760,000
No. 1 SR	"	1500	120	390	1500	1,760,000
No. 2 Dense SR	"	1400	105	455	1050	1,760,000
No. 2 SR	"	1200	105	390	900	1,760,000
Dense Structural 86	5″ thick & up	2400	150	455	1800	1,760,000
Dense Structural 72	"	2000	135	455	1550	1,760,000

TABLE 3–1. ALLOWABLE UNIT STRESSES FOR STRESS-GRADE LUMBER (Continued)
THE ALLOWABLE STRESSES BELOW ARE FOR NORMAL LOADING CONDITIONS

Don't Forget. New Girder & Beam

Species and Commercial Grade		Allowable Unit Stresses in Pounds per Square Inch				
		Extreme fiber in Bending, *f*, and Tension Parallel to Grain, *t*	Horizontal Shear, *H*	Compression Perpendicular to Grain, $c\perp$	Compression Parallel to Grain, *c*	Modulus of Elasticity, *E*
PINE SOUTHERN						
Dense Structural 65	5″ thick & up	1800	120	455	1400	1,760,000
Dense Structural 58	"	1600	105	455	1300	1,760,000
No. 1 Dense SR	"	1600	120	455	1500	1,760,000
No. 1 SR	"	1400	120	390	1300	1,760,000
No. 2 Dense SR	"	1400	105	455	1050	1,760,000
No. 2 SR	"	1200	105	390	900	1,760,000
OAK, RED and WHITE						
2150 *f* Grade	J.&P.	2150	145	600	1550	1,650,000
1900 *f* Grade	J.&P.–B.&S.	1900	145	600	1375	1,650,000
1700 *f* Grade	J.&P.–B.&S.	1700	145	600	1200	1,650,000
1450 *f* Grade	J.&P.–B.&S.	1450	120	600	1050	1,650,000
1300 *f* Grade	B.&S.	1300	120	600	950	1,650,000
1325 *c* Grade	P.&T.	....	...	600	1325	1,650,000
1200 *c* Grade	P.&T.	....	...	600	1200	1,650,000
1075 *c* Grade	P.&T.	....	...	600	1075	1,650,000
REDWOOD						
Dense Structural	J.&P.–B.&S.	1700	110	320	1450	1,320,000
Heart Structural	J.&P.–B.&S.	1300	95	320	1100	1,320,000
Dense Structural	P.&T.	....	...	320	1450	1,320,000
Heart Structural	P.&T.	....	...	320	1100	1,320,000
SPRUCE, EASTERN						
1450 *f* Structural Grade	J.&P.	1450	110	300	1050	1,320,000
1300 *f* Structural Grade	J.&P.	1300	95	300	975	1,320,000
1200 *f* Structural Grade	J.&P.	1200	95	300	900	1,320,000

Abbreviations: J.&P. = Joists and Planks, B.&S. = Beams and Stringers, P.&T. = Posts and Timbers, SR = Stress Rated.

Reproduced by permission of the National Lumber Manufacturers Association.

satisfactory as a general basis for competent engineering design of wood structures and are for normal loading conditions. Throughout this text the stresses used in the illustrative examples and problems conform with no specific building code; the stresses are taken from a number of different codes. Unless otherwise specified, the stresses to be used in the solution of problems are those found in Table 3–1.

Strength tests on various species of wood are commonly made on specimens 2 x 2 in. in cross section. But tests made of sizes used in practice show that stress data are applicable only to the sizes employed. Because of this, Table 3–1, in addition to species and grade, also gives the manner in which the material is used. Note that the abbreviation J.&P. refers to joists and planks, B.&S. to beams and stringers, and P.&T. indicates posts and timbers. As an example, consider the No. 1 SR grade of southern pine. Table 3–1 gives f, the allowable extreme fiber stress in bending, to be 1500 psi for material 3 and 4 in. in thickness, but for material 5 in. or more in thickness this stress is only 1400 psi.

In the design of structural timber the working stresses required as data are extreme fiber in bending and tension parallel to grain, horizontal shear, compression parallel to the grain, compression perpendicular to the grain, and the modulus of elasticity. These data are found in Table 3–1.

3–2. Duration of Stress. One of the characteristics of lumber is that the time during which a load is applied must be given consideration in determining the size of the member. A suddenly applied force of a few seconds' duration may cause no damage to a member, but the same force if applied for a longer period might cause failure. The working stresses given in Table 3–1 are for normal loading conditions.

A normal loading condition indicates the application of the full maximum normal design load for a duration of approximately ten years or 90% of the maximum design load continuously during the life of the structure.

When the duration of the full maximum load does not exceed the period indicated, the allowable unit stresses given in Table 3–1 may be increased as follows:

15% for two months' duration, as for snow
25% for seven days' duration
$33\frac{1}{3}$% for wind or earthquake
100% for impact

3–3. Decay Hazards. A timber that is constantly wet, a timber below water level for instance, or a member that remains dry, as in covered structures, is not subject to decay. Since it is almost impossible to determine the extent of decay, any form of decay is prohibited in structural grades of lumber.

3–4. Compression Parallel to Grain. The working stresses for compression parallel to grain apply to posts, columns, and struts, as given in Table 3–1. In designing a timber column using the formula given in Art. 13–3, note that $\frac{P}{A}$, the allowable unit stress, must not exceed c given in Table 3–1. For short members, such as posts, the maximum allowable unit stress is c, the allowable compressive stress parallel to the grain.

3–5. Compression Perpendicular to Grain. The stresses for compression perpendicular to the grain apply to stresses in the portions of beams where they bear on supports or where concentrated loads come in contact with beams. These allowable stresses are found in Table 3–1; they are for material that is surface-seasoned when installed and apply to bearings of any length at the ends of beams and to all bearings 6 in. or more in length at any other location. For bearings less than 6 in. in length they may be increased in accordance with the factors explained in Art. 7–1.

3–6. Loads on Surfaces Inclined to Grain. In framing timbers the condition illustrated in Fig. 3–1 frequently occurs. The load

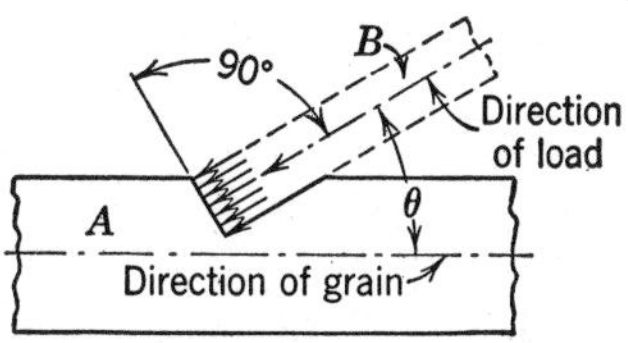

FIG. 3–1

from timber B exerts a compressive stress on timber A on a surface inclined to the grain. The formula recommended for computing the working unit stress on the inclined surface is known as the Hankinson formula; it is

$$N = \frac{PQ}{P \sin^2 \theta + Q \cos^2 \theta}$$

in which N = the allowable compressive unit stress perpendicular to the inclined surface

P = the allowable unit stress in compression parallel to the grain

Q = the allowable unit stress in compression perpendicular to the grain

θ = the angle between the direction of the load and the direction of the grain

When the load is applied parallel to the grain, θ is zero. When the load is applied perpendicular to the grain, θ is 90°. Table 3–2 gives values of $\sin^2 \theta$ and $\cos^2 \theta$ for various values of θ.

TABLE 3–2. VALUES OF $SIN^2\ \theta$ AND $COS^2\ \theta$ FOR VARIOUS VALUES OF θ

$\sin^2 \theta$	θ (degrees)	$\cos^2 \theta$	$\sin^2 \theta$	θ (degrees)	$\cos^2 \theta$
0.00000	0	1.00000	0.50000	45	0.50000
0.00760	5	0.99240	0.58682	50	0.41318
0.03015	10	0.96985	0.67101	55	0.32899
0.06698	15	0.93302	0.75000	60	0.25000
0.11698	20	0.88302	0.82140	65	0.17860
0.17860	25	0.82140	0.88302	70	0.11698
0.25000	30	0.75000	0.93302	75	0.06698
0.32899	35	0.67101	0.96985	80	0.03015
0.41318	40	0.58682	0.99240	85	0.00760
0.50000	45	0.50000	1.00000	90	0.00000

Example. Two 6-in.-wide timbers of Southern pine, No. 1 Dense SR grade, are framed together as indicated in Fig. 3–1. The angle between the direction of the load and the direction of the grain is 30°. Compute the allowable unit stress on the inclined bearing surface.

SOLUTION. Referring to Table 3–1, we find that the allowable compressive unit stress parallel to the grain is 1500 psi, term P in the formula. Likewise, 455 psi is the allowable compressive unit stress perpendicular to the grain. This is term Q in the formula. Then

$$N = \frac{PQ}{P \sin^2 \theta + Q \cos^2 \theta}$$

or

$$\frac{1500 \times 455}{(1500 \times 0.25) + (455 \times 0.75)} = 950 \text{ psi}$$

the allowable unit stress on the inclined surface. In this equation the quantities 0.25 and 0.75 are taken from Table 3–2, the $\sin^2 \theta$ and $\cos^2 \theta$, respectively, for the angle of 30°.

Problem 3–6–A. Two 6-in.-wide members at the heel of a roof truss are framed together as indicated in Fig. 3–1. The angle between the two members is 45° and the timbers are of the Dense Construction grade of Douglas fir. Determine the allowable compressive unit stress on the inclined bearing surface.

3–7. Tensile Unit Stresses. For working stresses for members in which tensile forces are applied parallel to the grain the working stress is t similar to f, the "extreme fiber in bending" given in Table 3–1. In the design of timber trusses it will be found that the strength of members in tension is usually determined by the strength of the connection at the joints rather than by the cross-sectional area of the member.

3–8. Nominal and Dressed Sizes. A timber is designated by the dimensions or size of its cross section; the size is indicated by the breadth and depth of the cross section in inches. As an example, we speak of a 6 x 12 in., and by this we mean a timber having a cross section 6 in. in breadth and 12 in. in depth; the length is a variable. For this particular section 6 x 12 in. is the *nominal size*, the name of the section. The terms *actual size* and *dressed size* (American Standard Dressed Size) are used synonymously, and they indicate the size of a timber that has been dressed on four sides, "S4S." Referring to Table 3–3, we note that both the nominal and dressed sizes are given in identifying specific timbers. The timber having 6 x 12 in. for its nominal size has a dressed size of $5\frac{1}{2}$ x $11\frac{1}{2}$ in.

Lumber is sold on the basis of the contents of the nominal size expressed in terms of *board feet.* A board foot is the content of a

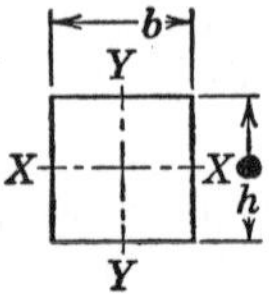

TABLE 3–3. PROPERTIES OF AMERICAN STANDARD SIZES OF YARD LUMBER AND TIMBERS *

Nominal Size, in Inches	American Standard Dressed Size (S4S), in Inches	Area of Section, in Inches²	Moment of Inertia, in Inches⁴		Section Modulus, in Inches³	
			$I_{X-X} = bh^3/12$	$I_{Y-Y} = b^3h/12$	$S_{X-X} = bh^2/6$	$S_{Y-Y} = b^2h/6$
b h	b h	$A = b \times h$				
2 x 4	1⅝ x 3⅝	5.89	6.45	1.30	3.56	1.60
2 x 6	1⅝ x 5⅝	9.14	24.10	2.01	8.57	2.48
2 x 8	1⅝ x 7½	12.19	57.13	2.68	15.23	3.30
2 x 10	1⅝ x 9½	15.44	116.10	3.40	24.44	4.18
2 x 12	1⅝ x 11½	18.69	205.95	4.11	35.82	5.06
2 x 14	1⅝ x 13½	21.94	333.18	4.83	49.36	5.94
2 x 16	1⅝ x 15½	25.19	504.27	5.54	65.07	6.82
2 x 18	1⅝ x 17½	28.44	725.75	6.25	82.94	7.70
3 x 4	2⅝ x 3⅝	9.52	10.42	5.46	5.75	4.16
3 x 6	2⅝ x 5⅝	14.77	38.93	8.48	13.84	6.46
3 x 8	2⅝ x 7½	19.69	92.29	11.30	24.61	8.61
3 x 10	2⅝ x 9½	24.94	187.55	14.32	39.48	10.91
3 x 12	2⅝ x 11½	30.19	332.69	17.33	57.86	13.21
3 x 14	2⅝ x 13½	35.44	538.21	20.35	79.73	15.50
3 x 16	2⅝ x 15½	40.69	814.60	23.36	105.11	17.80
3 x 18	2⅝ x 17½	45.94	1,172.36	26.38	133.98	20.10
4 x 4	3⅝ x 3⅝	13.14	14.39	14.39	7.94	7.94
4 x 6	3⅝ x 5⅝	20.39	53.76	22.33	19.12	12.32
4 x 8	3⅝ x 7½	27.19	127.44	29.77	33.98	16.43
4 x 10	3⅝ x 9½	34.44	259.00	37.71	54.53	20.81
4 x 12	3⅝ x 11½	41.69	459.43	45.65	79.90	25.19
4 x 14	3⅝ x 13½	48.94	743.24	53.59	110.11	29.57
4 x 16	3⅝ x 15½	56.19	1,124.92	61.53	145.15	33.95
4 x 18	3⅝ x 17½	63.44	1,618.98	69.47	185.03	38.33
6 x 6	5½ x 5½	30.25	76.26	76.26	27.73	27.73
6 x 8	5½ x 7½	41.25	193.36	103.98	51.56	37.81
6 x 10	5½ x 9½	52.25	392.96	131.71	82.73	47.90
6 x 12	5½ x 11½	63.25	697.07	159.44	121.23	57.98
6 x 14	5½ x 13½	74.25	1,127.67	187.17	167.06	68.06
6 x 16	5½ x 15½	85.25	1,706.78	214.90	220.23	78.15
6 x 18	5½ x 17½	96.25	2,456.38	242.63	280.73	88.23
8 x 8	7½ x 7½	56.25	263.67	263.67	70.31	70.31
8 x 10	7½ x 9½	71.25	535.86	333.98	112.81	89.06
8 x 12	7½ x 11½	86.25	950.55	404.30	165.31	107.81

* Reproduced by permission of the Timber Engineering Company.

TABLE 3–3. PROPERTIES OF AMERICAN STANDARD SIZES OF YARD LUMBER AND TIMBERS (Continued)

Nominal Size, in Inches	American Standard Dressed Size (S4S), in Inches	Area of Section, in Inches²	Moment of Inertia, in Inches⁴		Section Modulus, in Inches³	
			$I_{X-X} = bh^3/12$	$I_{Y-Y} = b^3h/12$	$S_{X-X} = bh^2/6$	$S_{Y-Y} = b^2h/6$
b h	b h	$A = b \times h$				
8 x 14	7½ x 13½	101.25	1,537.73	474.61	227.81	126.56
8 x 16	7½ x 15½	116.25	2,327.42	544.92	300.31	145.31
8 x 18	7½ x 17½	131.25	3,349.61	615.23	382.81	164.06
10 x 10	9½ x 9½	90.25	678.76	678.76	142.90	142.90
10 x 12	9½ x 11½	109.25	1,204.03	821.65	209.40	172.98
10 x 14	9½ x 13½	128.25	1,947.80	964.55	288.56	203.06
10 x 16	9½ x 15½	147.25	2,948.07	1,107.44	380.40	233.15
10 x 18	9½ x 17½	166.25	4,242.84	1,250.34	484.90	263.23
12 x 12	11½ x 11½	132.25	1,457.51	1,457.51	253.48	253.48
12 x 14	11½ x 13½	155.25	2,357.86	1,710.98	349.31	297.56
12 x 16	11½ x 15½	178.25	3,568.71	1,964.46	460.48	341.65
12 x 18	11½ x 17½	201.25	5,136.07	2,217.94	586.98	385.73
14 x 14	13½ x 13½	182.25	2,767.92	2,767.92	410.06	410.06
14 x 16	13½ x 15½	209.25	4,189.36	3,177.98	540.56	470.81
14 x 18	13½ x 17½	236.25	6,029.30	3,588.05	689.06	531.56
14 x 20	13½ x 19½	263.25	8,341.73	3,998.11	855.56	592.31

volume 12 x 12 x 1 in., 144 cu in., or $\frac{1}{12}$ cu ft. The properties of various cross sections, area, moment of inertia, and section modulus, given in Table 3–3, are based on dressed-size dimensions. As the reduction in area affects the strength of a piece of timber, actual or dressed dimensions only must be used in computations.

CHAPTER 4

PROPERTIES OF SECTIONS

4–1. Properties of Sections. In the design of structural members the computations involve the properties or elements of the members. As the computation of these properties of rectangular shapes presents no difficulty, the values are presented in Table 3–3; this table will be found to be of great convenience in the design of members. In general, the letter b represents the breadth in inches of the beam face on which the load is applied. The letter h represents the height or depth in inches of the beam face parallel to the direction of the line of action of the load. Sometimes the depth is represented by the letter d. The properties of the various sizes are based on the actual or American Standard dressed sizes, S4S, surfaced four sides.

4–2. Area. The *area of section* given in Table 3–3 is the area of the cross section of the member taken perpendicular to its longitudinal axis. As an example, consider a timber whose nominal size is 10 x 12 in. The actual size of this member is $9\frac{1}{2}$ x $11\frac{1}{2}$ in.; hence $9\frac{1}{2} \times 11\frac{1}{2} = 109.25$ sq in., the area given in the table.

4–3. Neutral Surface. Consider a simple beam subjected to a load or loads that produce bending. There is a tendency for the beam to be depressed on the upper surface; the fibers in the upper portion of the beam are in compression, and the fibers in the lower portion are in tension. The imaginary plane above which the fibers are in compression and below which they are in tension is called the *neutral surface.* The neutral surface is indicated by a line on the cross section of the member and is called the *neutral axis.* If the stresses in the fibers of the beams do not exceed the elastic limit of the material, the neutral axis of a rectangular section is perpendicular to the depth of the cross section and lies halfway between the upper and lower surfaces. Consider a 6 x 12 in. beam. Table 3–3 shows the actual size of this beam to be $5\frac{1}{2}$ x $11\frac{1}{2}$ in. As the depth is $11\frac{1}{2}$ in. the neutral surface is $11\frac{1}{2} \times \frac{1}{2}$ or 5.75 in. from the upper and lower surfaces.

The *centroid* of a plane area is the point that corresponds to the *center of gravity* of an extremely thin homogeneous plate of the same shape and area. The neutral axis of a cross section passes through the centroid of the section.

4–4. Moment of Inertia. A rectangular cross section of breadth b and depth h is shown in Fig. 4–1 (a). The distance from the fiber

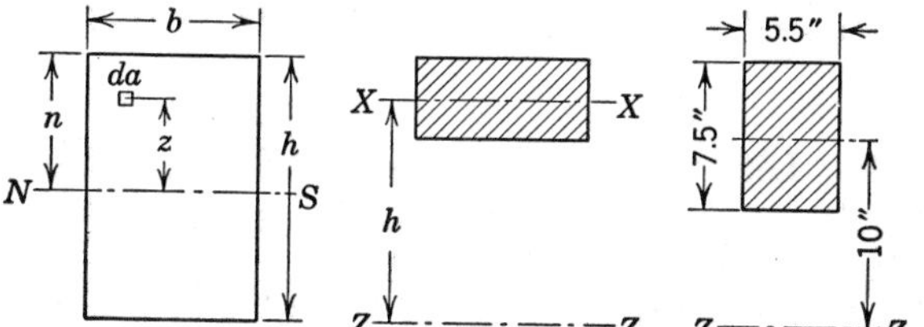

FIG. 4–1

most remote from the neutral surface is n; for rectangular cross sections it is one half the depth, or $\frac{h}{2}$. On this area consider an infinitely small area, da, at z distance from the neutral axis as indicated. This tiny area multiplied by the square of its distance from the neutral surface is $da \times z^2$. Because the elementary area is infinitely small, there are infinite numbers of these areas in the entire cross section. The maximum distance of an elementary area from the neutral axis is $\frac{h}{2}$, or n. If we use the Greek letter Σ to indicate the sum of an infinite number, $\Sigma da \times z^2$ is a quantity called the *moment of inertia* of the cross section. It may be defined as the sum of the products of each elementary area by the square of its distance from the neutral axis of the cross section, and it is represented by the letter I. As each area, although infinitely small, is in units of square inches and as z^2 is inches squared, the moment of inertia of a cross section is in units of inches to the fourth power, as, for instance, 750 in.^{4}

The formula for computing the moment of inertia is most readily derived by use of the calculus. Regardless of its derivation, the equation itself is of importance to us. Timber sections are invariably rectangular, and the moment of inertia of a rectangular cross section about an axis through its centroid parallel to the base is $\frac{bh^3}{12}$, that is,

$$I = \frac{bh^3}{12} \qquad \text{(See Art. 9–4)}$$

Remember, however, that this applies only to *rectangular* cross sections.

Example. Let us compute the moment of inertia of an 8 x 12 in. From Table 3–3 we find the actual size is $7\frac{1}{2}$ x $11\frac{1}{2}$ in. If this section is used as a beam, its greatest strength occurs when the long axis is vertical, that is, when $b = 7\frac{1}{2}$ and $h = 11\frac{1}{2}$. Then

$$I = \frac{bh^3}{12} = \frac{7.5 \times 11.5^3}{12} = 950.55 \text{ in.}^4, \text{ the moment of inertia}$$

Note that this is the value given in Table 3–3.

If, for some reason, this beam is turned so that the short axis is vertical, $b = 11\frac{1}{2}$ in. and $h = 7\frac{1}{2}$ in. Then

$$I = \frac{bh^3}{12} = \frac{11.5 \times 7.5^3}{12} = 404.30 \text{ in.}^4$$

This value is also given in Table 3–3.

4–5. Transferring Moments of Inertia. If we wish to design a beam whose cross section is not rectangular, for instance an L shape, it is necessary to compute the moment of inertia of the cross section by transferring moments of inertia from one axis to another. Consider Fig. 4–1 (*b*).

Let

A = the area of any cross section, such as indicated by the hatched area, in square inches

I_0 = the moment of inertia of the area A about an axis X–X passing through its centroid, in inches^4

Z–Z = any axis parallel to the axis X–X

h = the normal distance between the axes X–X and Z–Z, in inches

I_1 = the moment of inertia of the area A with respect to the axis Z–Z, in inches^4

Then

$$I_1 = I_0 + Ah^2$$

This formula for transferring moments of inertia from one axis to another may be stated thus: *the moment of inertia of a plane area with respect to any axis is equal to the moment of inertia of the area with respect to a parallel axis passing through its centroid plus the area of the section multiplied by the square of the normal distance between the two axes.*

Example. Figure 4–1 (*c*) indicates a rectangular cross section having a breadth of 5.5 in. and a depth of 7.5 in. Compute the moment of inertia of this area with respect to a parallel axis, Z–Z, 10 in. from the neutral axis of the cross section.

SOLUTION. A, the area of the cross section, $= 5.5 \times 7.5 = 41.25$ sq in. The moment of inertia of the cross section about an axis passing through its centroid is

$$I_0 = \frac{bh^3}{12} = \frac{5.5 \times 7.5^3}{12} = 193.36 \text{ in.}^4$$

(See Table 3–3)

In this problem the distance between axes $h = 10$ in. Then

$$I_1 = I_0 + Ah^2 = 193.36 + (41.25 \times 10^2) = 4318.36 \text{ in.}^4$$

the moment of inertia of the 5.5 x 7.5 in. cross section with respect to the axis marked Z–Z.

4–6. Section Modulus. The property of areas used most frequently in the design of beams is the section modulus. Referring to Fig. 4–1 (*a*), note that h is the depth of the section and that the neutral axis lies at the middepth, that is, distance n is one half distance h. A rectangular section is symmetrical, and therefore the neutral axis always lies halfway between the upper and lower surfaces. In the flexure formula (to be discussed later) we find the term n. For any beam n is the distance of the most remote fiber of the cross section from the neutral axis. For unsymmetrical sections, as, for instance, an angle section, the distance n must be computed, but for rectangular sections, $n = \frac{h}{2}$. The *section modulus* is simply the moment of inertia of the cross section divided by the distance of the fiber most remote from the neutral surface, $\frac{I}{n}$. The letter S is used to represent the section modulus; hence $S = \frac{I}{n}$. Since

$$I = \frac{bh^3}{12} \quad \text{and} \quad n = \frac{h}{2}, \qquad S = \frac{bh^3}{12} \times \frac{2}{h} \quad \text{or} \quad S = \frac{bh^2}{6}$$

(See Art. 9–4)

It should be noted that, since I is in units of inches^4 and n is a linear dimension, $\frac{I}{n}$, the section modulus, is in units of inches^3.

Briefly, the section modulus has this practical value. A beam and its loading are given as data. By simple mathematics the maximum tendency to fail by bending is computed (the maximum bending moment), and this quantity is divided by a number corresponding to the species and grade of the timber (the allowable extreme fiber stress). The quotient is the required section modulus of the beam. The beam size to use is determined by selecting from a table of properties of beams, such as Table 3–3, a beam whose section modulus is equal to or somewhat greater than that required. This is explained in detail later.

Example. Compute the section modulus of a 10 x 14 in.

SOLUTION. The actual size of a 10 x 14 in. is 9.5 x 13.5 in. (Table 3–3); hence $b = 9.5$ in. and $h = 13.5$ in.

$$S = \frac{I}{n} = \frac{bh^3}{12} \times \frac{2}{h} = \frac{9.5 \times 13.5^3}{12} \times \frac{2}{13.5} = 288.56 \text{ in.}^3$$

or

$$S = \frac{bh^2}{6} = \frac{9.5 \times 13.5^2}{6} = 288.56 \text{ in.}^3$$

Note that this value is given in Table 3–3.

Problem 4–6–A. Compute the cross-sectional areas, based on dressed-size dimensions, of the following nominal sizes: (1) 3 x 12 in.; (2) 6 x 8 in.; (3) 10 x 10 in.; (4) 12 x 16 in.; (5) 14 x 14 in.

Problem 4–6–B. Compute the moment of inertia with respect to the X–X axis, using dressed-size dimensions, of the following nominal sizes (1) 2 x 12 in.; (2) 3 x 14 in.; (3) 6 x 12 in.; (4) 8 x 12 in.; (5) 12 x 14 in.

Problem 4–6–C. Compute the moment of inertia of a 10 x 6 in. with respect to an axis parallel to the 10-in. face and 8 in. from the neutral axis of the cross section. Use dressed-size dimensions.

Problem 4–6–D. If b is the breadth of a rectangular cross section and h is the depth, compute, by use of the formula for transferring moments of inertia from one axis to another, the moment of inertia of the cross section about an axis taken through its base.

Problem 4–6–E. Compute the moment of inertia of an 8 x 12 in. about an axis taken through an 8-in. face. Use dressed-size dimensions.

Problem 4–6–F. Compute the section modulus, with respect to the X–X axis, of the following nominal sizes: (1) 2 x 10 in.; (2) 3 x 12 in.; (3) 6 x 12 in.; (4) 10 x 14 in. Use dressed-size dimensions.

CHAPTER 5

BENDING MOMENTS AND SHEAR

5–1. Moments. A *moment* may be defined as the tendency of a force to cause rotation about a given point or axis. When we speak of the moment of a force it is important that we have clearly in mind the point or axis about which the force tends to cause rotation; such a point or axis is sometimes called the *center of moments*. The magnitude of the moment of a force is the magnitude of the force (usually pounds) multiplied by the *perpendicular* distance (generally feet or inches) between the line of action of the force and the point about which the moment is taken. This distance is called the *lever arm*. Since a moment is the product of a force multiplied by a distance, the unit of a moment is foot-pounds or inch-pounds, depending on the units employed.

Consider the cantilever beam 10 ft 0 in. in length shown in Fig. 5–1. A force of 500 lb is placed at 4 ft 0 in. from the face of the wall. Then the moment of the force of 500 lb *about point A* at the face of the wall is 500 × 4 or 2000 ft-lb. If the 500 lb is moved to the unsupported end of the beam, shown by the dotted line, the moment of the force about point A is 500 × 10 or 5000 ft-lb. It should be noted that 2000 ft-lb and 5000 ft-lb are equivalent to 24,000 in-lb and 60,000 in-lb, respectively. When writing moments be sure to designate the units; this will help to avoid errors.

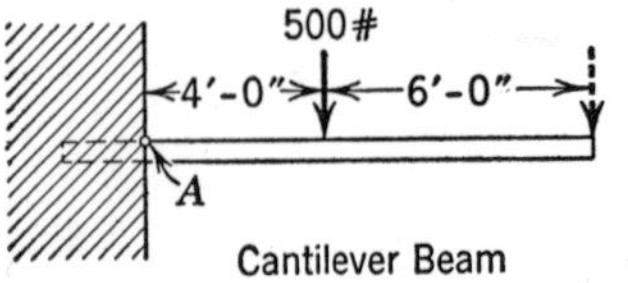

Cantilever Beam

FIG. 5–1

5–2. Laws of Equilibrium. Figure 5–2 represents a structural member in equilibrium. Equilibrium, in this sense, is a condition in which forces acting simultaneously produce no motion, a state of rest. All structural members in buildings are in a state of equilibrium.

If a body subjected to various forces is in equilibrium, the three basic laws of equilibrium apply:

1. The algebraic sum of all the vertical forces equals zero.
2. The algebraic sum of all the horizontal forces equals zero.
3. The algebraic sum of the moments of all the forces about any point equals zero.

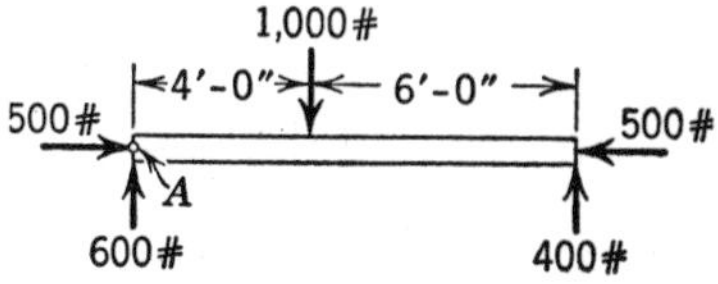

FIG. 5–2

The vertical forces shown in Fig. 5–2 consist of the downward force of 1000 lb, and the two upward forces of 600 and 400 lb. Calling the downward force positive and the upward forces negative, $1000 - 600 - 400 = 0$. This is an example of the first law of equilibrium. When a beam is subjected to vertical loads, the first law of equilibrium may be stated: *the sum of the loads equals the sum of the reactions.* The *reactions* are the vertical upward forces at the supports of the beam.

The two horizontal forces are 500 lb each. One force acts toward the left and the other toward the right. These forces have the same line of action. Then $500 - 500 = 0$, an example of the second law of equilibrium.

Now consider point A, a point in the line of action of the force of 600 lb, the left reaction. We take this point as the center of moments in our consideration of the moments of the forces acting on the member. The force 1000 lb tends to cause a clockwise rotation about point A, and its moment is 1000×4 or 4000 ft-lb. The force 400 lb tends to cause a counterclockwise rotation about point A, and its moment is 400×10 or 4000 ft-lb. If we call the clockwise moments positive and the counterclockwise moments negative, we may write

$$(1000 \times 4) - (400 \times 10) = 0$$

or

$$4000 \text{ ft-lb} = 4000 \text{ ft-lb}$$

Perhaps you wonder about the 600 lb, the left reaction. Because this force has its line of action through point A, it has a lever arm of zero. Its moment, then, is 600×0, or zero, and may be ignored in writing the equation of moments.

For a beam in equilibrium the third law of equilibrium may be stated thus: *the sum of the moments of the forces that tend to cause clockwise rotation about any point equals the sum of the moments of the forces that tend to cause counterclockwise rotation about the same point.* It is this third law of equilibrium that enables us to compute the upward forces or reactions of beams.

5–3. Reactions. The *reactions* of a beam are the upward supporting forces that hold in equilibrium the downward forces or loads. For symmetrically loaded simple beams each reaction is equal to one half the sum of the loads. In the design of unsymmetrically loaded beams it is generally necessary that the magnitudes of the reactions be computed. It is convenient to distinguish between the two reactions by using the symbols R_1 and R_2 to represent the left and right reactions, respectively. This system is followed in this book.

Consider first a simple beam having a span of 20 ft 0 in. with a concentrated load of 2400 lb at the center of the span as indicated in Fig. 5–3 (a). Since this beam is symmetrically loaded and the

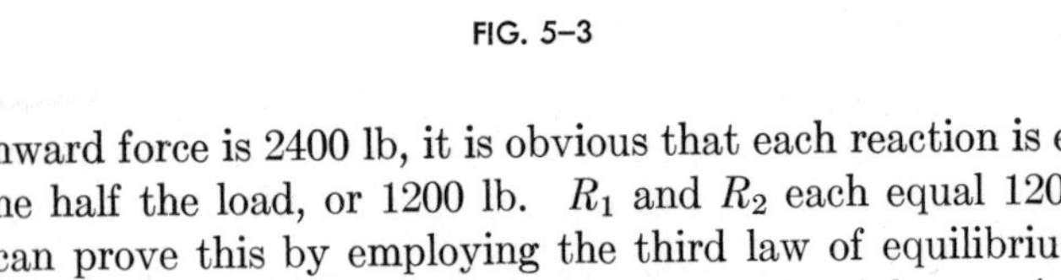

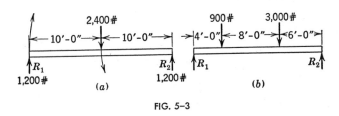

FIG. 5–3

downward force is 2400 lb, it is obvious that each reaction is equal to one half the load, or 1200 lb. R_1 and R_2 each equal 1200 lb. We can prove this by employing the third law of equilibrium as previously stated. Let us take a point at R_2, the right reaction, as the center of moments. The force R_1 tends to produce a clockwise rotation about this point, and its moment is $R_1 \times 20$. The downward force, the load, tends to cause a counterclockwise rotation about the same point, and its moment is 2400×10. Note the arrows that show the directions of rotation. As the sum of the moments tending to cause clockwise rotation equals the sum of the moments that tend to cause counterclockwise rotation, we may write

$$R_1 \times 20 = 2400 \times 10$$
$$20R_1 = 24{,}000$$
$$R_1 = 1200 \text{ lb}$$

In a similar manner we can show that $R_2 = 1200$ lb.

Now let us consider the simple beam with two loads as indicated in Fig. 5–3 (*b*). This beam is not symmetrically loaded; hence the reactions are not necessarily equal. Let us compute their magnitudes.

We select a point on the line of action of R_2 as the center of moments. With respect to this point, the only force that tends to cause a clockwise rotation is R_1, and its moment is $R_1 \times 18$. For the same center of moments the loads 900 and 3000 lb tend to produce counterclockwise rotation, and their moments are (900×14) and (3000×6), respectively. Then, in accordance with the law,

$$18 \times R_1 = (900 \times 14) + (3000 \times 6)$$
$$18R_1 = 30{,}600$$
$$R_1 = 1700 \text{ lb}$$

Taking R_1 as a center of moments, we may write

$$18 \times R_2 = (900 \times 4) + (3000 \times 12)$$
$$18R_2 = 39{,}600$$
$$R_2 = 2200 \text{ lb}$$

The magnitudes of the reactions just computed may be readily checked by employing the first law of equilibrium. In effect, this law states that the sum of the downward forces equals the sum of the upward forces or *the sum of the loads equals the sum of the reactions.* Thus

$$900 + 3000 = 1700 + 2200$$

or

$$3900 \text{ lb} = 3900 \text{ lb}$$

This example involves the computation of the reactions for a simple beam with concentrated loads. Now let us consider a beam with a uniformly distributed load. *As far as the reactions are concerned,* a distributed load has the same effect as a concentrated load of the same magnitude acting at the center of gravity of the distributed load.

Example. Compute the reactions for the beam and loading shown in Fig. 5–4 (*a*).

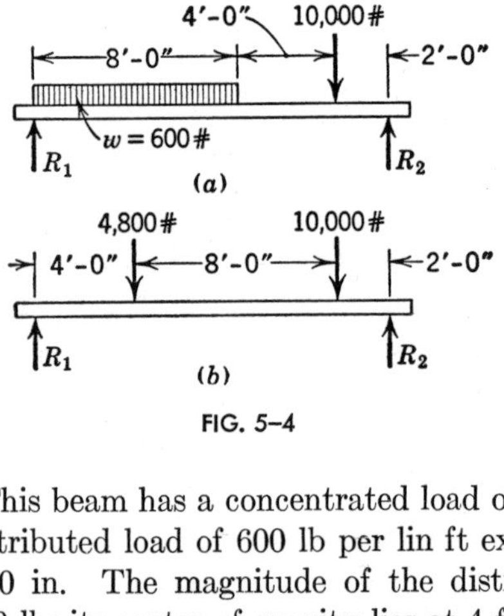

FIG. 5–4

SOLUTION. This beam has a concentrated load of 10,000 lb and a uniformly distributed load of 600 lb per lin ft extending over a length of 8 ft 0 in. The magnitude of the distributed load is 8×600 or 4800 lb; its center of gravity lies at 4 ft 0 in. from R_1 and at 10 ft 0 in. from R_2. With respect to the reactions, the beams and loads shown in Figs. 5–4 (*a*) and (*b*) are similar.

Consider Fig. 5–4 (*a*) and take R_2 as the center of moments. Then

$$14 \times R_1 = (8 \times 600 \times 10) + (10{,}000 \times 2)$$

$$R_1 = 4857.1 \text{ lb}$$

In this equation 8×600 is the magnitude of the distributed load and 10 is its lever arm about R_2.

Taking R_1 as the center of moments,

$$14 \times R_2 = (8 \times 600 \times 4) + (10{,}000 \times 12)$$

$$R_2 = 9942.9 \text{ lb}$$

To check,

$$(8 \times 600) + 10{,}000 = 4857.1 + 9942.9$$
$$14{,}800 \text{ lb} = 14{,}800 \text{ lb}$$

Example. Compute the reactions for the overhanging beam with a uniformly distributed load shown in Fig. 5–5.

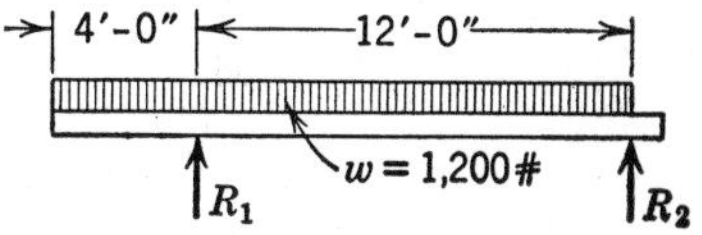

FIG. 5–5

SOLUTION. Note that the center of gravity of the uniformly distributed load lies at 8 ft 0 in. from R_2 and at 4 ft 0 in. from R_1. Then, selecting R_2 as the center of moments,

$$12 \times R_1 = (16 \times 1200 \times 8)$$
$$R_1 = 12{,}800 \text{ lb}$$

With R_1 as the center of moments,

$$12 \times R_2 = (16 \times 1200 \times 4)$$
$$R_2 = 6400 \text{ lb}$$

Check:

$$(16 \times 1200) = 12{,}800 + 6400$$
$$19{,}200 \text{ lb} = 19{,}200 \text{ lb}$$

Example. Compute the reactions for the overhanging beam and loading shown in Fig. 5–6.

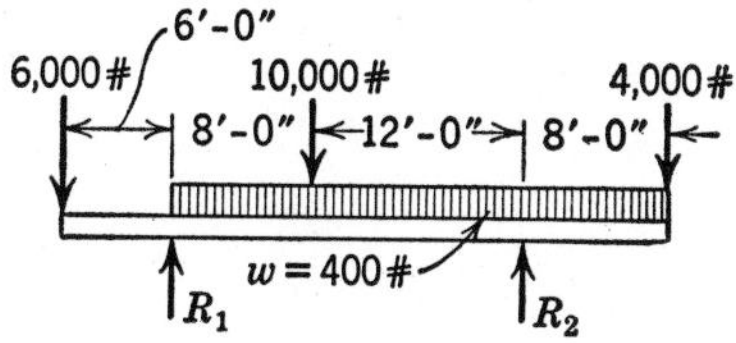

FIG. 5–6

SOLUTION. Note that the distributed load has its center of

gravity at 6 ft from R_2 and at 14 ft from R_1. Select R_2 as the center of moments. Then

$$(20 \times R_1) + (4000 \times 8)$$
$$= (6000 \times 26) + (10{,}000 \times 12) + (28 \times 400 \times 6)$$
$$20R_1 = 311{,}200$$
$$R_1 = 15{,}560 \text{ lb}$$

Taking R_1 as the center of moments,

$$(20 \times R_2) + (6000 \times 6)$$
$$= (10{,}000 \times 8) + (4000 \times 28) + (28 \times 400 \times 14)$$
$$20R_2 = 312{,}800$$
$$R_2 = 15{,}640 \text{ lb}$$

Check:

$$6000 + 10{,}000 + 4000 + (28 \times 400) = 15{,}560 + 15{,}640$$
$$31{,}200 \text{ lb} = 31{,}200 \text{ lb}$$

Problems 5–3–A–B–C–D–E–F. Compute the magnitudes of the reactions for the beams and loads shown in Figs. 5–7 (*a*), (*b*), (*c*), (*d*), (*e*), and (*f*).

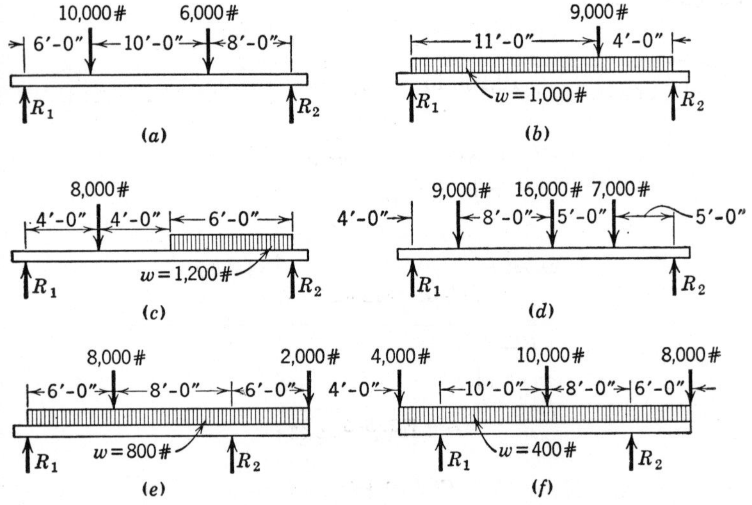

FIG. 5–7

5–4. Vertical Shear. The tendency for a beam to fail by dropping down between supports was mentioned in Art. 2–4. See Fig. 2–2 (*b*). This tendency for one part of a beam to move vertically with respect to an adjacent part is called *vertical shear*, and the stresses within the member that resist this tendency to fail are shearing stresses. The magnitude of the vertical shear at any section of a beam is the algebraic sum of the vertical forces on either the right or left of the section. A convenient form of this statement is: *the vertical shear at any section of a beam is equal to the reactions minus the loads to the left of the section.* Since the vertical shear is *reactions minus loads*, the vertical shear is generally in units of pounds. The letter V is used to identify the vertical shear.

There are two important reasons for investigating the vertical shear in beams. First, it is important to know the maximum value of the vertical shear, and, second, the section of the beam at which the shear changes from a plus to a minus quantity is the section at which we find the greatest tendency to fail by bending.

A *shear diagram* is a graphical representation of the values of the vertical shear throughout the length of a beam. A horizontal line (the base line) is drawn directly below the beam diagram, and the values of the shear at various sections of the beam are plotted to a convenient scale, plus values above and minus values below the base line.

Example. A simple beam 20 ft 0 in. in length has two concentrated loads as indicated in Fig. 5–8 (*a*). Now construct the shear diagram.

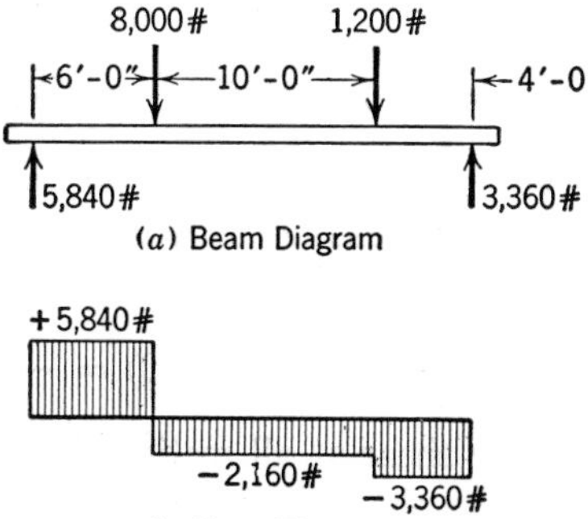

(*a*) Beam Diagram

(*b*) Shear Diagram

FIG. 5–8

SOLUTION. The first step is to compute the reactions as explained in Art. 5–3.

$$20R_1 = (8000 \times 14) + (1200 \times 4)$$

$$20R_1 = 116{,}800$$

$$R_1 = 5840 \text{ lb}$$

$$20R_2 = (8000 \times 6) + (1200 \times 16)$$

$$20R_2 = 67{,}200$$

$$R_2 = 3360 \text{ lb}$$

To designate the section at which we wish to compute the value of the shear, it is convenient to use a subscript: $V_{(x=4)}$. This indicates that the value of the shear is taken at a section 4 ft from the left end of the beam.

First consider a section 1 ft to the right of R_1. Since the shear is equal to the reactions minus the loads to the left of the section and the reaction to the left is 5840 lb and there are no loads to the left, we may write

$$V_{(x=1)} = 5840 - 0 = 5840 \text{ lb}$$

This is a positive quantity, and a point is plotted at a convenient scale above the base line at 1 ft to the right of R_1.

Note that there are no loads between R_1 and the load of 8000 lb 6 ft from R_1. Hence the vertical shear from R_1 up to the first concentrated load is 5840 lb.

Next consider a section 8 ft from R_1. We write

$$V_{(x=8)} = 5840 - 8000 = -2160 \text{ lb}$$

This is a negative value and is plotted *below* the base line. The value of the shear does not change between the two concentrated loads. In the same manner,

$$V_{(x=18)} = 5840 - (8000 + 1200) = -3360 \text{ lb}$$

This is the value of the shear at all sections between the 1200-lb load and R_2. Thus the shear diagram is completed. See Fig. 5–8 (*b*). Note that all the vertical distances (ordinates) in the shear diagram show the values of the vertical shear for all sections of the beam.

Having completed the shear diagram, let us see what it discloses. First we note that the maximum value of the vertical shear is 5840 lb. It occurs at all sections between the left reaction and the concentrated load of 8000 lb. It is obvious that for simple beams the maximum vertical shear occurs at the greater reaction and is equal to the greater reaction in magnitude. We see also that the value of the shear changes sign (from positive values to negative values) directly under the 8000-lb load, at 6 ft from R_1. Later it will be seen that this is the section at which the maximum bending moment occurs. This value is critical in the design of beams.

The weight of a beam constitutes a uniformly distributed load. Note that it has been ignored in computing the values of the vertical shear in the foregoing example.

Example. The simple beam shown in Fig. 5–9 (*a*) has both a concentrated and a uniformly distributed load. Construct the shear diagram; note the value of the maximum shear and the section at which the shear passes through zero.

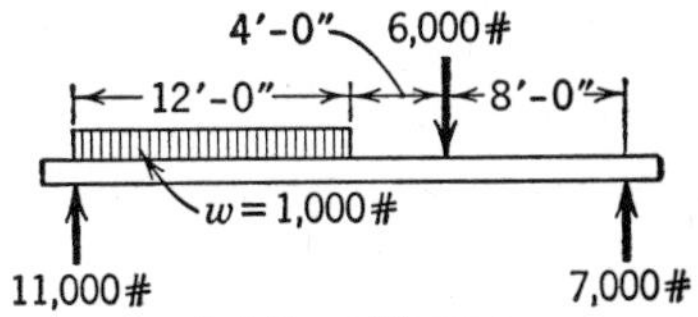

(*a*) Beam Diagram

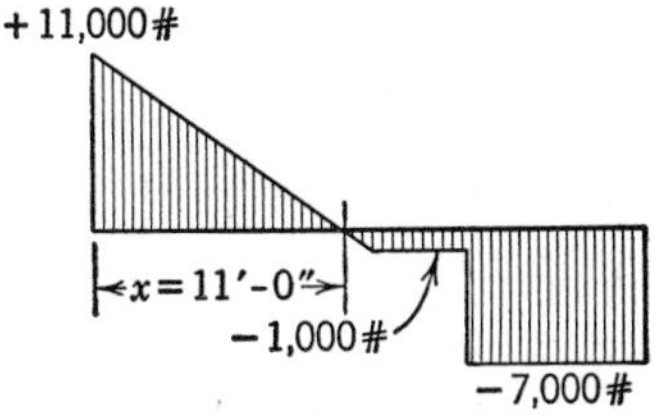

(*b*) Shear Diagram

FIG. 5–9

SOLUTION. Computing the reactions,

$$24R_1 = (12 \times 1000 \times 18) + (6000 \times 8)$$

$$24R_1 = 264{,}000$$

$$R_1 = 11{,}000 \text{ lb}$$

$$24R_2 = (12 \times 1000 \times 6) + (6000 \times 16)$$

$$24R_2 = 168{,}000$$

$$R_2 = 7000 \text{ lb}$$

At the left reaction the value of V is 11,000 lb. Since the magnitude of the uniformly distributed load is 1000 lb per lin ft, we may write

$$V_{(x=1)} = 11{,}000 - (1 \times 1000) = 10{,}000 \text{ lb}$$

$$V_{(x=2)} = 11{,}000 - (2 \times 1000) = 9000 \text{ lb}$$

$$V_{(x=12)} = 11{,}000 - (12 \times 1000) = -1000 \text{ lb}$$

$$V_{(x=16-)} = 11{,}000 - (12 \times 1000) = -1000 \text{ lb}$$

$$V_{(x=16+)} = 11{,}000 - [(12 \times 1000) + 6000] = -7000 \text{ lb}$$

$$V_{(x=24)} = 11{,}000 - [(12 \times 1000) + 6000] = -7000 \text{ lb}$$

In these equations $V_{(x=16-)}$ indicates a section close to but not including the 6000-lb load. Also, $V_{(x=16+)}$ designates a section slightly to the right of the 6000-lb load. Note that under the uniformly distributed load the shear diagram is a sloping line. In plotting the shear for a beam having only a uniformly distributed load it is necessary to compute only the shear values at the two ends of the distributed load.

From the shear diagram in Fig. 5–9 (b), it is observed that the value of the maximum vertical shear is 11,000 lb; it occurs at the left reaction. We notice also that the shear passes through zero

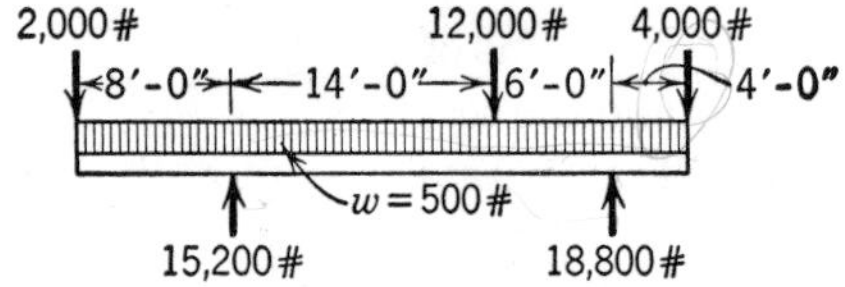

(a) Beam Diagram

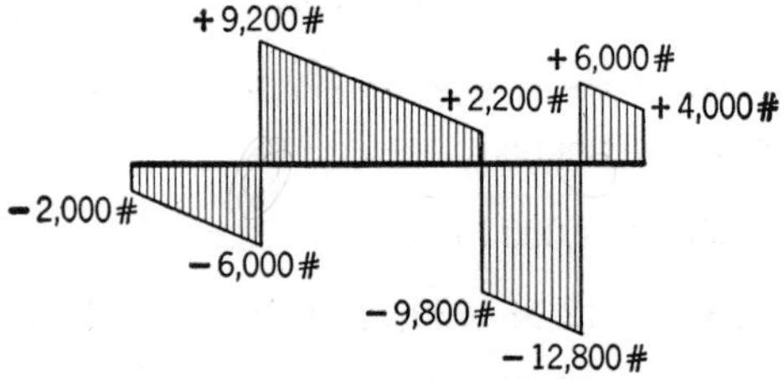

(b) Shear Diagram

FIG. 5–10

at some point between the left end of the beam and the end of the distributed load. To find the exact location of this section, let us call it x feet from R_1. Next, we write an expression for the shear at this section and equate it to zero, since the value of V at this section is zero. Then

$$11{,}000 - (1000 \times x) = 0$$

$$1000x = 11{,}000$$

and $x = 11$ ft, the section at which the shear passes through zero.

Example. Figure 5–10 (a) shows a beam overhanging both ends. A uniformly distributed load extends over the entire length of the beam, and in addition there are three concentrated loads. Construct the shear diagram. Note the magnitude of the maximum vertical shear and also the sections at which the shear passes through zero.

SOLUTION. Computing the reactions,

$$20R_1 + (4000 \times 4)$$

$$= (12{,}000 \times 6) + (2000 \times 28) + (32 \times 500 \times 12)$$

$$20R_1 = 304{,}000$$

$$R_1 = 15{,}200 \text{ lb}$$

$$20R_2 + (2000 \times 8)$$

$$= (12{,}000 \times 14) + (4000 \times 24) + (32 \times 500 \times 8)$$

$$20R_2 = 376{,}000$$

$$R_2 = 18{,}800 \text{ lb}$$

The value of the shear at a short distance to the right of the left end of the beam is -2000 lb.

$$V_{(x=8-)} = -[2000 + (8 \times 500)] = -6000 \text{ lb}$$

$$V_{(x=8+)} = 15{,}200 - [2000 + (8 \times 500)] = +9200 \text{ lb}$$

$$V_{(x=22-)} = 15{,}200 - [2000 + (22 \times 500)] = +2200 \text{ lb}$$

$$V_{(x=22+)} = 15{,}200 - [2000 + 12{,}000 + (22 \times 500)] = -9800 \text{ lb}$$

$$V_{(x=28-)} = 15{,}200 - [2000 + 12{,}000 + (28 \times 500)] = -12{,}800 \text{ lb}$$

$$V_{(x=28+)} = (15{,}200 + 18{,}800) - [2000 + 12{,}000 + (28 \times 500)]$$
$$= +6000 \text{ lb}$$

$$V_{(x=32-)} = (15{,}200 + 18{,}800) - [2000 + 12{,}000 + (32 \times 500)]$$
$$= +4000 \text{ lb}$$

The shear diagram is plotted in accordance with these computations and is shown in Fig. 5–10 (*b*). It is seen that the value of the maximum vertical shear is 12,800 lb; it occurs immediately to the left of the right reaction. It is noted also that the shear passes through zero at three different sections, at R_1, at R_2, and under the 12,000-lb load. The significance of this fact is explained in Art. 5–5.

Problems 5–4–A–B–C–D–E–F. For the beams and loads shown in Figs. 5–11 (*a*), (*b*), (*c*), (*d*), (*e*), and (*f*), draw the shear diagrams; note the values of the maximum vertical shear and the section or sections at which the shear passes through zero.

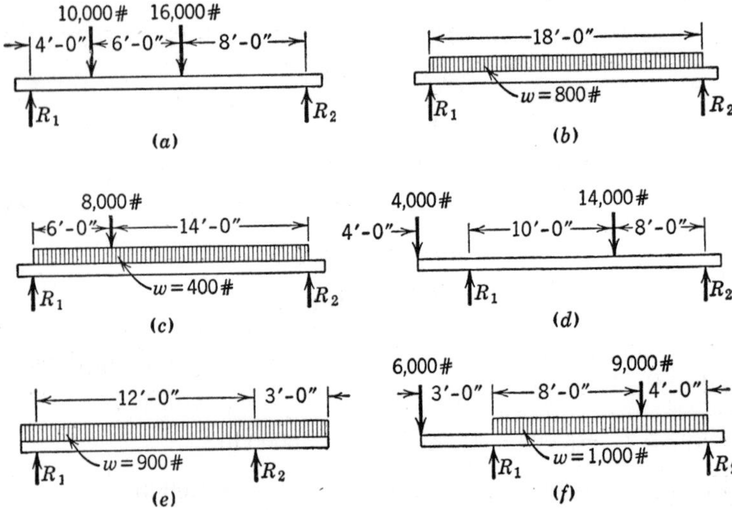

FIG. 5–11

5–5. Bending Moments. The maximum tendency of a beam to fail by bending is called the maximum bending moment. The bending moment represents the energy exerted by the loads to cause the beam to bend. The magnitude of the bending moment varies throughout the length of a beam, and the maximum value is used in determining the proper size of beam to use. It is readily computed. The maximum bending moment occurs at that section of the beam at which the shear changes from a plus to a minus quantity.

The magnitude of the bending moment at any section of a beam is equal to the algebraic sum of the moments of the forces on either the right or the left of the section. It is convenient to remember this statement in the following form: *the magnitude of the bending moment at any section of a beam is equal to the moments of the reactions minus the moments of the loads to the left of the section.* Shear and bending moment are often confused. Remember that the shear is *reactions minus loads* and that the bending moment is *moments of reactions minus moments of loads.* As a moment is the result of multiplying a force by a distance, bending moments are generally given in units of *foot-pounds* or *inch-pounds.*

To illustrate how readily this rule is applied, let us consider a simple beam supporting a concentrated load at the center of the span. We will let L be the span and P the magnitude of the concentrated load, as in Fig. 5–12 (a). Then, since the beam is symmetrically loaded, each reaction is $\frac{P}{2}$ and the shear diagram is constructed as shown in Fig. 5–12 (b). Note that the value of the maximum shear is $\frac{P}{2}$ and that the shear passes through zero at the center of the span. At this section the bending moment will be maximum. To compute its value, we apply this rule: *the bending moment at any section is equal to the moments of the reactions minus the moments of the loads to the left of the section.* The section we are considering is at $x = \frac{L}{2}$, the cen-

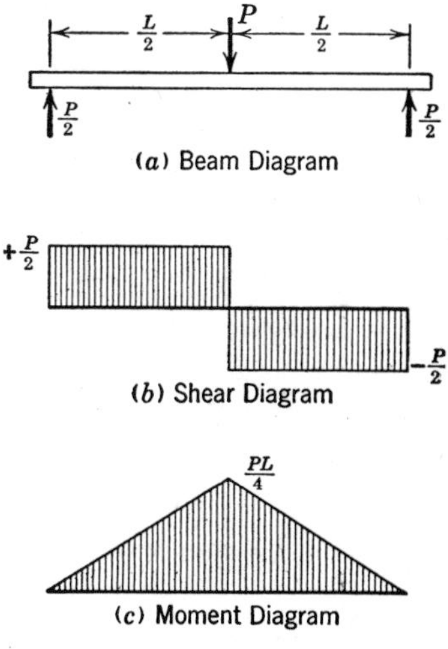

FIG. 5–12

ter of the span. We note that the reaction to the left is $\frac{P}{2}$ and its lever arm is $\frac{L}{2}$; therefore the moment of reaction is $\frac{P}{2} \times \frac{L}{2}$. Notice that there are no loads to the left. If the load P is considered, it has a lever arm of zero and thus its moment is $P \times 0$ or zero. Therefore

$$M_{(x=L/2)} = \frac{P}{2} \times \frac{L}{2} = \frac{PL}{4}$$

the maximum bending moment.

It is well to remember this value, for a simple beam with a concentrated load at the center of the span is a condition that occurs frequently in practice. The bending moment diagram is constructed as shown in Fig. 5–12 (*c*).

Another typical case is a simple beam with a uniformly distributed load extending over the full length of the beam. Let L be the length of the span and w the magnitude of the uniformly distributed load per linear foot. See Fig. 5–13 (*a*).

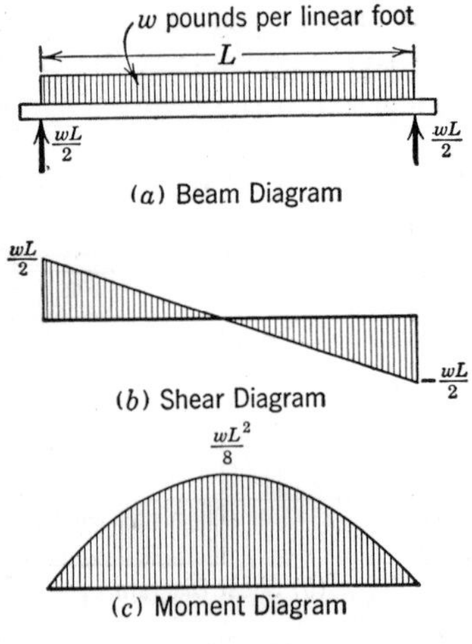

FIG. 5–13

This beam is symmetrically loaded. The total distributed load, is wL; therefore each reaction is $\frac{wL}{2}$. The shear diagram is shown in Fig. 5–13 (*b*). The maximum vertical shear is $\frac{wL}{2}$, and we note that the shear passes through zero at the center of the span, the section at which the bending moment will have a maximum value. For this section the reaction to the left is $\frac{wL}{2}$, and its lever arm is $\frac{L}{2}$. The load to the left of the section is $\frac{wL}{2}$, and its lever arm (since it acts at its center of gravity) is $\frac{L}{4}$. Then

$$M_{(x=L/2)} = \left(\frac{wL}{2} \times \frac{L}{2}\right) - \left(\frac{wL}{2} \times \frac{L}{4}\right)$$

$$M = \frac{wL^2}{4} - \frac{wL^2}{8}$$

$$M = \frac{wL^2}{8}, \text{ the maximum bending moment}$$

This value should be remembered also, for it will be used many times. In this problem the load is given as w lb per lin ft. As the beam is L ft in length, the *total* uniformly distributed load is $w \times L$, which is represented by W. Hence the maximum bending moment is either $\frac{wL^2}{8}$ or $\frac{WL}{8}$, depending on whether the load is given as pounds per foot or as the total distributed load.

The bending moment diagram for a simple beam with a uniformly distributed load is a parabola as shown in Fig. 5–13 (c).

Example. A simple beam has a span of 18 ft 0 in. with a concentrated load of 8000 lb at the center of the span. Compute the maximum bending moment.

SOLUTION. We have found that the value of the maximum bending moment for this beam and load is $\frac{PL}{4}$. For this illustrative problem $P = 8000$ lb and $L = 18$ ft 0 in. Then

$$M = \frac{PL}{4} \quad \text{or} \quad M = \frac{8000 \times 18}{4} = 36{,}000 \text{ ft-lb}$$

For the design of beams it is generally necessary that the bending moment be in units of inch-pounds. To convert foot-pounds to inch-pounds, we merely multiply the magnitude in foot-pounds by 12. Thus 36,000 ft-lb = 36,000 × 12 = 432,000 in-lb, the magnitude of the maximum bending moment.

Example. A simple beam has a span of 22 ft 0 in. and a uniformly distributed load of 300 lb per lin ft. Compute the maximum bending moment.

SOLUTION. For this typical case we have found the maximum bending moment to be $\frac{wL^2}{8}$. In this problem $w = 300$ lb and $L = 22$ ft 0 in. Then

$$M = \frac{wL^2}{8} = \frac{300 \times 22 \times 22}{8} = 18{,}150 \text{ ft-lb}$$

$18{,}150 \times 12 = 217{,}800$ in-lb, the maximum bending moment

If the load had been given as 6600 lb, the total uniformly distributed load, instead of 300 lb per lin ft, then W would be 6600 lb.

$$M = \frac{WL}{8} = \frac{6600 \times 22}{8} = 18{,}150 \text{ ft-lb} \quad \text{or} \quad 217{,}800 \text{ in-lb}$$

Example. Compute the maximum bending moment for the simple beam with two concentrated loads as shown in Fig. 5–14 (*a*).

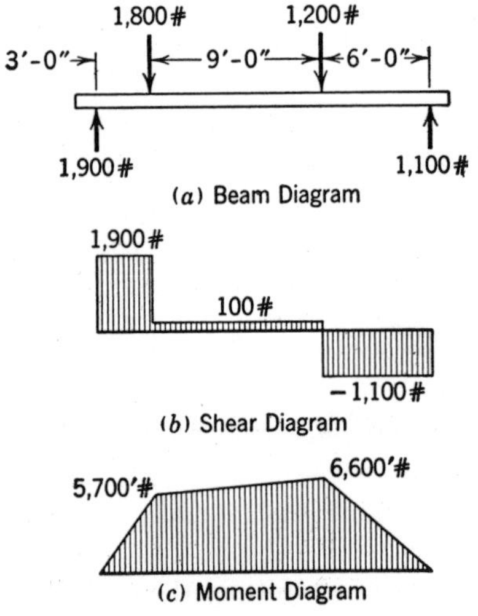

FIG. 5–14

SOLUTION. To compute the maximum bending moment, we must first determine its location; this necessitates constructing the shear diagram. First, the reactions are found.

$$18R_1 = (1800 \times 15) + (1200 \times 6)$$
$$18R_1 = 34{,}200$$
$$R_1 = 1900 \text{ lb}$$
$$18R_2 = (1800 \times 3) + (1200 \times 12)$$
$$18R_2 = 19{,}800$$
$$R_2 = 1100 \text{ lb}$$

The shear diagram is constructed as explained in Art. 5–4. It is shown in Fig. 5–14 (*b*), and we find that the shear passes through zero at the section 12 ft 0 in. from the left end of the beam. This is the section of the maximum bending moment. Then

$$M_{(x=12)} = (1900 \times 12) - (1800 \times 9) = 6600 \text{ ft-lb}$$
$$6600 \times 12 = 79{,}200 \text{ in.-lb, the maximum bending moment}$$

To construct the bending moment diagram, we need only to compute the bending moment under the 1800-lb load.

$$M_{(x=3)} = 1900 \times 3 = 5700 \text{ ft-lb} \quad \text{or} \quad 68{,}400 \text{ in-lb}$$

The bending moment diagram is shown in Fig. 5–14 (*c*).

Example. Compute the maximum bending moment for the overhanging beam shown in Fig. 5–15 (*a*). A uniformly distributed load of 600 lb per lin ft extends over the entire length of the beam.

SOLUTION. This is another illustration of a beam for which it is necessary to find first the section at which the shear passes through zero in order to compute the magnitude of the maximum bending moment. To determine the reactions,

$$20R_1 = (26 \times 600 \times 7)$$
$$20R_1 = 109{,}200$$
$$R_1 = 5460 \text{ lb}$$
$$20R_2 = (26 \times 600 \times 13)$$
$$20R_2 = 202{,}800$$
$$R_2 = 10{,}140 \text{ lb}$$

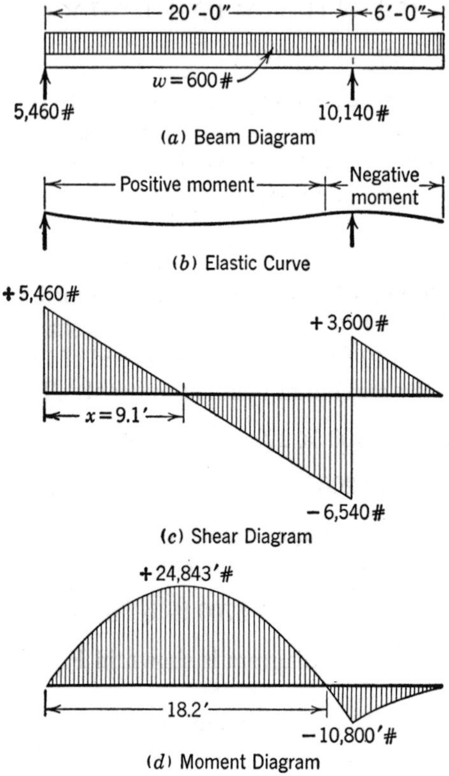

FIG. 5–15

The shear diagram is constructed as shown in Fig. 5–15 (*c*). We find that the maximum vertical shear is 6540 lb and that the shear passes through zero at two places: one at some point between the two reactions and the other directly above the right reaction. To find the exact position of the first section, we will call it x ft from R_1, write an expression for the shear at this section and equate it to zero:

$$5460 - (600 \times x) = 0$$

$$600x = 5460$$

$$x = 9.1 \text{ ft}$$

Then

$$M_{(x=9.1)} = (5460 \times 9.1) - (600 \times 9.1 \times 4.55) = +24{,}843 \text{ ft-lb}$$

$$M_{(x=20)} = (5460 \times 20) - (600 \times 20 \times 10) = -10{,}800 \text{ ft-lb}$$

It should be noted that the bending moment at 9.1 ft from R_1 is a positive quantity and that the bending moment at R_2 is negative. See Fig. 5–15 (*d*). When the fibers above the neutral surface of a beam resist compressive stresses, we say the bending moment is positive. However, when the fibers above the neutral surface resist tensile stresses, the bending moment is negative. Figure 5–15 (*b*) shows the curve the beam tends to take as it bends under the uniformly distributed load. Note that a portion of the beam is concave upward and that the remaining portion is concave downward. This shows graphically the extent of positive and negative bending moments. The section of the beam at which the bending moment is zero is called the *inflection point;* it is the section at which the elastic curve changes from concave to convex.

To find the position of the inflection point let us call it x ft from R_1. For this section we will write an expression for the bending moment and equate it to zero:

$$(5460 \times x) - \left(600 \times x \times \frac{x}{2}\right) = 0$$

$$\frac{600x^2}{2} - 5460x = 0$$

$$x^2 - 18.2x = 0$$

Completing the square,

$$x^2 - 18.2x + 82.81 = 82.81$$

Extracting the square root of both sides,

$$x - 9.1 = 9.1$$

$$x = 18.2 \text{ ft}$$

The position of the inflection point for steel and timber beams is relatively unimportant, but it is of vital importance that its position be known in the design of reinforced concrete.

For this particular beam the maximum bending moment is 24,843 ft-lb. The negative bending moment is of lesser magnitude. In the design of such a beam the bending moment having the greater numerical value is the moment used in computations, regardless of whether it is positive or negative.

Problems 5–5–A–B–C–D–E–F. For the beams shown in Figs. 5–16 (*a*), (*b*), (*c*), (*d*), (*e*), and (*f*), draw the shear and moment diagrams. In each instance

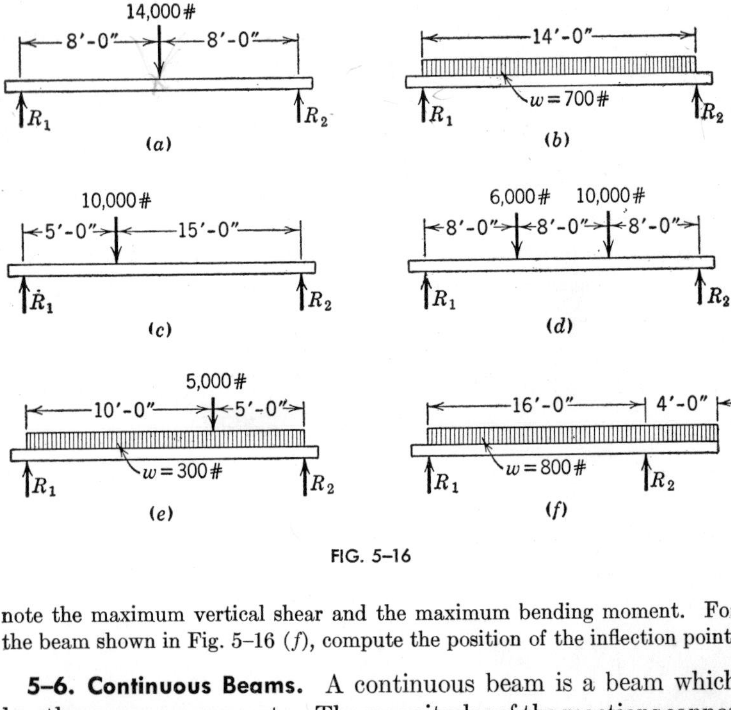

FIG. 5–16

note the maximum vertical shear and the maximum bending moment. For the beam shown in Fig. 5–16 (*f*), compute the position of the inflection point.

5–6. Continuous Beams. A continuous beam is a beam which has three or more supports. The magnitudes of the reactions cannot be determined solely by the principle of moments employed for beams having only two supports, and a discussion of the necessary computations is beyond the scope of this text.* Continuous beams are common in reinforced concrete structures but they occur rather infrequently in timber construction.

Figure 5–17 shows a number of typical beams and loads. The

* See Chapter 9 of *Simplified Mechanics and Strength of Materials*, Second Edition, by Harry Parker, John Wiley and Sons, New York, 1961.

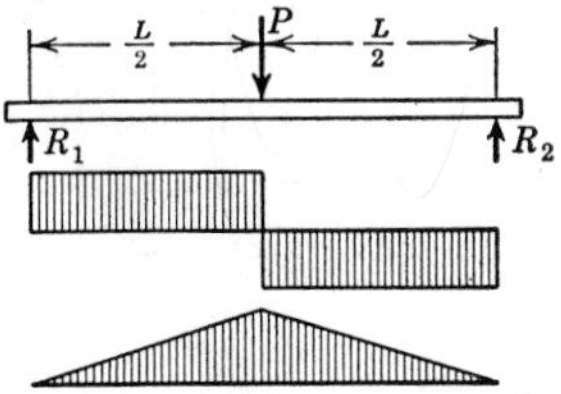

Case I $R_1 = R_2 = \frac{P}{2}$ Max. $V = \frac{P}{2}$

Max. $M = \frac{PL}{4}$ $D = \frac{Pl^3}{48EI}$

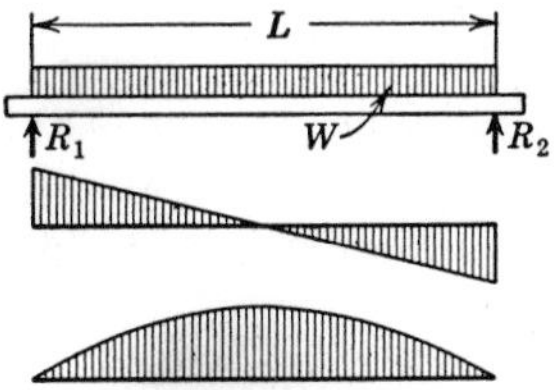

Case II $R_1 = R_2 = \frac{W}{2}$ Max. $V = \frac{W}{2}$

Max. $M = \frac{WL}{8}$ $D = \frac{5}{384} \times \frac{Wl^3}{EI}$

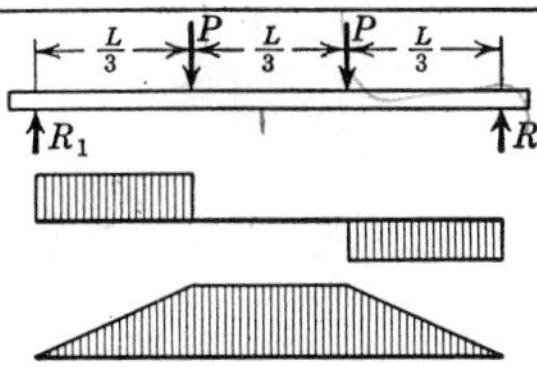

Case III $R_1 = R_2 = P$ Max. $V = P$

Max. $M = \frac{PL}{3}$ $D = \frac{23}{648} \times \frac{Pl^3}{EI}$

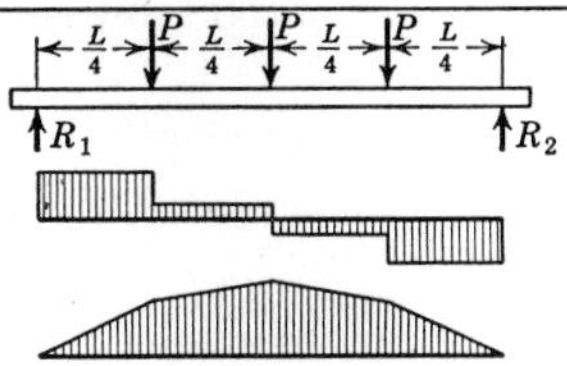

Case IV $R_1 = R_2 = \frac{3P}{2}$ Max. $V = \frac{3P}{2}$

Max. $M = \frac{PL}{2}$ $D = \frac{19}{384} \times \frac{Pl^3}{EI}$

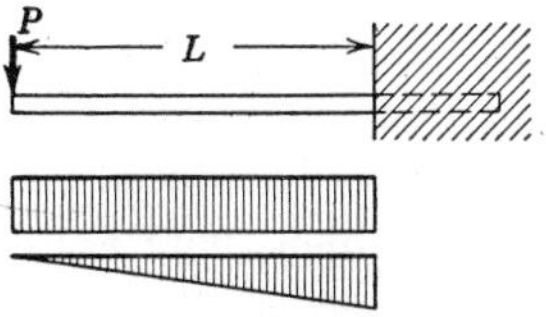

Case V $R = P$ Max. $V = P$

Max. $M = PL$ $D = \frac{Pl^3}{3EI}$

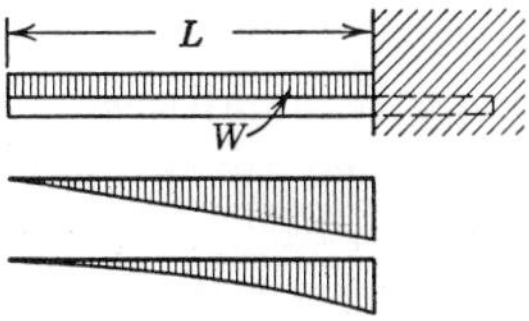

Case VI $R = W$ Max. $V = W$

Max. $M = \frac{WL}{2}$ $D = \frac{Wl^3}{8EI}$

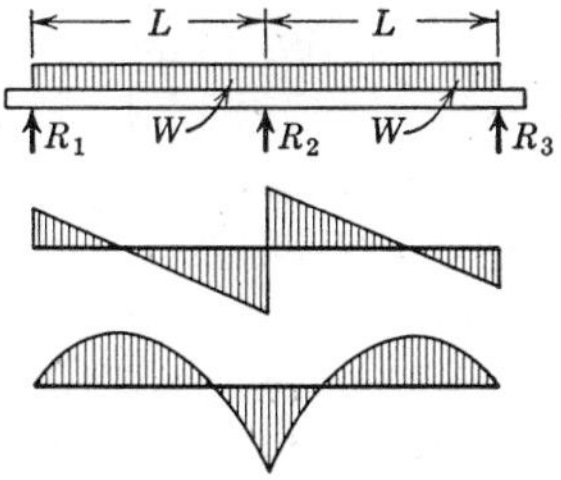

Case VII $R_1 = R_3 = \frac{3}{8} W$ $R_2 = \frac{10}{8} W$

Max. $V = \frac{5}{8} W$ Max. $M = \frac{WL}{8}$

$D = \frac{Wl^3}{185EI}$

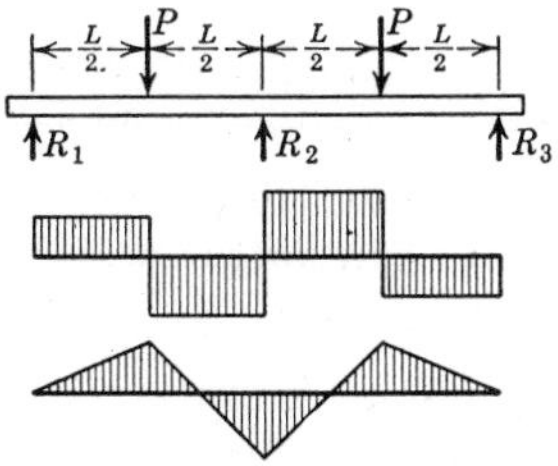

Case VIII $R_1 = R_3 = \frac{5}{16} P$ $R_2 = \frac{22}{16} P$

Max. $V = \frac{11}{16} P$ Max. $M = \frac{6}{32} PL$

FIG. 5–17

beams shown include simple beams, cantilever beams, and two continuous beams. The diagrams indicate the shear and moment distribution as well as the values of the maximum shear, the maximum bending moments, and the maximum deflections. In using the values given, note the significance of the letters and terms:

P = the concentrated load, in pounds
W = the total uniformly distributed load, in pounds; if in problems the load is given in pounds per linear foot, w, the total distributed load is wL or W, in which L is the span length in feet
L = the span length, in feet
l = the span length, in inches
V = the maximum vertical shear, in pounds
M = the maximum bending moment, in foot-pounds
D = the maximum deflection in inches; in giving the maximum deflection note that the term l^3 occurs; l is the span length, *in inches*

Cases VII and VIII show continuous beams in which the central support is equidistant from the two end supports. Case VII, showing a continuous beam with a uniformly distributed load of W pounds for each span, and Case VIII, in which there are concentrated loads of P pounds each at the centers of the spans, illustrate conditions that sometimes occur in timber construction. For these two cases, the maximum bending moment occurs over the central support and is a negative quantity. The maximum positive moments for Case VII and Case VIII are $\frac{WL}{14.2}$ and $\frac{5PL}{32}$, respectively. In the design of beams the maximum value is considered regardless of whether it is positive or negative.

Example. A continuous beam has two equal spans of 10 ft 0 in. each and a uniformly distributed load of 10,000 lb extending over *each* span. Construct the shear and bending-moment diagrams and note the magnitudes of the maximum shear and maximum bending moment. The beam diagram is shown in Fig. 5–18 (a). Note that there will be two inflection points.

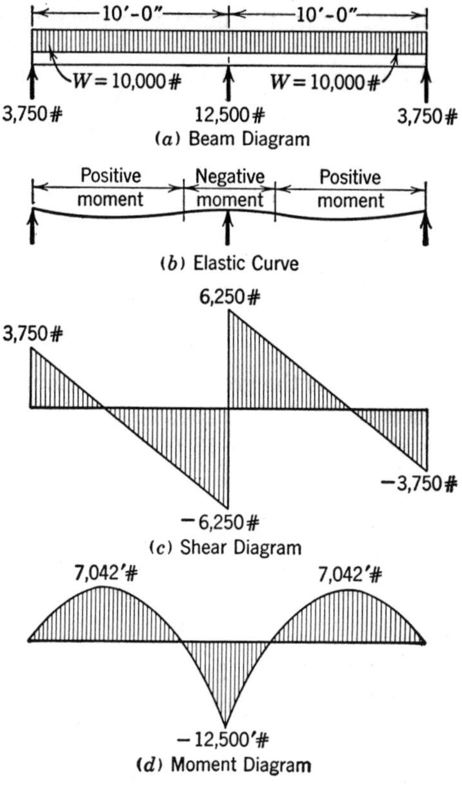

FIG. 5–18

SOLUTION. The first step is to determine the magnitudes of the reactions. Referring to Fig. 5–17, Case VII, we see that R_1 and R_3, the end reactions, $= \frac{3}{8}W$. Then

$$R_1 = R_3 = \tfrac{3}{8}W = \tfrac{3}{8} \times 10{,}000 = 3750 \text{ lb}$$

R_2, the center reaction, $= \frac{10}{8}W = \frac{10}{8} \times 10{,}000 = 12{,}500$ lb

As explained in Art. 5–4, the magnitudes of the vertical shear are computed in various sections of the beam, and the shear diagram is plotted as shown in Fig. 5–18 (c). Note that Fig. 5–17, Case VII, shows the maximum vertical shear to be $V = \frac{5}{8}W$ or $V = \frac{5}{8} \times$ 10,000 or 6250 lb. For a continuous beam of two equal spans with uniformly distributed loads, the maximum positive bending moment is $\frac{WL}{14.2}$ and the maximum negative moment is $\frac{WL}{8}$. Therefore

$$M = \frac{WL}{14.2} = \frac{10{,}000 \times 10}{14.2} = 7042 \text{ ft-lb, the maximum positive bending moment}$$

$$M = \frac{WL}{8} = \frac{10{,}000 \times 10}{8} = 12{,}500 \text{ ft-lb, the maximum negative bending moment}$$

Since the negative value is the greater, the maximum bending moment in the beam is 12,500 ft-lb or 150,000 in-lb. The bending moment diagram is shown in Fig. 5–18 (*d*).

Problem 5–6–A. The two spans of a continuous beam are each 10 ft 0 in. in length. There are concentrated loads of 4000 lb each at the center of each span. Construct the shear and moment diagrams and note the magnitude of the maximum shear and the maximum bending moment. *Note:* See Fig. 5–17, Case VIII.

5–7. Concentrated Loads on Beams. We assume that floor boards exert a uniformly distributed load on the joists on which they are supported. When the joists frame into or are supported by beams, the joists exert concentrated loads on the beams at uniform intervals.

Consider a 20 x 18 ft floor area that is supported by a simple beam having a span of 20 ft. The dead plus live load on the floor area is 100 psf. Hence 20 × 18 × 100 or 36,000 lb is the total floor load to be supported by the beam. If this load is uniformly distributed on the beam, the values of the vertical shear and bending moments are computed as previously described, and the shear and moment diagrams are constructed as shown in Fig. 5–19(*a*). Note that the maximum bending moment is 90,000 ft-lb and that the bending moment curve is a parabola. See Fig. 5–17, Case II.

Now imagine the same floor load transferred to the beam by smaller beams spaced 10 ft apart over the floor area. This, then, consists of a beam at the center of the 20 ft span with other beams framing to the 20-ft beam at its supports. Only the beam at the center of the span produces bending stresses in the 20-ft beam.

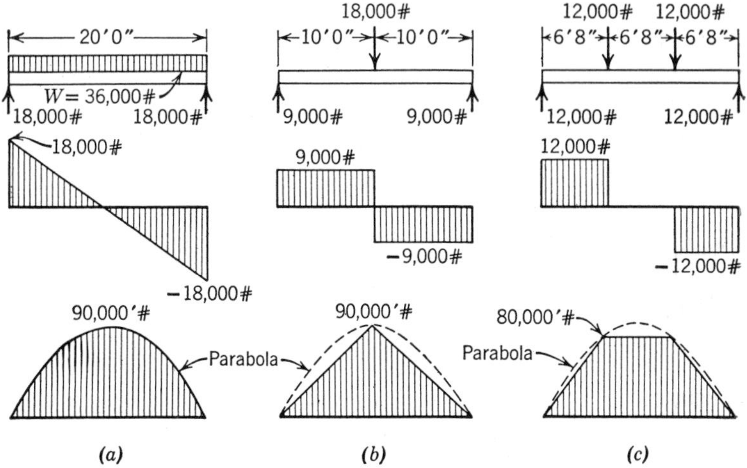

FIG. 5–19

The concentrated load at the center of the span is 10 × 18 × 100 or 18,000 lb. This loading is similar to that shown in Fig. 5–17, Case I. The values of the shear and moment are computed in the usual manner, and the shear and moment diagrams are constructed as shown in Fig. 5–19 (*b*). Note that the value of the maximum bending moment is also 90,000 ft-lb and that the moment curve is a triangle inscribed in a parabola similar to that shown in Fig. 5–19 (*a*).

Regardless of the number of equal concentrated loads into which this 36,000-lb floor load is divided, the bending moment diagram will be a polygon inscribed in a parabola, the greatest ordinate (greatest height) of which will be 90,000 ft-lb. These concentrated loads may be exerted by joists, beams, or columns. The value of the maximum bending moment will always be equal to $\frac{Wl}{8}$ if one of the concentrated loads is located at the center of the span and, if one of the loads does not occur at the center of the span, the moment is something less than $\frac{Wl}{8}$. Consequently, for this type of loading it is always safe to design a beam loaded with concentrated loads as though the total load on the floor area is distributed uniformly on the beam.

For joists (or beams) equally spaced, the bending moment is exactly equal to $\frac{Wl}{8}$ *if the number of spaces is even. If the number of spaces is odd, the moment is reduced by the ratio of* $\frac{1}{(\textit{number of spaces})^2}$. For example, if there are five spaces, $M = \frac{Wl}{8} - \left(\frac{1}{5^2} \times \frac{Wl}{8}\right)$.

Suppose that the 36,000-lb load on the floor panel is transferred to the 20-ft beam by concentrated loads at the third points of span. Then, $\frac{20}{3} \times 18 \times 100 = 12{,}000$ lb, the magnitude of each of the concentrated loads. Figure 5–17, Case III, shows the maximum bending moment for this type of loading to be $M = \frac{Pl}{3}$ or $M = 12{,}000 \times \left(\frac{20}{3}\right) = 80{,}000$ ft-lb. The shear and moment diagrams are shown in Fig. 5–19 (*c*). Now let us test the foregoing rule. The maximum bending moment for this loading is $90{,}000 - \left(\frac{1}{3^2} \times 90{,}000\right)$ or 80,000 ft-lb, which, of course, is the same value previously found. And, if there are 5 equal spaces, $M = 90{,}000 - \left(\frac{1}{5^2} \times 90{,}000\right)$ or 86,400 ft-lb.

Problem 5–7–A. Floor joists spaced 16 in. on centers transfer a total floor load of 20,000 lb to a simple beam, the span of which is 20 ft 0 in. Compute the maximum bending moment on the beam.

Problem 5–7–B. A floor load of 21,600 lb is transferred to a simple beam, having a span of 20 ft, by floor joists. (*a*) Compute the maximum bending moment in the beam if the joists are spaced 12 in. on centers. (*b*) What is the maximum bending moment if the joist spacing is 16 in. on centers?

CHAPTER 6

SHEARING STRESSES IN BEAMS

6–1. Vertical Shear. The shearing stresses in beams have been referred to in Art. 2–4. The tendency for a beam to fail by vertical shear is illustrated in Fig. 2–2 (*b*). This type of shear actually is cross-grain shear; failures of this type seldom occur, and ordinarily it is unnecessary to investigate cross-grain or vertical shearing unit stresses. For simple beams the maximum vertical shear has the magnitude of the greater reaction. The computations for determining the magnitude of the vertical shear V are explained in Art. 5–4.

6–2. Horizontal Shear in Rectangular Beams. Any beam subjected to vertical shear is also subjected to horizontal shear. Horizontal shear is the tendency of one part of a beam to slide horizontally on an adjacent part. This type of failure is illustrated in Fig. 2–2 (*c*). The stresses are not equally distributed over the cross-sectional area, and for rectangular beams the greatest horizontal shearing unit stress is at the neutral surface. The formula used to compute the maximum horizontal shearing unit stress for unchecked *rectangular* beams is

$$q = \frac{3V}{2bh}$$

in which q = the maximum horizontal shearing unit stress, in pounds per square inch
V = the maximum vertical shear, in pounds
b = the width of the beam, in inches
h = the depth of the beam, in inches

In some textbooks the letters v and d are used instead of q and h, respectively. When so used, the formula for shear becomes

$$v = \frac{3V}{2bd}$$

This formula is derived in Art. 6–3; it applies only to rectangular cross sections. It errs on the side of safety, for it indicates greater shearing stresses than actually occur. In computing the value of the reactions, smaller magnitudes may be found by using the procedure explained later.

In investigating the shearing stress, it is customary to begin by using the above formula; if q is found to be not in excess of H, the allowable shearing stress, the beam is accepted for shear. However, if q exceeds H, q is again computed, using one of the procedures given below.

The allowable horizontal shearing stress for various species and grades of lumber is found in Table 3–1. It is identified by the letter H. Some building codes permit unit shearing stresses to be 50 per cent greater in joint details than the horizontal shearing stresses otherwise permitted.

In nearly all structural lumber checks and shakes are present. Because of their presence, the upper and lower portions of a beam act partly as two beams and partly as a unit. The following procedure for computation of the horizontal shear takes into account this two-beam action.

In computing the horizontal shearing unit stress on the neutral surface in checked rectangular beams, the Forest Products Laboratory recommends:

1. Use of the ordinary shear formula given above.
2. Use of the allowable shearing unit stresses, H, given in Table 3–1.

In calculating the reactions for use in the formula, (*a*) neglect all loads within a distance equal to the height of the beam from both supports; (*b*) if there are any moving loads, place the largest one at three times the depth of the beam from the support or at the quarter point, whichever is closer to the support.

If the beam does not qualify for shear resistance under the foregoing procedure, the reactions may be determined by these formulas:

For a concentrated load

$$R = \frac{10P(l - x)\left(\frac{x}{h}\right)^2}{9l\left[2 + \left(\frac{x}{h}\right)^2\right]}$$

For a uniformly distributed load

$$R = \frac{W}{2}\left(1 - \frac{2h}{l}\right)$$

in which R = the modified reaction, in pounds
P = the magnitude of the concentrated load, in pounds
W = total uniformly distributed load, in pounds
l = the span length of the beam, in inches
x = the distance from the reaction to the load P, in inches
h = the depth of the beam, in inches

Example. A simple beam having a span of 14 ft 0 in. has a uniformly distributed load of 800 lb per lin ft. A 10 x 14 in. timber of No. 2 SR grade of Southern pine is used. Is the beam safe with respect to horizontal shear?

SOLUTION. Referring to Table 3–1, we find H, the allowable horizontal shearing unit stress, to be 105 psi. Table 3–3 shows that the dressed size of a 10 x 14 in. section is 9.5 x 13.5 in.

The total load on the beam is 14 × 800 or 11,200 lb; therefore each reaction is $11{,}200 \times \frac{1}{2} = 5600$ lb. This, then, is V, the maximum vertical shear. To compute the maximum horizontal shearing unit stress, we use the formula

$$q = \frac{3V}{2bh} \quad \text{or} \quad q = \frac{3 \times 5600}{2 \times 9.5 \times 13.5} \quad \text{and} \quad q = 66 \text{ psi}$$

the shearing unit stress.

We see that 66 psi is well below 105 psi, the allowable stress; hence the beam is safe with respect to horizontal shear. The foregoing procedure is usually followed. However, if the stress had been found to be greater than the allowable, the method of neglecting a portion of the distributed load at each end of the beam in computing V could be investigated. Although unnecessary in this problem, the following explains how the method is employed.

In using this method of determining the horizontal shearing unit stress, it is noted above that all loads for a distance equal to the height of the beam from both supports are to be neglected. As the depth of the beam is 14 in., or 1.166 ft, the loaded length of span to be considered is (14 − 2.33) ft. The load per linear foot is 800 lb; hence each modified reaction (V, in formula) is $\frac{800 \times (14 - 2.33)}{2}$ or 4668 lb. Then $q = \frac{3V}{2bh} = \frac{3 \times 4668}{2 \times 9.5 \times 13.5} = 55$ psi, the maximum horizontal shearing unit stress. Since this is less than the allowable stress of 105 psi given in Table 3–1, the beam is safe with respect to horizontal shear.

Example. A simple beam has a span of 16 ft 0 in. and a concentrated load of 8000 lb at the center of the span. The timber used is a 12 x 14 in. for which the allowable horizontal shearing unit stress is 120 psi. Investigate the horizontal shearing unit stress.

SOLUTION. Since the beam is symmetrically loaded, each reaction is equal to $\frac{8000}{2}$ or 4000 lb. Then

$$q = \frac{3V}{2bh} = \frac{3 \times 4000}{2 \times 11.5 \times 13.5} = 39 \text{ psi}$$

the maximum horizontal shearing unit stress. As this stress is less than 120 psi, the allowable, the 12 x 14 in. beam is adequate with respect to horizontal shear.

Example. A 12 x 14 in. timber of the Select Structural grade of Douglas fir has a span of 20 ft 0 in. Two loads of 8000 and 4000 lb, 6 ft 0 in. apart, roll over the beam; they constitute a condition of moving loads. Investigate the horizontal shearing unit stress.

SOLUTION. In Table 3–1 we find the allowable shearing unit stress for this timber to be 120 psi. A 12 x 14 in. beam has a dressed size of 11.5 x 13.5 in.

In accordance with the foregoing instructions for computing the reactions, place the 8000-lb load at (3 × 13.5) or 3.37 ft from the left reaction. The two moving loads now take the positions shown in Fig. 6–1. One fourth the span length is 20 × ¼ or 5 ft. At 3.37

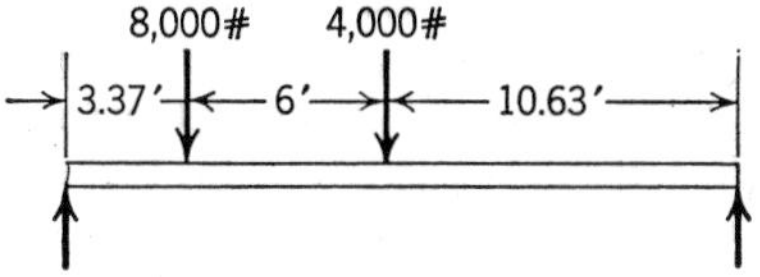

FIG. 6–1

ft, the 8000-lb load is closer to the support than one fourth the span length. With the loads in the positions shown in Fig. 6–1, we compute R_1. Thus

$$20R_1 = (8000 \times 16.63) + (4000 \times 10.63)$$

and

$$R_1 = 8778 \text{ lb}$$

Then

$$V = 8778 \text{ lb, the maximum vertical shear}$$

Substituting in the equation $q = \frac{3}{2} \times \frac{V}{bh}$, $q = \frac{3}{2} \times \frac{8778}{11.5 \times 13.5}$ and $q = 85$ psi, the maximum horizontal shearing unit stress. Since this stress is less than 120 psi, the allowable, the timber is accepted for horizontal shear.

In the design of beams it is customary first to determine the size of the beam to withstand the bending stresses. When the beam dimensions have thus been established, the beam is investigated for horizontal shear. Is or is not the beam of adequate dimensions to result in a horizontal shearing unit stress that does not exceed the allowable? Consequently, the formula $q = \frac{3}{2} \times \frac{V}{bh}$ is tried. If q is found to exceed the allowable, the beam is further investigated by making use of modified reactions as explained in the foregoing discussion. This procedure may be employed in solving the following problems.

Problem 6–2–A. A simple Southern pine beam has a span of 12 ft 0 in. and a uniformly distributed load of 1200 lb per lin ft. If the timber is a 10 x 12 in., for which the allowable horizontal shearing unit stress is 105 psi, is the beam large enough with respect to horizontal shear?

Problem 6–2–B. A 10 x 14 in. timber is used for a beam having a span of 15 ft 0 in. with a concentrated load of 9000 lb at 5 ft 0 in. from one end. Compute the horizontal shearing unit stress.

Problem 6–2–C. A simple beam having a span of 20 ft 0 in. has a concentrated load of 8000 lb at 6 ft 0 in. from the left support and a concentrated load of 1200 lb at 4 ft 0 in. from the right support. If the timber is a 12 x 14 in., compute the horizontal shearing unit stress.

6–3. Horizontal Shear. In Art. 6–2 we used the formula

$$q = \frac{3V}{2bh}$$

to determine the maximum horizontal shearing stress for beams having a rectangular cross section. The timber beams commonly used have rectangular cross sections, hence this formula is generally appropriate. In recent years great advances have been made in the fabrication of timber beams of various sizes and shapes. Glued laminated beams are often employed and I- and box beams are built-up to comply with special requirements. To find the horizontal shearing stresses for beams in which the cross sections are not rectangular, we use the general formula for shear

$$q = \frac{VQ}{Ib}$$

in which q = the horizontal shearing unit stress at any specific point in the cross section of the beam, in pounds per square inch

V = the total vertical shear in the beam at the section selected, in pounds

Q = the statical moment with respect to the neutral axis of the area of the cross section above (or below) the point at which q is to be determined, in units of inches^3; a statical moment is an area multiplied by the distance of its centroid to a given axis

I = the moment of inertia of the cross section of the beam with respect to its neutral axis, in units of inches^4

b = the width of the beam at the point at which q is to be computed, in inches

Consider the rectangular cross section of which b and d are the width and depth, respectively, as shown in Fig. 6–2 (a). Let us

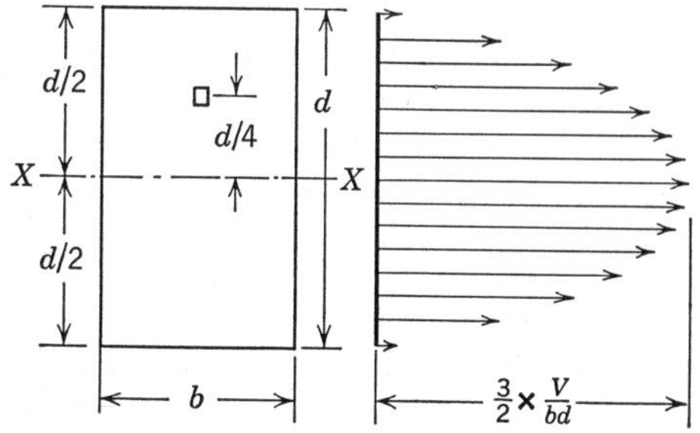

(a) (b)

FIG. 6–2

compute, by use of the general formula, the maximum horizontal shearing stress *at the neutral axis X–X.*

The area above the neutral axis is $\left(b \times \frac{d}{2}\right)$ and its centroid * is $\frac{d}{4}$ distance from the neutral axis.

$$Q = \left(b \times \frac{d}{2}\right) \times \frac{d}{4} = \frac{bd^2}{8}$$

From Art. 4–4 we know that the moment of inertia $I = \frac{bd^3}{12}$.

Then

$$q = \frac{VQ}{Ib} = \frac{V \times \frac{bd^2}{8}}{\frac{bd^3}{12} \times b} \quad \text{and} \quad q = \frac{3}{2} \times \frac{V}{bd}$$

the formula used to compute the maximum horizontal shearing unit stress for *rectangular* sections. Note that the letters d and h for the depth of the beam are used interchangeably. The horizontal shearing stresses are not equally distributed over the area of

* A centroid of a plane area is a point that corresponds to the center of gravity of a very thin homogeneous plate of the same area and shape.

the cross section. These stresses are indicated by the lengths of the arrows in Fig. 6–2 (*b*), the maximum stress being at the neutral surface.

Another use for the general formula for horizontal shear is to determine the stress at glue lines of built-up timber beams. The following is an example.

Example. Determine the shearing unit stress at the glue line of the box beam shown in Fig. 6–3 when the maximum vertical shear is 6400 lb.

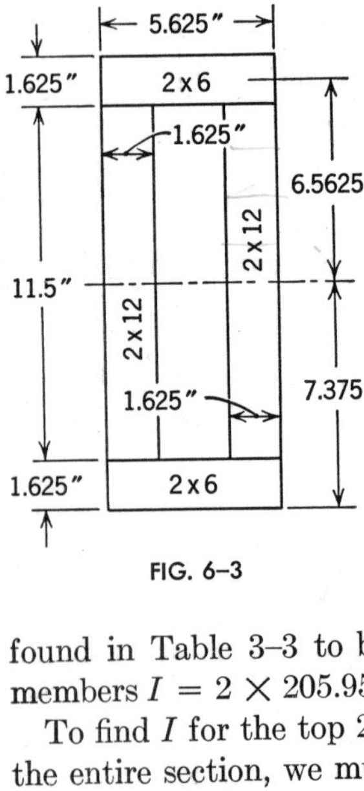

FIG. 6–3

SOLUTION. The key to the solution of this problem is the formula

$$q = \frac{VQ}{Ib}$$

We will determine the horizontal shearing stress in the glue joint under the upper 2 x 6 in. section. Then Q, the statical moment of the 2 x 6 in. top (or bottom) member of the box beam, $= (1.625 \times 5.625) \times 6.5625 = 60.$

Next, we will compute I, the moment of inertia of the beam cross section with respect to its neutral axis. The I for one 2 x 12 in. member is found in Table 3–3 to be 205.95 in.^{4}, and for the two 2 x 12 in. members $I = 2 \times 205.95$ or 412 in.^{4}

To find I for the top 2 x 6 in. member about the neutral axis of the entire section, we must use the transfer formula given in Art. 4–5.

$$I_1 = I_0 + Ah^2$$

Referring to Table 3–3, we see that I for a 2 x 6 in. section about an axis through its centroid *parallel to a long side* is 2.01 in.^{4} Its area is (1.625×5.625) or 9.14 sq in., and, from Fig. 6–3, $h =$ 6.5625 in. Substituting in the above formula,

$$I_1 = 2.01 + (9.14 \times 6.5625^2) \quad \text{and} \quad I = 395 \text{ in.}^4$$

For the two 2 x 6s, $I = 2 \times 395$ or 790 in.^{4} Then for the entire cross section $I = 412 + 790$ or 1202 in.^{4}

The width of the beam *at the glue line* is 2×1.625 or $b = 3.25$ in. Substituting these values in the general formula for horizontal shear,

$$q = \frac{VQ}{Ib} = \frac{6400 \times 60}{1202 \times 3.25}$$

and $q = 98$ psi, the shearing stress at the glue line.

Problem 6–3–A. Four pieces of timber are glued together to form a box beam similar to that shown in Fig. 6–3. The upper and lower members are 3 x 6s and the two vertical side members are 2 x 10s. The maximum vertical shear for this box beam is 4000 lb. Compute the shearing unit stress at the glue line.

CHAPTER 7

COMPRESSION PERPENDICULAR TO GRAIN

7–1. Beam Bearings. In addition to bending and shearing stresses in beams, beam bearings must have ample dimensions to result in compressive stresses perpendicular to the grain that do not exceed the allowable. The allowable stresses given in Table 3–1 apply to bearings of any length at the ends of beams and to all bearings 6 in. or more in length at any other location.

For bearings shorter than 6 in. in length and not nearer than 3 in. to the end of a member the maximum allowable load per square inch may be increased by multiplying the allowable unit stresses in compression perpendicular to the grain by the following factor:

$$\frac{l + \frac{3}{8}}{l}$$

in which l is the length in bearing, in inches, measured along the grain of the wood. These multiplying factors for the bearing lengths indicated are given in Table 7–1. For stress under a washer or other round bearing area, the same factor may be taken as for a bearing whose length equals the diameter of the washer.

In joists supported on a ribbon or ledger board and spiked to the studs the allowable stresses given in Table 3–1 for compression perpendicular to the grain may be increased 50 per cent.

Example. A beam of the No. 2 SR grade of Southern pine supports a load from a 4 x 6 in. post at the center of the span. Compute the maximum allowable load the post can exert on the beam.

SOLUTION. In Table 3–3 we find the dressed size of a 4 x 6 in. post to be $3\frac{5}{8}$ x $5\frac{5}{8}$ in. Table 3–1 shows the allowable compressive

TABLE 7–1. FACTORS FOR INCREASING WORKING STRESSES FOR DIFFERENT BEARING LENGTHS

Length of Bearings, in Inches	Factor
$\frac{1}{2}$	1.75
1	1.38
$1\frac{1}{2}$	1.25
2	1.19
3	1.13
4	1.10
6 or more	1.00

Reproduced by permission of the National Lumber Manufacturers Association.

unit stress perpendicular to the grain of the beam to be 390 psi.

The post has a bearing length of 3.625 in.; hence the factor to use in determining the allowable stress is

$$\frac{l + \frac{3}{8}}{l} \quad \text{or} \quad \frac{3.625 + 0.375}{3.625} = 1.1$$

Thus $390 \times 1.1 = 429$ psi. A $3\frac{5}{8}$ x $5\frac{5}{8}$ in. cross section contains 20.39 sq in. Therefore $20.39 \times 429 = 8750$ lb, the maximum allowable concentrated load on the beam from the 4 x 6 in. post.

Example. A Douglas fir beam of the Dense construction grade has a nominal width of 8 in. and a bearing length of 6 in. at its supports. With respect to compression perpendicular to the grain, compute the maximum reaction that is permitted for this beam.

SOLUTION. The dressed dimension of a nominal 8-in. width is 7.5 in. (Table 3–3). Hence the bearing area is 7.5×6 or 45.0 sq in. In Table 3–1 we find that the allowable compressive unit stress perpendicular to the grain for this grade of Douglas fir is 455 psi.

Therefore, since the area in bearing is 45 sq in., 455 $\times$ 45 = 20,470 lb, the maximum reaction.

Problem 7–1–A. A beam of the 1300 *f* grade of white oak supports 4 x 4 in. posts at various intervals in its length. With respect to compression perpendicular to the grain, compute the maximum load a 4 x 4 in. post is permitted to exert on the beam.

Problem 7–1–B. A 6 x 12 in. beam of the heart structural grade of redwood is supported at a girder by a metal beam hanger as indicated in Fig. 9–5 (*b*). The bearing length on the hanger is 2 in. Compute the maximum bearing stress permitted on the hanger.

CHAPTER 8

DEFLECTION OF BEAMS

8–1. Deflection of Beams. The deformation that accompanies bending is called *deflection*. It is the vertical distance moved by a point on the neutral surface when the beam bends. A certain degree of deflection exists in all beams, and the designer must see that the deflection does not exceed certain prescribed limits. It is important to understand that the dimensions of a beam may be adequate to support the imposed loads, but the deflection may be so great that cracks may develop in a plastered ceiling below or a floor may vibrate noticeably. In other words, a beam should be designed for strength in bending and also for *stiffness.*

The allowable limit for the deflection of beams in floor construction that supports plastered ceilings or partitions is generally taken to be $\frac{1}{360}$ of the span. For such construction an initial deflection due to the dead load (the weight of the materials of construction) occurs before the plaster is applied. It is for this reason that the dead load is sometimes omitted in the computations for determining deflection.

Some authorities consider the allowable deflection limit for beams that do not support plastering to be $\frac{1}{240}$ of the span length; for highway bridges the limit is frequently $\frac{1}{200}$ of the span.

When green timber is used, the deflection increases beyond the deflection that occurs immediately after the load is first applied. This is termed *sag.* When the timber is green, it is customary in computations to double the dead load but not the live load to provide for sag. When the design load is permanently applied, lumber acquires a permanent set about equal to the original deflection, but the strength is not reduced.

Example. A beam having a span of 18 ft 0 in. supports a plastered ceiling. What is the allowable deflection?

SOLUTION. The span length is 18 ft 0 in. or 216 in. As the allowable deflection is $\frac{1}{360}$ of the span, the allowable deflection is $\frac{1}{360} \times 216$ or 0.6 in.

8–2. Computations for Deflection. The investigation of a beam for deflection consists in computing the *actual deflection* and comparing it with the *allowable deflection*. As has been explained, for beams supporting plastered ceilings or partitions the allowable deflection limit is generally given in building codes as $\frac{1}{360}$ of the span. The formulas used to determine the actual deflection for several of the most common beams and loads are found in Fig. 5–17. In these formulas note the significance of the terms. Note particularly that l, the span length, is in *inches*.

D = the maximum vertical deflection, in inches
P = the concentrated load, in pounds
W = the total uniformly distributed load, in pounds
l = the span length, *in inches*
E = the modulus of elasticity of the beam material, in pounds per square inch
I = the moment of inertia of the beam cross section, in inches^4

Example. A 12 x 16 in. Southern pine simple beam has a span of 18 ft 0 in. and a total uniformly distributed load of 21,600 lb. If this beam supports a plastered ceiling, is the deflection excessive?

SOLUTION. Referring to Table 3–1 we find that E, the modulus of elasticity for this timber, is 1,760,000 psi. Table 3–3 shows I, the moment of inertia, of a 12 ft x 16 in. cross section to be 3,568.71 in.^{4} The formula used to compute the actual deflection for a simple beam with a uniformly distributed load is found in Fig. 5–17, Case II, to be

$$D = \frac{5}{384} \times \frac{Wl^3}{EI}$$

$$D = \frac{5}{384} \times \frac{21{,}600 \times (18 \times 12)^3}{1{,}760{,}000 \times 3{,}568.71} = 0.45 \text{ in., the maximum deflection}$$

The allowable deflection equals $\frac{1}{360}$ of the span, or $\frac{1}{360} \times$

$(18 \times 12) = 0.6$ in. Since the actual deflection, 0.45 in., is less than the allowable, the deflection is not excessive.

Example. A simple beam, 10 x 14 in. in cross section, has a span of 12 ft 0 in. with a concentrated load of 10,000 lb at the center of the span. The timber is Douglas fir. Does the deflection exceed $\frac{1}{360}$ of the span?

SOLUTION.

$$E = 1{,}760{,}000 \text{ psi} \qquad \text{(Table 3–1)}$$

I, for a 10 x 14 in. cross section, $= 1947.8 \text{ in.}^4$ (Table 3–3)

$$D = \frac{1}{48} \times \frac{Pl^3}{EI} \qquad \text{(Fig. 5–17, Case I)}$$

Then

$$D = \frac{1}{48} \times \frac{10{,}000 \times (12 \times 12)^3}{1{,}760{,}000 \times 1947.8} = 1.8 \text{ in., the actual deflection}$$

$$\text{Allowable deflection} = \frac{12 \times 12}{360} = 0.4 \text{ in.}$$

Since 1.8 in., the actual deflection, is less than 0.4 in., the allowable, the beam will not deflect excessively.

A condition that occurs frequently consists of a combination of a uniformly distributed load and a concentrated load or loads acting simultaneously. If the maximum deflection for each type of loading occurs at the same section in the length of the beam, the deflection for each loading may be computed separately and their sum will be the total maximum deflection of the beam.

Example. A 12 x 14 in. Douglas fir, coast region, simple beam has a span of 18 ft 0 in. The beam supports a total uniformly distributed load of 6000 lb, and, in addition, there are two concentrated loads of 5000 lb each placed at the third points of the span. Compute the maximum deflection.

SOLUTION.

$$E = 1{,}760{,}000 \text{ psi} \qquad \text{(Table 3–1)}$$

$$I = 2357.86 \text{ in.}^4 \qquad \text{(Table 3–3)}$$

The deflection resulting from the uniformly distributed load is found by the formula

$$D = \frac{5}{384} \times \frac{Wl^3}{EI} \qquad \text{(Fig. 5–17, Case II)}$$

Then

$$D = \frac{5}{384} \times \frac{6000 \times (18 \times 12)^3}{1{,}760{,}000 \times 2357.86} = 0.19 \text{ in.}$$

Figure 5–17, Case III, gives $D = \frac{23}{648} \times \frac{Pl^3}{EI}$ for the maximum deflection resulting from two equal concentrated loads placed at the third points of the span. Then the deflection due to the concentrated loads is

$$D = \frac{23}{648} \times \frac{5000 \times (18 \times 12)^3}{1{,}760{,}000 \times 2357.86} = 0.43 \text{ in.}$$

For this beam the maximum vertical deflection due to both the uniformly distributed load and the concentrated loads occurs at the center of the span. Therefore, $0.19 + 0.43 = 0.62$ in., the maximum deflection that results from the combined loading.

Problem 8–2–A. A 10 x 10 in. Southern pine simple beam is 18 ft 0 in. in length and supports a uniformly distributed load of 6000 lb. If the beam supports a plastered ceiling, is the deflection excessive?

Problem 8–2–B. A 6 x 12 in. simple beam supports a concentrated load of 3400 lb at the center of a 14 ft 0 in. span. If the timber is redwood, compute the deflection.

Problem 8–2–C. A cantilever beam 6 ft 0 in. in length supports a concentrated load of 4000 lb at its free end. The timber is redwood and has a cross-sectional area of 12 x 12 in. Compute the deflection.

Problem 8–2–D. A simple beam of 10 x 12 in. Douglas fir, coast region, has a span of 12 ft 0 in. with a uniformly distributed load of 4000 lb and two concentrated loads of 3000 lb each placed at the third points of span. Compute the deflection.

8–3. Deflections Found by Coefficients. A somewhat simpler method of computing the deflection of beams involves the use of coefficients. This method requires that we know the *actual* extreme fiber stress that results from the size of the timber and the imposed loads. Examples illustrating deflections found in this manner are given in Art. 9–5.

For uniformly distributed loads and timber for which E = 1,760,000 psi the following rules may be used to find the limiting span, the span length that will result in a deflection of $\frac{1}{360}$ of the span.

When

$$f = 1000 \text{ psi}, \qquad L = 1.95 \times h$$

$$f = 1200 \text{ psi}, \qquad L = 1.63 \times h$$

$$f = 1400 \text{ psi}, \qquad L = 1.40 \times h$$

$$f = 1600 \text{ psi}, \qquad L = 1.22 \times h$$

$$f = 1800 \text{ psi}, \qquad L = 1.08 \times h$$

in which f = the extreme fiber stress, in pounds per square inch
L = the span length, in feet
h = the depth of the beam, in inches

As an example, a timber beam 14 in. in depth has a modulus of elasticity of 1,760,000 psi and a uniformly distributed load that produces an extreme fiber stress of 1200 psi. What is the limiting span length?

The actual depth of the beam is 13.5 in.; hence $L = 1.63 \times h$ or $L = 1.63 \times 13.5 = 22$ ft, the span length that will result in a deflection of $\frac{1}{360}$ of the span.

CHAPTER 9

DESIGN OF BEAMS

9–1. Types of Beams. A *beam* is a structural member subjected to transverse loads. Generally, the loads act at right angles to the longitudinal axis of the beam. Compared with other structural members, the loads on a beam, as well as the weight of the beam itself, tend to bend rather than lengthen or shorten the member. For simple beams, the supports are at the ends, and the resisting upward forces are called *reactions.* A girder is a beam but the term *girder* is generally applied to the larger beams. A beam that supports smaller beams is called a girder.

In frame construction the beams that directly support the floor boards are called *joists.* In the more recent codes the terms *joist* and *plank* are used to identify lumber of rectangular cross sections having nominal thicknesses of 2 in. to but not including 5 in. and nominal widths of 4 or more inches. The beams that support roofing are called *rafters;* they are often inclined. In bridge construction the longitudinal beams on which the ties are placed are called *stringers.* Recent codes use the terms *beams* and *stringers* in referring to lumber rectangular in cross section having nominal dimensions of 5 in. and more in thickness and 8 in. and more in width.

A *simple beam* is a beam that rests upon a support at each end, there being no restraint at the supports. See Fig. 9–1 (*a*). The majority of beams in timber construction are simple beams.

A *cantilever beam* is a beam that projects beyond a support, such as a beam built into a wall and extending out beyond the face of the wall. This is illustrated in Fig. 9–1 (*b*).

A beam that projects beyond one or both supports is called an *overhanging beam;* it is indicated in Fig. 9–1 (*c*).

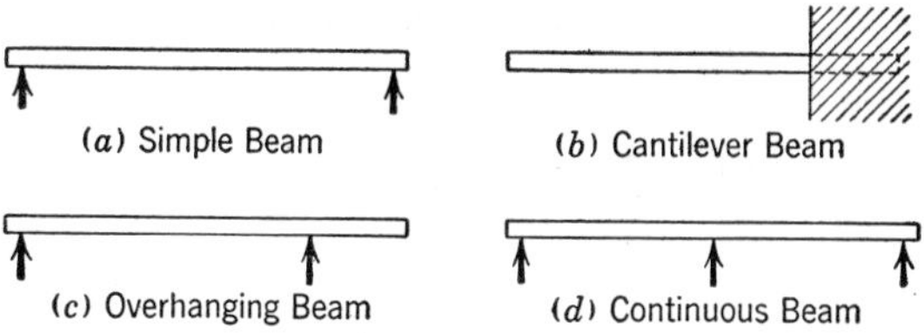

FIG. 9–1

A *continuous beam* is a beam that rests on three or more supports; see Fig. 9–1 (*d*).

A *fixed beam* is a beam having one or both ends restrained against rotation; such beams are found infrequently in timber construction.

Theoretically, the effective *span* of a beam is the horizontal distance between centers of the supports. Although it is improper, it is common practice, to consider the span to be the clear distance between faces of supports.

9–2. Design Procedure. The first step in the design of a beam is the computation of the load or loads the beam will be required to support. It will be advantageous to make a diagram showing the magnitude of the loads and their positions on the beam. A glance at such a diagram will frequently indicate the procedure required in subsequent design computations.

The design of a beam consists first in determining by computations the dimensions of a cross section in which the extreme fiber stress does not exceed the allowable stress for the material used. This is what we mean when we say the beam is first designed for strength in bending or flexure. Having determined a cross section to meet this requirement, we then investigate it to see that the allowable horizontal shearing stress is not exceeded. If the shearing stresses are found to be excessive, a larger section will be required. Next, the beam is investigated with respect to deflection to see that the actual deflection will not exceed the prescribed limit. When a cross section that satisfies these requirements has been determined, the dimensions of the end bearings are determined to provide that the stresses in compression perpendicular to the grain do not exceed the allowable stresses given in the building code.

9–3. Bending Stresses, Flexure Formula, Modulus of Rupture, and Form Factor. Figure 9–2 (*a*) represents a simple beam subjected to various loads. The forces acting on the beam are in a state of equilibrium. Figure 9–2 (*b*) shows a larger-scale drawing of the left end of the beam cut off at section marked A–A. Let us consider the stresses in the fibers of the beam at this section.

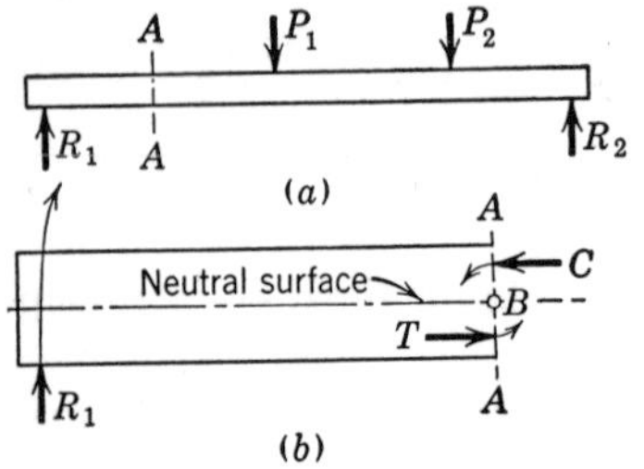

FIG. 9–2

From what we have learned in Art. 5–5, we know that the left reaction R_1 tends to produce a *clockwise* rotation about the point marked B. Point B is a line (or axis) on the neutral surface at the section A–A. The tendency for R_1 to cause rotation about this axis is the bending moment at this section of the beam, and we know its magnitude in this instance is the magnitude of the reaction multiplied by the normal distance between R_1 and the section A–A.

But there is no rotation, no motion, because the stresses in the fibers of the beam at this section tend to produce a *counterclockwise* rotation, the moments of the stresses in the fibers exactly balancing the moment of the reaction.

As this is a simple beam, we know that the fibers above the neutral surface are compressive stresses and that the fibers below the neutral surface are tensile stresses. The resultant of all the compressive stresses is indicated by the arrow marked C, and the resultant of the tensile stresses is indicated by the arrow marked T. The sum of the moments of all the stresses in the fibers of the section is called the *resisting moment* because it holds in equilibrium the *bending moment*. Thus

$$\text{bending moment} = \text{resisting moment}$$

We have been discussing a specific section of the beam but what we have said applies to any section, and, in the design of beams, the section with which we are particularly concerned is that at which the bending moment is maximum. This is the section at which the beam is most likely to fail by bending.

Although it is not appropriate or necessary in this text to develop the formula showing the relation of the bending moment to the resisting moment, it can be shown * that the resisting moment is $f \times S$. Then

$$\text{bending moment} = \text{resisting moment}$$

or

$$M = f \times S$$

in which M = the bending moment, *in inch-pounds*,
f = the unit stress on the fiber most remote from the neutral surface, the extreme fiber stress, in pounds per square inch,
S = the section modulus of the cross section, in units of inches^3

This formula, $M = fS$, is known as the *flexure formula*, and its use enables us to design homogeneous beams with respect to bending or flexure. Its application is quite simple. Since $M = fS$, $\frac{M}{f} = S$. Then, to design a beam for bending, we divide the maximum bending moment by f, the allowable extreme fiber stress, and the quotient is the required section modulus. Referring to Table 3–3, we select a beam with a section modulus equal to or greater than that which is required.

Consider a beam placed in a testing machine and investigated for the phenomenon of bending. The beam is loaded until failure occurs, and the bending moment for this loading is computed. If we use this bending moment in the flexure formula, $\frac{M}{S} = f$, the stress f that results is called the *modulus of rupture* of the material.

The size of standard test specimens is often a 2 x 2 in. cross section. When the height of a beam of rectangular cross section is increased, the modulus of rupture decreases slightly. A *form factor* is the ratio of the unit strength value of a beam of structural size to the corresponding unit value for a beam 2 x 2 in. in cross section. The form factor has already been included in the recommended allowable unit stresses in Table 3–1. See Art. 3–1.

* See Chapter 11 of *Simplified Mechanics and Strength of Materials*, Second Edition, by Harry Parker, John Wiley and Sons, New York, 1961.

9–4. Moment of Inertia and Section Modulus of Rectangles. In Arts. 4–4 and 4–6 it was stated that the moment of inertia and section modulus of rectangular cross sections are $\frac{bh^3}{12}$ and $\frac{bh^2}{6}$, respectively. Since timber beams are invariably rectangular in cross section, these quantities are used repeatedly in designing. Let us investigate the compressive and tensile stress in the fibers of a beam.

Figure 9–3 (*a*) represents a rectangular cross section of a beam;

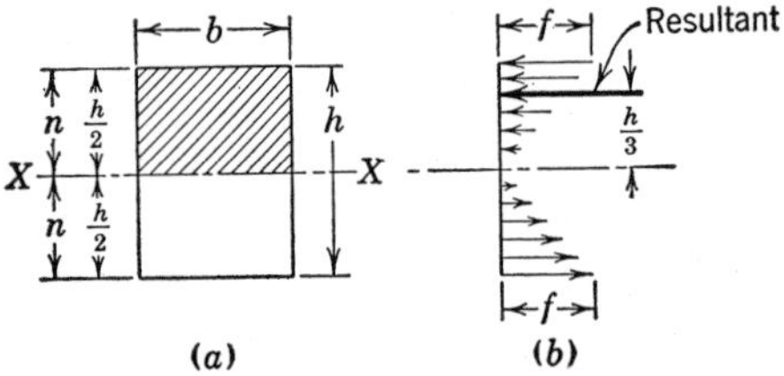

FIG. 9–3

b is the breadth, and *h* is the height or depth. Since the neutral surface passes through the centroid of the section, X–X, the neutral surface, is midway between the upper and lower surfaces of the beam. Let n = the distance of the most remote fiber from the neutral surface; thus $n = \frac{h}{2}$.

For a simple beam in bending, the fibers above the neutral surface are in compression and those below are in tension. For the present let us consider the compressive stresses indicated by the hatched area. This area is $b \times \frac{h}{2}$. The fibers in compression are not stressed equally, and their magnitudes are directly proportional to their distances from the neutral surface. The stress distribution is shown graphically in Fig. 9–3 (*b*). Let f = the unit stress on the fiber at n distance from the neutral surface. In building codes this is often identified as the *extreme fiber stress.* Since the stress on the fibers at the neutral surface is zero, the *average* unit stress on the fibers in compression is $\frac{f}{2}$. Then, since the area under compression is $b \times \frac{h}{2}$, the total compressive stress is $\left(b \times \frac{h}{2}\right) \times \frac{f}{2}$. We know that the centroid of a triangle lies at a point one third of the distance between the base and the apex. Then the resultant of all the compressive stresses passes through a point $\frac{2}{3} \times \frac{h}{2}$ or $\frac{h}{3}$ distance above the neutral surface; see Fig. 9–3 (*b*). The *resultant* of a number of forces is a single force having the same effect as the forces acting simultaneously. As the resultant of all the compressive stresses is $b \times \frac{h}{2} \times \frac{f}{2}$ and its moment arm about the neutral surface is $\frac{h}{3}$, the sum of the moments of all the compressive stresses about the neutral surface is $\left(b \times \frac{h}{2} \times \frac{f}{2}\right) \times \frac{h}{3}$. This quantity is the moment of the compressive stresses only, and, if we multiply it by 2 (to include the moments of all the tensile stresses below the neutral surface), we have an expression representing the sum of the moments of all the stresses in the cross section with respect to the neutral surface. This quantity is known as the *resisting moment*, and it is equal in magnitude to the bending moment.

Thus

$$2 \times \left(b \times \frac{h}{2} \times \frac{f}{2} \times \frac{h}{3}\right) = M$$

$$f \times \frac{bh^2}{6} = M$$

and

$$\frac{M}{f} = \frac{bh^2}{6}$$

This is a form of the flexure formula to use when applied to beams having a rectangular cross section.

Since $\frac{M}{f} = S$, $S = \frac{bh^2}{6}$, the value of the section modulus of a rectangular cross section about an axis through the centroid parallel to the base.

From Art. 4–6 we know that $S = \frac{I}{n}$. Since $n = \frac{h}{2}$,

$$I = S \times n = \frac{bh^2}{6} \times \frac{h}{2}$$

$$I = \frac{bh^3}{12}$$

Thus

$$S = \frac{bh^2}{6} \quad \text{and} \quad I = \frac{bh^3}{12}$$

To illustrate how readily the flexure formula is applied in the design of timber beams, consider the following example.

Example. The maximum bending moment for a beam has been found to be 250,000 in.-lb. If f, the allowable extreme fiber stress of the timber, is 1200 psi, design the beam with respect to bending.

SOLUTION. The key to the solution of this problem is the flexure formula, $\frac{M}{f} = S$. Then $\frac{250{,}000}{1200} = 208.3$ in.^{3}, the required section modulus. Referring to Table 3–3, we find

for a 6 x 16 in., $S = 220.23$ in.^{3}

for an 8 x 14 in., $S = 227.81$ in.^{3}

for a 10 x 12 in., $S = 209.40$ in.^{3}

Since all of these sections have a section modulus equal to or greater than the section modulus required, any one of the sections is acceptable.

Sometimes the formula is used in this manner: let us suppose that we wish to use a timber 10 in. in width (9.5 in. actual width). Then, since the required section modulus is 208.3 in.^{3}, $\frac{bh^2}{6} = 208.3$. Substituting 9.5 for the value of b, $\frac{9.5 \times h^2}{6} = 208.3$, and

$$h^2 = 131.5 \quad \text{and} \quad h = 11.4 \text{ in.}$$

A beam having a nominal depth of 12 in. has an actual depth of 11.5 in.; hence a 10 x 12 in. beam is acceptable.

9–5. Deflections Found by Coefficients. Before continuing with the design of beams let us explain the method of determining deflections by the use of coefficients given in Table 9–1. This method requires that we know f, the actual extreme fiber stress; this stress is readily found now that we know the flexure formula to be $M = fS$. It should be noted that the deflection coefficients given in Table 9–1 are for simple timber beams with uniformly distributed loads. For other types of loads refer to the footnote to the table.

TABLE 9–1. DEFLECTION COEFFICIENTS FOR UNIFORMLY * LOADED TIMBER BEAMS
$f = 1000$ PSI

Span, in Feet	$E =$ 1,760,000 psi	$E =$ 1,650,000 psi	$E =$ 1,600,000 psi	$E =$ 1,500,000 psi	$E =$ 1,320,000 psi	$E =$ 1,210,000 psi	$E =$ 1,200,000 psi
12	2.46	2.62	2.70	2.88	3.28	3.57	3.60
13	2.88	3.07	3.16	3.38	3.84	4.18	4.22
14	3.34	3.56	3.67	3.92	3.46	4.87	4.90
15	3.83	4.08	4.21	4.50	5.12	5.58	5.62
16	4.37	4.65	4.80	5.12	5.59	6.09	6.15
17	4.92	5.26	5.41	5.78	6.57	7.17	7.22
18	5.52	5.89	6.07	6.48	7.36	8.05	8.10
19	6.16	6.55	6.76	7.22	8.20	8.95	9.02
20	6.82	7.28	7.50	8.00	9.09	9.91	10.00
21	7.51	8.02	8.26	8.82	10.05	10.90	11.02
22	8.26	8.79	9.07	9.68	11.00	11.98	12.10
23	9.00	9.60	9.91	10.58	12.06	13.12	13.22
24	9.84	10.48	10.80	11.52	13.10	14.26	14.40
25	10.66	11.40	11.71	12.50	14.22	15.50	15.62
26	11.52	12.30	12.67	13.52	15.38	16.78	16.90

* For concentrated center load, coefficient = 0.80 of above values. For triangular loading, apex at C.L., coefficient = 0.96 of above values. For equal concentrated loads at $\frac{1}{3}$ points, coefficient = 1.02 of above values. For irregular loading (approx.), coefficient = 0.92 of above values.

To find the deflection of a simple timber beam having a uniformly distributed load, divide the coefficient in the table corresponding to E, the modulus of elasticity of the timber and the span length in feet, by the depth of the beam in inches. This gives the maximum deflection of the beam in inches *for an extreme fiber stress of* 1000 psi. If the actual extreme fiber stress is not 1000 psi, divide the actual extreme fiber stress by 1000 and multiply the quotient by the appropriate coefficient divided by the depth of the beam in inches.

Example. A 12 x 16 in. Southern pine simple beam has a span of 18 ft 0 in. and a uniformly distributed load of 21,600 lb. Compute the deflection by the use of Table 9–1.

SOLUTION. The first step is to find f, the actual extreme fiber stress. For this type of loading

$$M = \frac{Wl}{8}$$

$$M = \frac{21{,}600 \times 18 \times 12}{8} = 583{,}200 \text{ in-lb.}$$

From Table 3–3, the section modulus S for a 12 x 16 in. section is 460.48 in.^{3} Then $M = fS$ or $f = \frac{M}{S} = \frac{583{,}200}{460.48} = 1260$ psi, the actual extreme fiber stress. Referring to Table 3–1, we find E for southern pine to be 1,760,000 psi. The coefficient in Table 9–1 for $E = 1{,}760{,}000$ psi and a span of 18 ft 0 in. is 5.52. Then, since the actual depth of the beam is 15.5 in., $\frac{1260}{1000} \times \frac{5.52}{15.5} = 0.45$ in., the maximum deflection of the beam. Note that this is the first example given in Art. 8–2; the result is the same.

Example. A simple beam, 10 x 14 in. in cross section, has a span of 12 ft 0 in. with a concentrated load of 10,000 lb at the center of the span. If the timber is Southern pine, compute the maximum deflection.

SOLUTION. For this type of loading, $M = \frac{Pl}{4}$, Fig. 5–17, Case I.

Then $M = \frac{10{,}000 \times 12 \times 12}{4} = 360{,}000$ in-lb

For a 10 x 14 in. section the depth of the beam is 13.5 in. and

$$S = 288.56 \text{ in.}^3 \qquad \text{(Table 3–3)}$$

$$f = \frac{M}{S} = \frac{360{,}000}{288.56} = 1245 \text{ psi, the actual extreme fiber stress}$$

$$E, \text{ for Southern pine, } = 1{,}760{,}000 \text{ psi} \quad \text{(Table 3–1)}$$

The coefficient in Table 9–1 corresponding to $E = 1{,}760{,}000$ psi and a span of 12 ft 0 in. is 2.46. Since this is a concentrated load at the center of the span, the footnote to the table directs that the deflection is to be multiplied by 0.8. Then $\frac{1245}{1000} \times \frac{2.46}{13.5} \times 0.8 = 0.18$ in., the maximum deflection. Refer to the second example in Art. 8–2.

Example. A 12 x 14 in. Douglas fir, coast region, simple beam has a span of 18 ft 0 in. The beam supports a uniformly distributed load of 6000 lb, and, in addition, there are two concentrated loads of 5000 lb each placed at the third points of span. Compute the maximum deflection by the use of Table 9–1.

SOLUTION. Since there are two different types of loading, each type will be considered separately and the deflection computed for each; their sum will be the maximum deflection of the beam.

For the uniformly distributed load,

$$M = \frac{Wl}{8} \quad \text{(Fig. 5–17, Case II)}$$

$$M = \frac{6000 \times 18 \times 12}{8} = 162{,}000 \text{ in-lb}$$

For the concentrated loads,

$$M = \frac{Pl}{3} \quad \text{(Fig. 5–17, Case III)}$$

$$M = \frac{5000 \times 18 \times 12}{3} = 360{,}000 \text{ in-lb}$$

For a 12 x 14 in. section,

$$S = 349.31 \text{ in.}^3 \quad \text{(Table 3–3)}$$

For the uniformly distributed load,

$$M = fS \quad \text{or} \quad f = \frac{M}{S}$$

$$f = \frac{162{,}000}{349.31} = 464 \text{ psi, the actual extreme fiber stress}$$

For the concentrated loads,

$$f = \frac{M}{S}$$

$$f = \frac{360{,}000}{349.31} = 1031 \text{ psi, the actual extreme fiber stress}$$

$$E = 1{,}760{,}000 \text{ psi for Douglas fir, coast region} \qquad \text{(Table 3–1)}$$

Deflection coefficient for $E = 1{,}760{,}000$ psi, and a span of 18 ft 0 in. is 5.52 (Table 9–1). Then, since the depth of the beam is 13.5 in.,

$$\frac{464}{1000} \times \frac{5.52}{13.5} = 0.19 \text{ in.}$$

the maximum deflection that results from the uniformly distributed load.

In the table footnote we read that the deflection coefficient must be multiplied by 1.02 for concentrated loads at the third points of span. Then

$$\frac{1031}{1000} \times \frac{5.52}{13.5} \times 1.02 = 0.43 \text{ in.}$$

the maximum deflection due to the concentrated loads.

Since the maximum deflection due to each of the two types of loading occurs at the center of the length of the beam, they may be added. Then $0.19 + 0.43 = 0.62$ in., the maximum deflection due to the combined loads. This is the same result found in the third example in Art. 8–2.

Problem 9–5–A. Compute the deflection for the beam given in Problem 8–2–A by use of Table 9–1.

Problem 9–5–B. By the use of Table 9–1, compute the deflection for the beam given in Problem 8–2–B.

Problem 9–5–C. A beam having both a uniformly distributed load and concentrated loads is given in Problem 8–2–D. Compute the deflection by use of Table 9–1.

9–6. Design of Beams for Flexure. As explained in Art. 9–2, the design of a beam includes several steps. The usual procedure is first to determine a cross section in which the extreme fiber stress does not exceed the allowable stress given in the governing building code. This is called designing the beam for flexure or strength in bending. In the next steps the beam is investigated for horizontal shear and finally for deflection.

The design of a beam for flexure is accomplished by use of the flexure formula, $\frac{M}{f} = S$, as explained in Art. 9–3. The maximum bending moment divided by the allowable extreme fiber stress gives the required section modulus, and a beam cross section having a section modulus equal to or slightly larger than that which is required may be selected by referring to Table 3–3. Obviously many different sections may meet this requirement. Practical considerations govern the choice of sections; adjacent construction may limit the depth of a member. A beam that is relatively narrow tends to bend sidewise, but the deeper the beam the less will be the deflection. When not governed by other factors, the widths are generally $\frac{1}{3}$ to $\frac{1}{2}$ the depth. The designer should always have in mind the sizes that are available in the local markets.

It should be remembered that the weight of the beam produces bending stresses. However, the weight of wood beams is usually small compared with the superimposed loads, and consequently it is often neglected in preliminary computations. When it is deemed advisable to provide for the weight of the beam, it is customary to consider the weight of lumber to be 40 lb per cu ft. See the second example that follows. To provide for the weight of the beam as a load producing bending stresses, its weight may be estimated and added to the uniformly distributed load. When the size of the beam has been determined by computations, its weight is compared with the weight that was estimated to see that an ample load was assumed. For simplicity of explanation the weight of the beam has purposely been omitted in many of the following examples.

Before the complete design of a beam is presented examples are given to illustrate how the beam is first designed for flexure.

Example. Design for flexure a simple beam having a span of 14 ft 0 in. with a uniformly distributed load, including the weight of the beam, of 800 lb per lin ft. The allowable extreme fiber stress is 1400 psi.

SOLUTION. The flexure formula is $\frac{M}{f} = S$ (Art. 9–3). The maximum bending moment for this beam is $M = \frac{wl^2}{8}$ (Fig. 5–17, Case II). Then

$$M = \frac{wl^2}{8} = \frac{800 \times 14 \times 14 \times 12}{8} = 235{,}200 \text{ in-lb, the maximum bending moment}$$

$$\frac{M}{f} = S = \frac{235{,}200}{1400} = 168 \text{ in.}^3\text{, the required section modulus}$$

Referring to Table 3–3, we find a number of choices. A 10 x 12 in. cross section has a section modulus of 209.40 in.^{3} and is acceptable for flexure. An 8 x 12 in. has a section modulus of 165.31 in.^{3}, slightly less than that required.

Example. A simple beam has a span of 15 ft 0 in. with two concentrated loads of 4000 lb each placed at the third points of span. If the allowable extreme fiber stress is 1200 psi, design the beam for flexure.

SOLUTION.

$$M = \frac{Pl}{3} \qquad \text{(Fig. 5–17, Case III)}$$

Then

$$M = \frac{4000 \times 15 \times 12}{3} = 240{,}000 \text{ in-lb, the maximum bending moment}$$

$$\frac{M}{f} = S = \frac{240{,}000}{1200} = 200 \text{ in.}^3\text{, the required section modulus}$$

We find in Table 3–3 that a 10 x 12 in. section has a section modulus of 209.40 in.^{3} and is accepted.

In this example no allowance has been made for the weight of the beam. Let us investigate.

Since a section modulus of 200 in.^{3} is required and the 10 x 12 in.

section has a section modulus of 209.40 in.^{3}, $209.40 - 200 = 9.4$ in.^{3}, the section modulus in excess of that required for the concentrated loads. The weight of a 10 x 12 in. $= \frac{9.5 \times 11.5}{144} \times 40$ or 30.3 lb per lin ft. This constitutes a uniformly distributed load, the weight of the beam. Then, referring to Fig. 5–17, Case II,

$$M = \frac{wl^2}{8} = \frac{30.3 \times 15 \times 15 \times 12}{8}$$

$= 10{,}226$ in-lb, the maximum bending moment due to the weight of the beam

$$\frac{M}{f} = S = \frac{10{,}226}{1200} = 8.5 \text{ in.}^3$$

the section modulus required for the weight of the beam. Since 9.4 in.^{3} is provided, the 10 x 12 in. beam is acceptable for flexure.

Example. A simple timber beam 12 ft 0 in. in length has a concentrated load of 6000 lb at 4 ft 0 in. from the left support and, in addition, a uniformly distributed load, including the weight of the beam, of 1000 lb per lin ft. The allowable extreme fiber stress of the lumber is 1600 psi, and the depth of the beam is limited by adjacent construction to 12 in. Design the beam for flexure.

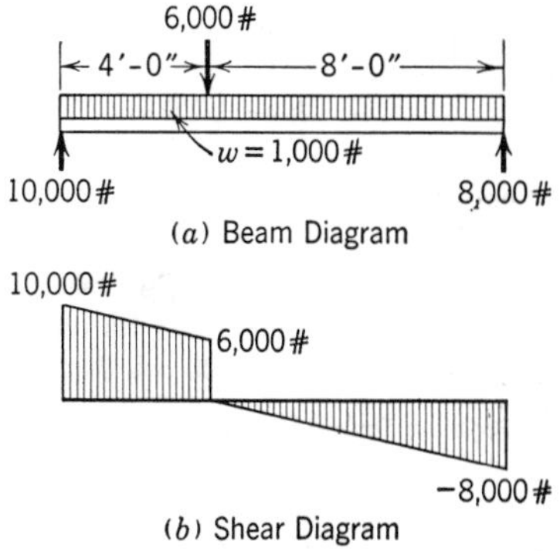

FIG. 9–4

SOLUTION. The beam diagram showing the position of the loads is drawn as indicated in Fig. 9–4 (*a*). This system of loading is not typical; hence we cannot use one of the formulas given in Fig. 5–17 to find the maximum bending moment. We must begin by computing the reactions.

$$12R_1 = (6000 \times 8) + (12 \times 1000 \times 6) \quad \text{and} \quad R_1 = 10{,}000 \text{ lb}$$

$$12R_2 = (6000 \times 4) + (12 \times 1000 \times 6) \quad \text{and} \quad R_2 = 8000 \text{ lb}$$

A shear diagram, Fig. 9–4 (b), is next constructed, and we find that the shear passes through zero at 4 ft 0 in. from the left support. See the second example in Art. 5–4. This is the section at which the bending moment will be maximum. Hence

$$M_{(x=4)} = (10{,}000 \times 4) - (4 \times 1000 \times 2)$$
$$= 32{,}000 \text{ ft-lb} = 384{,}000 \text{ in-lb}$$

$$S = \frac{M}{f} = \frac{384{,}000}{1600} = 240 \text{ in.}^3\text{, the required section modulus}$$

Since, by data, the depth of the beam is limited to 12 in., we find by referring to Table 3–3 that a 12 x 12 in. section has a section modulus of 253.48 in.^{3} and therefore is acceptable.

The section might have been determined thus:

$$S = \frac{bh^2}{6} \qquad \text{(Art. 9–4)}$$

Then, since a beam 12 in. in depth has an actual depth of 11.5 in.,

$$240 = \frac{b \times 11.5 \times 11.5}{6}$$

$$b = 10.9 \text{ in., the minimum required width}$$

Accept, therefore, a 12 x 12 in. section.

Problem 9–6–A. A simple timber beam 10 ft 0 in. in length has a uniformly distributed load, including its own weight, of 7000 lb. If the allowable extreme fiber stress is 1400 psi, design the beam for flexure.

Problem 9–6–B. A simple timber beam has a span of 16 ft 0 in. with a concentrated load of 6000 lb at the center of the span. If the allowable extreme fiber stress is 1200 psi, design the beam for flexure.

Problem 9–6–C. A simple timber beam having a span of 14 ft 0 in. has a concentrated load of 6000 lb at the center of the span and a uniformly distributed load of 1000 lb per lin ft. Design the beam for flexure, using 1600 psi as the allowable extreme fiber stress.

Problem 9–6–D. A concentrated load of 8000 lb is placed at 5 ft 0 in. from one of the supports of a simple beam whose span length is 20 ft 0 in. The allowable extreme fiber stress for the timber is 1600 lb. Design the beam for flexure.

9–7. Investigation of Beams. A problem that may arise is the investigation of a beam to determine whether or not it is safe with respect to strength in bending. In such a problem we are given as data the dimensions of the cross section, the span length, the loading, and the species and grade of the lumber. Knowing the species and grade, we know also the allowable extreme fiber stress. The procedure, therefore, is to determine the *actual* extreme fiber stress and to compare it with the allowable.

Example. A 6 x 10 in. simple beam of the dense structural 58 grade of Southern pine has a span of 12 ft 0 in. and a total uniformly distributed load of 8600 lb. Is the beam safe in bending?

SOLUTION. This being a member in bending, the flexure formula is the key to the solution:

$$M = fS \quad \text{or} \quad f = \frac{M}{S}$$

The maximum bending moment for this loading is

$$M = \frac{Wl}{8} \qquad \text{(Fig. 5–17, Case II)}$$

$$M = \frac{8600 \times 12 \times 12}{8} = 154{,}800 \text{ in-lb}$$

Table 3–3 gives the section modulus of a 6 x 10 in. to be 82.73 in.^{3} Then

$$f = \frac{M}{S} = \frac{154{,}800}{82.73} = 1870 \text{ psi, the actual extreme fiber stress}$$

Referring to Table 3–1, we find the allowable extreme fiber stress for this grade of lumber to be 1600 psi, and, since the actual stress is in excess of the allowable, the beam is unsafe with respect to bending.

In the following problems consider the weight of the beam as a uniformly distributed load.

Problem 9–7–A. Investigate for bending an 8 x 12 in. timber beam having a span of 14 ft 0 in. and a uniformly distributed load of 10,000 lb, including the weight of the beam. The allowable extreme fiber stress for the timber is 1400 psi.

Problem 9–7–B. A 10 x 12 in. beam has a span of 16 ft 0 in. with a concentrated load of 6500 lb at the center of the span. If the allowable extreme fiber stress of the timber is 1600 psi, investigate the beam for bending.

Problem 9–7–C. A 10 x 10 in. timber beam, whose allowable extreme fiber stress is 1500 psi, has a span of 15 ft 0 in. with two concentrated loads of 4000 lb each placed at the third points of span. Is the beam safe with respect to bending?

9–8. Safe Loads for Beams. The flexure formula may also be used to find the safe load a beam of given cross section and span will support. In using the formula M, the maximum bending moment, is expressed in terms of W or P in accordance with the type of loading.

Example. What uniformly distributed load will a 10 x 14 in. timber beam support if the span length is 15 ft 0 in. and the allowable extreme fiber stress of the timber is 1700 psi?

SOLUTION. The maximum bending moment for this beam is

$$M = \frac{Wl}{8} \qquad \text{(Fig. 5–17, Case II)}$$

$$M = \frac{W \times 15 \times 12}{8} = 22.5W \text{ in-lb}$$

From Table 3–3, $S = 288.56$ in.^{3} for a 10 x 14 in. cross section. Then $M = fS$ or $22.5W = 1700 \times 288.56$, and $W = 21{,}800$ lb, the total allowable uniformly distributed load.

Example. An 8 x 14 in. timber beam having an allowable extreme fiber stress of 1400 psi has a span of 18 ft 0 in. Ignoring the weight of the beam, determine the magnitude of a concentrated load that may be placed at the center of the span.

SOLUTION. For this type of loading $M = \frac{Pl}{4}$ (Fig. 5–17, Case I).

Then

$$M = \frac{P \times 18 \times 12}{4} = 54P \text{ in-lb}$$

From Table 3–3, $S = 227.81$ in.^{3}, the section modulus of an 8 x 14 in. Then $M = fS$ or $54P = 1400 \times 227.81$, and $P = 5906$ lb, the magnitude of the concentrated load that may be placed at the center of the span.

In the computations used to determine the loads in the following problems, ignore the weight of the beams.

Problem 9–8–A. A 6 x 12 in. timber beam having an allowable extreme fiber stress of 1200 psi has a span of 14 ft 0 in. What is the magnitude of the total uniformly distributed load the beam will support?

Problem 9–8–B. A 12 x 14 in. timber beam has a span of 20 ft 0 in. with a concentrated load at the center of the span. If the allowable extreme fiber stress is 1700 psi, what is the maximum magnitude of the concentrated load?

Problem 9–8–C. A simple beam 15 ft 0 in. in length has a concentrated load at 5 ft 0 in. from one of the supports. If the cross section of the beam is 10 x 14 in. and the allowable extreme fiber stress is 1600 psi, what is the maximum concentrated load the beam will support?

Problem 9–8–D. Two loads of equal magnitude are placed at the third points of span of an 8 x 12 in. timber beam having a length of 18 ft 0 in. If the allowable extreme fiber stress of the timber is 1700 psi, compute the magnitude of the loads.

9–9. Safe-Load Tables for Beams. Since many species and grades of lumber are used for structural members, numerous different safe-load beam tables might be computed. Table 9–2 gives safe uniformly distributed loads for simple beams rectangular in cross section and 1 in. in width. Note particularly that this table is to be used for beams having an allowable extreme fiber stress of 1200 psi, an allowable horizontal shearing unit stress of 100 psi, and a modulus of elasticity of 1,600,000 psi. Tables 9–3 and 9–4 are similar tables with the exception that the extreme fiber stresses are 1400 and 1600 psi, respectively. The loads above the heavy horizontal lines are determined by horizontal shear. When two loads are given for a specific span, the upper load is computed for strength in bending or flexure and the lower load, in italics, is computed for a deflection that does not exceed $\frac{1}{360}$ of the span. Attention is called to the fact that *the loads given are for beams 1 in. in width* and that the heights 5.5, 7.5, 9.5 in., etc., correspond to the nominal heights of 6, 8, and 10 in., respectively.

Art. 9–14 explains how these safe load tables can be used for any extreme fiber stress or modulus of elasticity.

TABLE 9–2. SAFE DISTRIBUTED LOADS * IN POUNDS FOR SIMPLE RECTANGULAR BEAMS 1 IN. IN WIDTH

$f = 1200$ psi

1,200 psi = extreme fiber stress
100 psi = horizontal shearing unit stress
1,600,000 psi = modulus of elasticity

Span of Beam, in Feet	$h = 5\frac{1}{2}''$	$h = 7\frac{1}{2}''$	$h = 9\frac{1}{2}''$	$h = 11\frac{1}{2}''$	$h = 13\frac{1}{2}''$	$h = 15\frac{1}{2}''$	$h = 17\frac{1}{2}''$
6	672	1,000	1,267	1,533	1,800	2,066	2,333
7	576	1,000	1,267	1,533	1,800	2,066	2,333
8	504	937	1,267	1,533	1,800	2,066	2,333
9	448 / *407*	833	1,267	1,533	1,800	2,066	2,333
10	403 / *329*	750	1,203	1,533	1,800	2,066	2,333
11	366 / *272*	681	1,093	1,533	1,800	2,066	2,333
12	336 / *228*	625 / *578*	1,002	1,468	1,800	2,066	2,333
13	310 / *194*	577 / *493*	927	1,354	1,800	2,066	2,333
14	287 / *168*	536 / *425*	859	1,259	1,735	2,066	2,333
15		500 / *371*	802 / *750*	1,175	1,620	2,066	2,333
16		468 / *325*	753 / *659*	1,102	1,518	2,002	2,333
17		442 / *288*	708 / *584*	1,037	1,430	1,886	2,333
18			668 / *521*	979 / *927*	1,348	1,782	2,268
19			634 / *467*	928 / *832*	1,278	1,686	2,149
20			601 / *422*	881 / *755*	1,215	1,601	2,041
21				839 / *681*	1,155 / *1,104*	1,525	1,945
22				802 / *622*	1,102 / *1,006*	1,456	1,855
23				767 / *568*	1,054 / *922*	1,394 / *1,392*	1,774
24				734 / *522*	1,011 / *845*	1,335 / *1,276*	1,701
25					972 / *778*	1,282 / *1,175*	1,632
26					934 / *720*	1,232 / *1,088*	1,570 / *1,565*
27					900 / *668*	1,188 / *1,011*	1,512 / *1,451*
28						1,144 / *939*	1,458 / *1,350*
29						1,105 / *873*	1,408 / *1,257*
30						1,067 / *817*	1,361 / *1,175*

* Loads above heavy lines are determined by horizontal shear. Where two loads are given, the upper is calculated for strength in bending; the lower, which is in italics, is for deflection not to exceed 1/360 of the span.

TABLE 9–3. SAFE DISTRIBUTED LOADS * IN POUNDS FOR SIMPLE RECTANGULAR BEAMS 1 IN. IN WIDTH

$f = 1400$ psi

1,400 psi = extreme fiber stress
100 psi = horizontal shearing unit stress
1,600,000 psi = modulus of elasticity

Span of Beam, in Feet	$h = 5\frac{1}{2}''$	$h = 7\frac{1}{2}''$	$h = 9\frac{1}{2}''$	$h = 11\frac{1}{2}''$	$h = 13\frac{1}{2}''$	$h = 15\frac{1}{2}''$	$h = 17\frac{1}{2}''$
6	733	1,000	1,267	1,533	1,800	2,066	2,333
7	672	1,000	1,267	1,533	1,800	2,066	2,333
8	588 *515*	1,000	1,267	1,533	1,800	2,066	2,333
9	523 *407*	973	1,267	1,533	1,800	2,066	2,333
10	470 *329*	876 *834*	1,267	1,533	1,800	2,066	2,333
11	427 *272*	797 *688*	1,267	1,533	1,800	2,066	2,333
12	393 *228*	730 *578*	1,169	1,533	1,800	2,066	2,333
13	362 *194*	673 *493*	1,079 *1,002*	1,533	1,800	2,066	2,333
14	336 *168*	626 *425*	1,002 *862*	1,466	1,800	2,066	2,333
15	314 *146*	584 *371*	936 *750*	1,369 *1,333*	1,800	2,066	2,333
16	294 *128*	547 *325*	877 *659*	1,283 *1,179*	1,770	2,066	2,333
17		515 *288*	825 *584*	1,205 *1,040*	1,666	2,066	2,333
18		486 *257*	779 *521*	1,181 *927*	1,572 *1,510*	2,066	2,333
19			738 *467*	1,081 *832*	1,493 *1,345*	1,968	2,333
20			702 *422*	1,027 *755*	1,416 *1,217*	1,871 *1,840*	2,333
21				978 *681*	1,350 *1,104*	1,780 *1,668*	2,263
22				934 *622*	1,288 *1,006*	1,700 *1,520*	2,161
23				893 *568*	1,231 *922*	1,625 *1,392*	2,065 *2,000*
24				856 *522*	1,180 *845*	1,558 *1,276*	1,980 *1,835*
25					1,132 *778*	1,495 *1,175*	1,901 *1,692*
26					1,089 *720*	1,438 *1,088*	1,830 *1,565*
27					1,050 *668*	1,384 *1,011*	1,762 *1,451*
28						1,335 *939*	1,698 *1,350*
29						1,289 *873*	1,641 *1,257*
30						1,246 *817*	1,586 *1,175*

* Loads above heavy lines are determined by horizontal shear. Where two loads are given, the upper is calculated for strength in bending; the lower, which is in italics, is for deflection not to exceed 1/360 of the span

TABLE 9–4. SAFE DISTRIBUTED LOADS * IN POUNDS FOR SIMPLE RECTANGULAR BEAMS 1 IN. IN WIDTH

$f = 1600$ psi

1,600 psi = extreme fiber stress
100 psi = horizontal shearing unit stress
1,600,000 psi = modulus of elasticity

Span of Beam, in Feet	$h = 5\frac{1}{2}''$	$h = 7\frac{1}{2}''$	$h = 9\frac{1}{2}''$	$h = 11\frac{1}{2}''$	$h = 13\frac{1}{2}''$	$h = 15\frac{1}{2}''$	$h = 17\frac{1}{2}''$
6	733	1,000	1,267	1,533	1,800	2,066	2,333
7	733	1,000	1,267	1,533	1,800	2,066	2,333
8	672 *518*	1,000	1,267	1,533	1,800	2,066	2,333
9	597 *407*	1,000	1,267	1,533	1,800	2,066	2,333
10	537 *329*	1,000	1,267	1,533	1,800	2,066	2,333
11	488 *272*	909 *688*	1,267	1,533	1,800	2,066	2,333
12	447 *228*	832 *578*	1,267	1,533	1,800	2,066	2,333
13	413 *194*	769 *493*	1,234 *1,002*	1,533	1,800	2,066	2,333
14	383 *168*	713 *425*	1,145 *866*	1,533	1,800	2,066	2,333
15		666 *371*	1,069 *750*	1,533	1,800	2,066	2,333
16		625 *325*	1,002 *659*	1,469 *1,176*	1,800	2,066	2,333
17		588 *288*	944 *584*	1,382 *1,038*	1,800	2,066	2,333
18			892 *521*	1,305 *927*	1,800	2,066	2,333
19			844 *467*	1,238 *832*	1,704 *1,347*	2,066	2,333
20			802 *422*	1,175 *755*	1,620 *1,211*	2,066	2,333
21				1,118 *681*	1,541 *1,104*	2,034 *1,668*	2,333
22				1,068 *622*	1,472 *1,006*	1,942 *1,523*	2,333
23				1,021 *568*	1,405 *922*	1,855 *1,392*	2,333
24				981 *522*	1,349 *845*	1,780 *1,276*	2,262 *1,841*
25					1,295 *778*	1,702 *1,175*	2,173 *1,691*
26					1,245 *720*	1,644 *1,088*	2,090 *1,565*
27					1,200 *668*	1,582 *1,011*	2,010 *1,451*
28						1,525 *939*	1,940 *1,350*
29						1,472 *873*	1,875 *1,257*
30						1,423 *817*	1,813 *1,175*

* Loads above heavy lines are determined by horizontal shear. Where two loads are given, the upper is calculated for strength in bending; the lower, which is in italics, is for deflection not to exceed 1/360 of the span.

Example. A simple timber beam having an allowable extreme fiber stress of 1200 psi has a span of 16 ft 0 in. and a uniformly distributed load of 8000 lb. The modulus of elasticity of the timber is 1,600,000 psi. What size beam should be used?

SOLUTION. Table 9–2 shows that a beam having an actual depth of 11.5 in. (corresponding to a nominal depth of 12 in.) and 1 in. in width will support a distributed load of 1102 lb if the span is 16 ft 0 in. Then, 8000 ÷ 1102 = 7.25 in., the required width of the beam. As an 8 x 12 in. has actual dimensions of 7.5 x 11.5 in., this section is acceptable. If a beam 14 in. in depth is preferred 8000 ÷ 1518 = 5.27 in. Accept a 6 x 14 in. The deflection will not be excessive.

Example. Compute the safe uniformly distributed load that may be supported by a 6 x 10 in. beam having a span of 18 ft 0 in. The allowable extreme fiber stress of the timber is 1200 psi, the allowable horizontal shearing unit stress is 100 psi, and the modulus of elasticity is 1,600,000 psi. The deflection must not be excessive.

SOLUTION. We find, with respect to strength in bending, that a beam 1 in. in width having an actual depth of $9\frac{1}{2}$ in. will support a uniformly distributed load of 668 lb if the span is 18 ft 0 in. (Table 9–2). Therefore, since a 6 x 10 in. beam has 5.5 x 9.5 in. for its actual dimensions, 5.5 × 668 = 3670 lb, the uniformly distributed load the beam will safely support with respect to strength in bending. However, in Table 9–2 we find that 521 lb is the safe uniformly distributed load for a beam 1 in. in width and 9.5 in. in depth for a span of 18 ft 0 in. if the deflection is not to exceed $\frac{1}{360}$ of the span. Then, 521 × 5.5 = 2865 lb, the allowable uniformly distributed load permitted if the deflection is not to be excessive. The allowable distributed load determined by horizontal shear for the 5.5 x 9.5 in. beam is 5.5 × 1267 or 6968 lb. Of the three loads, 2865 lb is the smallest. Therefore this is the maximum distributed load the 6 x 10 in. beam will support. Deflection is the controlling factor.

The following problems are to be solved by the use of Table 9–2. For each problem the timber has an allowable extreme fiber stress of 1200 psi, an allowable horizontal shearing unit stress of 100 psi, and a modulus of elasticity of 1,600,000 psi. In each problem the deflection is not to be excessive.

Problem 9–9–A. Design a simple beam having a span of 14 ft 0 in. with a total uniformly distributed load of 6800 lb.

Problem 9–9–B. A simple beam has a total uniformly distributed load of 12,000 lb and a span length of 18 ft 0 in. What should be the size of the beam?

Problem 9–9–C. The span of a simple beam is 14 ft 0 in., and the total uniformly distributed load is 2300 lb. What should be the size of the beam?

Problem 9–9–D. A 10 x 12 in. beam is used to support a uniformly distributed load; the span length is 20 ft 0 in. What is the maximum load the beam will support?

Problem 9–9–E. The uniformly distributed load supported by an 8 x 10 in. beam whose span is 16 ft 0 in. is 5200 lb. Is the beam safe?

9–10. End Bearings of Beams. It is important in the design of timber beams to provide an ample end bearing. The area in bearing should be large enough to result in compressive unit stresses that do not exceed the allowable stresses given in Table 3–1 in the column "compression perpendicular to grain." For smaller beams supported by a wall, joists for example, 4 in. of length parallel to the length of the beam should be considered a minimum bearing length. For bearings less than 6 in. in length the bearing stresses may be increased in accordance with the factors given in Table 7–1. See Art. 7–1. For the larger beams, a general rule is to have the bearing length equal to the width of the beam plus 4 in. Bearing plates of cast iron or steel are generally used for the larger beams; these plates not only aid in distributing the compressive stresses over larger areas of the masonry but also assist in bringing the beams to the desired level. A cast iron bearing plate is illustrated in Fig. 9–5 (*a*). This type of bearing provides ventilation for the timber and the avoidance of dry rot. The length of the bearing plate parallel to the length of the beam, that is, the projection into the wall, must conform to the units of the masonry. As an example, a 13-in. brick wall may have a bearing plate 8 in. in length to provide a thickness of one brick to protect the end of the timber. The other dimension of the plate is determined by the bearing capacity of the masonry.

Other usual types of bearings, beams framed to girders, are illustrated in Figs. 9–5 (*b*), (*c*), and (*d*). Figure 9–5 (*d*) shows two beams butted together; such beams should be tied together with

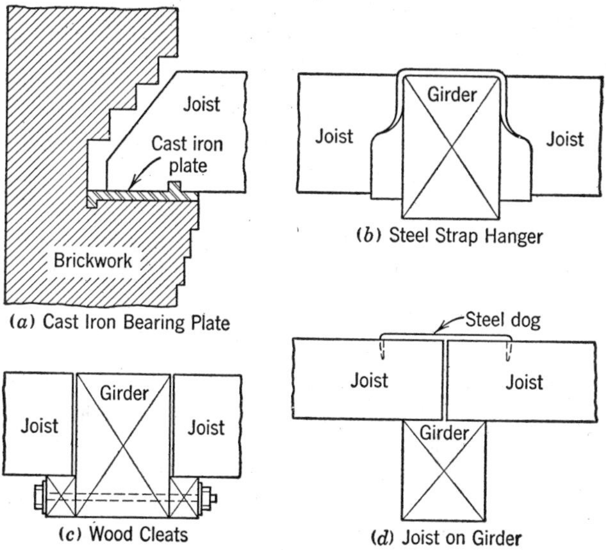

FIG. 9–5

steel dogs or straps. Figure 9–5 (*b*) illustrates the use of steel strap-hangers, and Fig. 9–5 (*c*) shows the beams supported on wood cleats.

It is obvious that the deflection of a beam results in an unequal distribution of stresses on the end bearing. In computing the bearing stresses, however, it is assumed that the stresses are distributed uniformly. The computations are quite simple and require merely some form of the basic formula $\frac{P}{f} = A$ as explained in Art. 2–3. It may be stated thus: *the end reaction of the beam, in pounds, divided by the allowable compressive unit stress of the timber perpendicular to the grain, in pounds per square inch, equals the minimum required bearing area, in square inches.*

Example. An 8 x 12 in. Southern pine beam, of No. 1 dense SR grade, has an end reaction of 8000 lb. The beam is supported on a brick wall by means of a bearing plate with an area of 8 x 8 in., similar to the bearing illustrated in Fig. 9–5 (*a*). Is the bearing area large enough?

SOLUTION. On referring to Table 3–1 we find that the allowable compressive unit stress perpendicular to the grain for this grade of Southern pine is 455 psi. Then

$$\frac{P}{f} = A$$

or

$$\frac{8000}{455} = 17.5 \text{ sq in., the minimum required bearing area of the beam on the plate}$$

Since the bearing area of the plate is 8 × 8 in. or 64 sq in. and only 17.5 sq in. are required, the bearing area is large enough.

The size of the bearing plate with respect to its bearing on the brick wall is investigated thus: since the beam reaction is 8000 lb and the plate has an area of 8 × 8 in., or 64 sq in., 8000 ÷ 64 = 125 psi, the compressive stress of the plate on the brickwork. Since brick masonry has an allowable bearing stress of 150 psi, 200 psi, etc., depending on the bricks and mortar that are used and the building code requirements, the bearing plate is amply large to distribute the load of 8000 lb.

Example. A 4 x 12 in., spruce beam supports a total uniformly distributed load of 5000 lb and is framed to a timber girder on cleats as indicated in Fig. 9–5 (*c*). What should be the size of the cleat upon which the beam rests?

SOLUTION. There is always a slight variation in the length of beams. In this instance let us assume that the beam will have at least a 2-in. length of bearing. Then, since the beam has a 3.625-in. width, 2 × 3.625 = 7.25 sq in., the bearing area. In Table 3–1 we find that the allowable compressive stress perpendicular to the grain for spruce is 300 psi. Referring to Table 7–1 we see that the bearing stress for a 2-in. bearing length may be increased by multiplying by a factor of 1.19. Therefore 300 × 1.19 = 357 psi, the allowable compressive unit stress.

The bearing area is 7.25 sq in.; hence 7.25 × 357 = 2590 lb, the allowable bearing stress on a bearing having a 2-in. length. The total distributed load on the beam is 5000 lb; consequently each reaction is 5000 × $\frac{1}{2}$ or 2500 lb. Since the allowable bearing stress,

2590 lb, exceeds this magnitude, a 2-in. bearing length is acceptable. If the cleat is a 3 x 4-in. piece, the total length for bearing is 2.625 in. The lengths of the beams may vary, but a minimum 2-in. bearing length is adequate. Accept, therefore, a 3 x 4-in. cleat.

Example. A 10 x 12 in. Douglas fir beam of dense construction grade having an end reaction of 14,000 lb is supported by a strap hanger as indicated Fig. 9–5 (*b*). What should be the dimensions of the hanger?

SOLUTION. Table 3–1 gives the allowable compressive stress perpendicular to the grain for this timber as 455 psi. As the beam has an actual width of 9.5 in., let x in. be the approximate bearing length; thus $9.5 \times x$ is the bearing area of the beam on the hanger. Then

$$\frac{P}{f} = A = \frac{14{,}000}{455} = (9.5 \times x)$$

and

$$x = 3.24 \text{ in., the approximate bearing length}$$

Now let us investigate a strap having a $3\frac{1}{2}$ in. bearing length.

For a strap width of $3\frac{1}{2}$ in., assume that the bearing length of the beam on the hanger will be at least 3 in. For a 3-in. bearing length Table 7–1 shows that 455×1.13 or 515 psi is the allowable compressive stress. The width of the beam being 9.5 in., $9.5 \times 3 =$ 28.5 sq in., the bearing area. Then $28.5 \times 515 = 14{,}700$ lb, the allowable compressive load on the hanger. Only 14,000 lb is required; hence the $3\frac{1}{2}$-in. wide strap is accepted.

Hangers of this type are usually made of malleable iron or of soft steel. If failure occurs in rupture of the hanger strap, the strap theoretically will fail at *two* sections as a result of tension or shear. Let A be the cross-sectional area of the strap. Then, assuming that the allowable shearing stress for this material is 9000 psi and that it is the controlling value, $(2 \times A \times 9000)$ lb is the allowable load that may be placed on one hanger.

In this example we have determined the width of the hanger strap to be $3\frac{1}{2}$ in., and, if t is the thickness of the strap, the cross-sectional area is $(3\frac{1}{2} \times t)$ sq in. Then $14{,}000 = 2 \times (3\frac{1}{2} \times t) \times 9000$, and $t = 0.22$ in., the minimum thickness of the hanger strap.

Accept, therefore, a hanger made of a strap whose minimum cross-sectional dimensions are $3\frac{1}{2} \times \frac{1}{4}$ in.

Problem 9–10–A. A 12 x 20 in. Southern pine beam supports a total uniformly distributed load of 44,000 lb and its end support is a 13-in. brick wall for which the allowable compressive stress is 200 psi. What should be the area of the bearing plate?

Problem 9–10–B. A 3 x 12 redwood beam is supported on a cleat bolted to a girder as illustrated in Fig. 9–5 (*c*). If the total uniformly distributed load on the beam is 2800 lb, what should be the size of the cleat?

9–11. Beams Laterally Unsupported. In the discussions so far it has been assumed that the beams have been laterally supported, that they have been restrained against the tendency to buckle or bend sidewise. This is the usual condition, for floor boards, bridging, or smaller beams framing into the beams afford the necessary lateral bracing.

Floor joists should be bridged at intervals not exceeding 8 ft or six times their depth (whichever is the greater) between bridging or between bridging and bearing.

The following approximate rules should be applied to provide lateral restraint for rectangular beams and joists.

1. If the ratio of depth to breadth is 2 to 1, no lateral support is needed.
2. If the ratio is 3 to 1, the ends should be held in position.
3. If the ratio is 4 to 1, the piece should be held in line by spiking or bolting as in a vertically laminated beam.
4. If the ratio is 5 to 1, one edge should be held in line, for example, by flooring nailed to the edge of a joist.
5. If the ratio is 6 to 1, diagonal bridging should be used as described above.
6. If the ratio is 7 to 1, both edges should be held in line.
7. If a beam is subject to both flexure and compression parallel to the grain, the ratio may be as much as 5 to 1 if one edge is held firmly in line, for example, by rafters (or by roof joists) and diagonal sheathing. If the dead load is sufficient to induce tension on the under side of the rafters, the ratio for the beam may be 6 to 1.

A method formerly used to design beams with no lateral support is described as follows. It is included in this discussion to show how a *reduced allowable extreme fiber stress* was determined for laterally unsupported beams.

When the span length of a timber beam *with no lateral support* exceeds 20 times the width of a member, the allowable extreme fiber stress may be found by the formula

$$f = f_1\left(1 - \frac{l}{100b}\right)$$

in which f = the allowable extreme fiber stress for a beam laterally unsupported, in pounds per square inch

f_1 = the allowable extreme fiber stress for the timber when the beam is laterally supported, in pounds per square inch

l = the unsupported span of the beam, in inches

b = the width of the beam, in inches

Example. A beam having a span length of 15 ft 0 in. has two concentrated loads of 3000 lb each at the third points of span. The beam is laterally unsupported. If the timber has an allowable extreme fiber stress of 1400 psi for a beam laterally supported and the allowable horizontal shearing unit stress is 120 psi, what should be the size of the beam?

SOLUTION. The maximum bending moment due to the concentrated loads is found by the formula

$$M = \frac{Pl}{3} \qquad \text{(Fig. 5–17, Case III)}$$

$$M = \frac{3000 \times 15 \times 12}{3} = 180{,}000 \text{ in-lb}$$

Assume that the weight of the beam is 30 lb per lin ft. Then

$$M = \frac{wl^2}{8} = \frac{30 \times 15 \times 15 \times 12}{8} = 10{,}125 \text{ in-lb}$$

(Fig. 5–17, Case II)

Since the maximum bending moment for these two types of loads occurs at the center of the span, they may be added. Thus 180,000

+ 10,125 = 190,125 in-lb, the maximum bending moment. We shall assume the width of the beam to be 7.5 in. Then $\frac{15 \times 12}{7.5} = 24$; this ratio exceeds 20; thus it will be necessary to use the formula to determine the reduced allowable extreme fiber stress.

$$f = f_1\left(1 - \frac{l}{100b}\right) = 1400\left(1 - \frac{15 \times 12}{100 \times 7.5}\right) = 1064 \text{ psi}$$

the permissible extreme fiber stress. Then

$$S = \frac{M}{f} = \frac{190{,}125}{1064} = 178.8 \text{ in.}^3, \text{ the required section modulus}$$

Referring to Table 3–3, we find that an 8 x 14 in. section has a section modulus of 227.81 in.^{3}, and therefore this section is acceptable with respect to bending. The weight of the beam per linear foot is $\frac{7.5 \times 13.5}{144} \times 40 = 28$ lb per lin ft; hence the weight allowance of 30 lb per lin ft was adequate.

Maximum vertical shear $V = \frac{3000 + 3000 + (28 \times 15)}{2}$

$$= 3210 \text{ lb}$$

$$q = \frac{3}{2} \times \frac{V}{bh} \qquad \text{(Art. 6–2)}$$

$$q = \frac{3}{2} \times \frac{3210}{7.5 \times 13.5} = 47.6 \text{ psi}$$

the maximum horizontal shearing unit stress. Since this stress is less than 120 psi, the allowable, the 8 x 14 in. section meets the requirements for both shear and bending and therefore is accepted.

Problem 9–11–A. A simple beam 14 ft 0 in. in length supports a uniformly distributed load, including its own weight, of 6500 lb. If the allowable extreme fiber stress of the timber, laterally supported, is 1200 psi and the allowable shearing unit stress is 100 psi, what should be the size of the beam if it is laterally unsupported?

9–12. Design of a Floor Panel. So far the various steps in the design of beams have been discussed. The usual procedure for the complete design is to compute the loads the beam will support and then determine the cross section of the beam to satisfy bending stresses. Following this, the beam is investigated for horizontal shear, deflection, and end bearing. The following example is an illustration of the design of a typical panel in a structure employing mill construction.

Example. A panel of a building of heavy timber framing, mill construction, has 12 x 12 in. columns spaced 15 ft 0 in. on centers both ways as shown in Fig. 9–6 (*a*). The beams frame into the

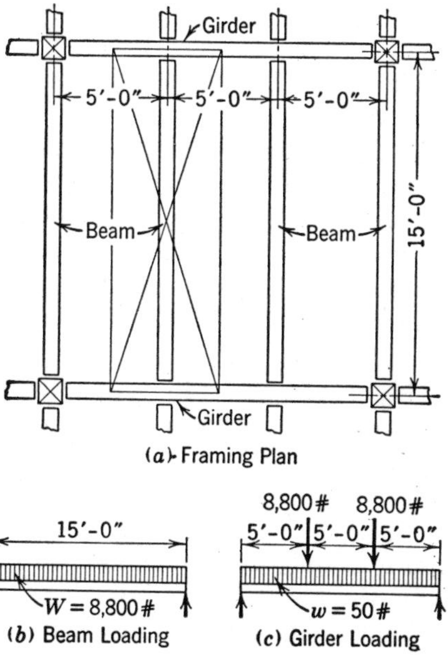

FIG. 9–6

girders at the third points, and the flooring consists of 3 in. planking on which is a $\frac{7}{8}$ in. maple top floor. The building is to be used for manufacturing purposes for which the live load is 100 psf. The allowable working stresses of the timber are

extreme fiber stress	=	1200 psi
horizontal shear	=	100 psi
compression perpendicular to grain	=	375 psi
modulus of elasticity	=	1,600,000 psi

SOLUTION. *Design of Beams.* As the loads on the girders are the loads that come from the beams, the beams are designed first.

The 3-in. planking runs from beam to beam, a span of 5 ft 0 in.; therefore each beam supports a floor area of 5×15 or 75 sq ft. This area is indicated by the diagonal lines in Fig. 9–6 (*a*). The weights of floor materials are given in Table 9–5.

3-in. plank flooring	=	9
$\frac{7}{8}$-in. top flooring	=	3
Live load	=	100
Total	=	112 psf

Note that a live load of 100 psf was given as a design requirement. If the live load had not been specified, it would have been necessary to refer to the local building code to find the live load appropriate for the type of occupancy. As a convenience, Table 9–6 gives certain minimum live loads, but the designer should refer to the code that governs the design of structures in his city.

Since each beam supports 75 sq ft and the floor load is 112 psf, $75 \times 112 = 8400$ lb = the floor load, not including the weight of the beam.

Assuming the beam to be an 8 x 12 in. and weighing 40 lb per cu ft, the estimated weight of the beam 15 ft 0 in. in length is

$$\frac{8 \times 12}{144} \times 40 \times 15 = 400 \text{ lb}$$

Thus the total uniformly distributed load on the beam is 8400 + 400 = 8800 lb. See Fig. 9–6 (*b*).

This being a simple beam with a uniformly distributed load, the maximum bending moment is

$$M = \frac{Wl}{8} \qquad \text{(Fig. 5–17, Case II)}$$

$$M = \frac{8800 \times 15 \times 12}{8} = 198{,}000 \text{ in-lb}$$

$$\frac{M}{f} = S$$

$$S = \frac{198{,}000}{1200} = 165 \text{ in.}^3, \text{ the required section modulus}$$

Referring to Table 3–3, we find that an 8 x 12 in. cross section has a section modulus of 165.31 in.^{3}, and therefore this beam is adequate to resist bending stresses. Since the allowable extreme fiber stress of the timber is 1200 psi, attention is called to the fact that Table 9–2 might have been used in selecting the beam. A beam 1 in. in width, having an actual depth of $11\frac{1}{2}$ in. and a span of 15 ft 0 in., will support a uniformly distributed load of 1175 lb. Then, 8800 ÷ 1175 = 7.48 in., the required width of the beam. Accept, therefore, an 8 x 12 in.

To investigate this 8 x 12 in. beam for horizontal shear, we first find the value of V. In accordance with the instructions in Art. 6–2, we may neglect all loads within a distance equal to the height of the beam from both ends. The total distributed load is 8800 lb, and, since the beam is 15 ft 0 in. in length, 8800 ÷ 15 = 586 lb per lin ft. Then the vertical shear to use in determining the horizontal shearing unit stress is

$$V = \frac{586 \times (15 - 2)}{2} = 3809 \text{ lb}$$

$$q = \frac{3}{2} \times \frac{V}{bh} \qquad \text{(Art. 6–2)}$$

$$q = \frac{3}{2} \times \frac{3809}{7.5 \times 11.5} = 66.3 \text{ psi}$$

the maximum horizontal shearing unit stress. Since this stress is less than 100 psi, the allowable, the beam is acceptable for horizontal shear.

To investigate the beam for deflection we shall use the deflection coefficients explained in Art. 9–5. This requires that we first determine the *actual* extreme fiber stress. Note that the section modulus of an 8 x 12 in. cross section is 165.31 in.^{3} (Table 3–3). Then

$$\frac{M}{f} = S$$

$$f = \frac{M}{S} = \frac{198{,}000}{165.31} = 1195 \text{ psi, the actual extreme fiber stress}$$

The deflection coefficient corresponding to $f = 1000$ psi, $E =$

TABLE 9–5. WEIGHTS OF BUILDING MATERIALS

Floors

Materials	Pounds per Square Foot
Board flooring, per inch of thickness	3
Granolithic flooring, " " " "	12
Floor tile, " " " "	10
Asphalt mastic, " " " "	12
Wood block, " " " "	4
Cinder-concrete fill, " " " "	6
Stone-concrete slab, " " " "	12
Slag-concrete slab, " " " "	10
Ceiling, suspended, metal lath and plaster	10
Ceiling, pressed steel	2

Roofs

Materials	Pounds per Square Foot
Three-ply roofing felt and gravel	5½
Five-ply roofing felt and gravel	6½
Roofing tile, cement	15 to 20
Roofing tile, clay, shingle type	12 to 14
Roofing tile, Spanish	8 to 10
Slate, ¼″ thick	9½
Slate, ⅜″ thick	14½
2″ Book tile	12
Sheathing, wood, 1″ thick	3
Skylight, ⅜″ glass in galvanized iron frame	7½

Walls and Partitions

Materials	Pounds per Square Foot
9″ Brick wall	95
13″ Brick wall	135
18″ Brick wall	190
4″ Brick, 8″ tile backing	75
9″ Brick, 4″ tile backing	100
8″ Wall tile	35
12″ Wall tile	45
3″ Clay-tile partition	18
4″ Clay-tile partition	19
6″ Clay-tile partition	25
3″ Gypsum-block partition	11
4″ Gypsum-block partition	13
2″ Solid plaster partition	20
4″ Stud partition, plastered both sides	22
Steel sash, glazed	10

Masonry

Materials	Pounds per Cubic Foot
Ashlar masonry, granite	165
Ashlar masonry, limestone	160
Ashlar masonry, sandstone	140
Brick masonry, common	125
Brick masonry, pressed	140
Concrete, plain stone	145
Concrete, reinforced stone	150
Concrete, cinder	110
Rubble masonry, limestone	150
Rubble masonry, sandstone	130

TABLE 9–6. MINIMUM LIVE LOADS

Occupation or Use	Live Load, Pounds per Square Foot
Apartments	
Private suites	40
Corridors	100
Rooms for assembly	100
Buildings for public assembly	
Corridors	100
Rooms with fixed seats	60
Rooms with movable seats	100
Dwellings	40
Factories	125
Garages	100
Hotels	
Private rooms	40
Public rooms	100
Office buildings	
Offices	80
Public spaces	100
Restaurants	100
Schools	
Assembly rooms	100
Classrooms with fixed seats	40
Classrooms with movable seats	80
Corridors	100
Stairways and firetowers	100
Stores	
First floors	125
Upper floors	75
Theatres	
Corridors, aisles, and lobbies	100
Fixed seats areas	60
Stage	150

1,600,000 psi, and a span of 15 ft 0 in. is 4.21 (Table 9–1). Therefore, $\frac{1195}{1000} \times \frac{4.21}{11.5} = 0.438$ in., the maximum deflection. The allowable deflection is $\frac{15 \times 12}{360} = 0.5$ in. Since the actual maximum deflection is less than 0.5 in., the allowable, the beam will not deflect excessively.

Let us assume that these beams frame into the girders by use of strap hangers as indicated in Fig. 9–5 (*b*). From the data the allowable compressive unit stress perpendicular to the grain for this timber is 375 psi.

We shall assume that the metal strap used for the hangers has a cross-sectional area of 2.5 x $\frac{3}{16}$ in. and that the bearing length of the beam on the hanger is 2 in. The factor for a 2-in. bearing length is found in Table 7–1 to be 1.19. Then, since the allowable compressive stress perpendicular to the grain for this timber is 375 psi, $375 \times 1.19 = 446$ psi, the allowable bearing stress on the hanger. The beam has a 7.5-in. width; hence the bearing area is 7.5×2 or 15 sq in. Thus $15 \times 446 = 6690$ lb, the allowable bearing stress on the hanger, and, since the reaction from the beam is only 4400 lb, the assumed hanger dimensions are acceptable for bearing.

The strap has 2.5×0.1875 or 0.468 sq in. in its cross section. There are two sections that may fail by shear and, if the allowable shearing stress of the metal is 9000 psi, $0.468 \times 9000 \times 2 = 8430$ lb, the allowable stress. Since this exceeds 4400 lb, the magnitude of the reaction, the assumed dimensions of the hanger are acceptable.

Design of Girders. Because beams frame into the girders from *both* sides, the concentrated loads on the girders are each 2×4400, or 8800 lb. These loads occur at the third points of span. The size of the girder must be estimated in order to make an allowance for its weight. Assume that the girder is a 12 x 16 in.; its weight at 40 lb per cu ft will be

$$\frac{12 \times 16}{144} \times 40 = 53 \text{ lb, say 50 lb per lin ft}$$

The diagram of the girder loading is shown in Fig. 9–6 (*c*).

The total load on the girder is $[8800 + 8800 + (15 \times 50)]$ or 18,350 lb. Each reaction is $18{,}350 \times \frac{1}{2} = 9175$ lb.

The maximum bending moment occurs at the center of the span; therefore

$$M_{(x=7.5)} = (9175 \times 7.5) - [(8800 \times 2.5) + (7.5 \times 50 \times 3.75)]$$
$$= 45{,}406 \text{ ft-lb} = 544{,}872 \text{ in-lb}$$

$$\frac{M}{f} = S = \frac{544{,}872}{1200} = 454 \text{ in.}^3, \text{ the required section modulus}$$

Table 3–3 shows the section modulus of a 12 x 16 in. to be 460.48 in.^{3}; therefore it is acceptable with respect to bending stresses.

To determine the horizontal shearing unit stress, we use the formula $q = \frac{3}{2} \times \frac{V}{bh}$ as explained in Art. 6–2. Then, since each reaction and, therefore, $V = 9175$ lb, $q = \frac{3}{2} \times \frac{9175}{11.5 \times 15.5} = 77$ psi, the horizontal shearing unit stress. This stress being less than 100 psi, the allowable, the 12 x 16 in. is approved for shear.

To investigate the deflection, first let us compute the actual extreme fiber stress.

$$\frac{M}{f} = S$$

$$f = \frac{M}{S} = \frac{544{,}872}{460.48} = 1180 \text{ psi}$$

The deflection coefficient for $f = 1000$ psi, $E = 1{,}600{,}000$ psi, and a span of 15 ft 0 in. is 4.21 (Table 9–1). The actual depth of the beam is 15.5 in.

In accordance with the footnote to the table, the coefficient will be multiplied by 1.02. The beam has equal concentrated loads at the third points of span, and, since the distributed load due to the weight of the beam is quite small in comparison to the concentrated loads, it will be ignored in computing the deflection. Then $\frac{1180}{1000} \times \frac{4.21}{15.5} \times 1.02 = 0.328$ in., the actual deflection. Allowable deflection $= \frac{15 \times 12}{360} = 0.5$ in. The actual deflection being less than the allowable, the deflection is not excessive.

The girders require special cast-iron bearing caps at the columns. We shall consider only the shelf upon which the girder is supported. The allowable compressive stress perpendicular to the grain for the timber in this problem is 375 psi. We shall assume that the bearing length is 3 in. In Table 7–1 we find the factor for a 3-in. bearing length to be 1.13. Thus 1.13 × 375 = 423 psi, the allowable bearing unit stress. The girder has an actual width of 11.5 in. and, since the bearing length is 3 in., 11.5 × 3 = 34.5 sq in., the bearing area. Then 34.5 × 423 = 14,600 lb, the allowable bearing load on the shelf. As the reaction of the girder is only 9175 lb, the bearing area is adequate.

Problem 9–12–A. Design the beams and girders for the floor panel shown in Fig. 9–7. The flooring consists of 4-in. planking with a $\frac{7}{8}$ in. finished flooring.

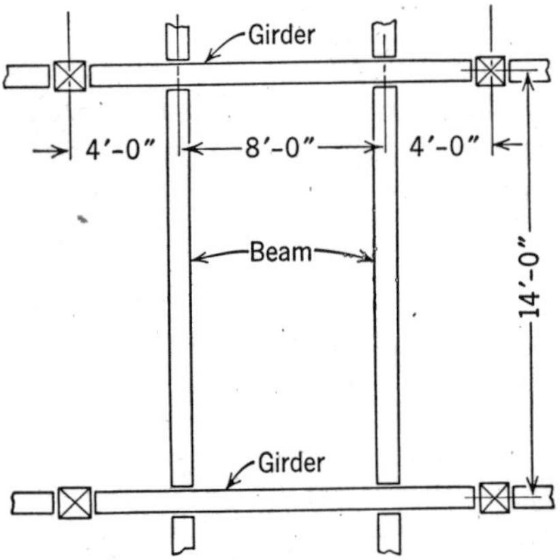

Framing Plan

FIG. 9–7

The live load is 100 psf. The allowable stresses to be used for the timber are f = 1700 psi, H = 120 psi, $c\perp$ = 455 psi, and E = 1,600,000 psi.

9–13. Depth Factor for Rectangular Beams. Let us suppose that a timber beam in a testing laboratory is loaded for bending with loads increasing in magnitude until failure occurs. The maximum bending moment for the load that occurs at failure is computed. This moment and S, the section modulus of the beam, are substituted in the flexure formula, $f = \frac{M}{S}$, and f, the extreme fiber stress that results, is called the *modulus of rupture.* It is not an accurate magnitude because the flexure formula is valid only when the extreme fiber stress does not exceed the elastic limit of the material. Nevertheless, the modulus of rupture is useful for purposes of comparison. In timber beams of rectangular cross section the modulus of rupture decreases slightly when the depth is increased. In assigning the bending stresses to structural grades of lumber a *depth factor* or *form factor* that corresponds approximately to a 12-in. depth was employed. In designing beams of the common sizes no additional depth factor need be used. When, however, the depth of the beam exceeds about 16 in., a depth factor should be computed by the empirical formula

$$F = 0.81 \frac{h^2 + 143}{h^2 + 88}$$

in which F is the depth factor and h is the depth of the beam in inches. Thus, for a beam 12 in. in depth, $F = 0.81 \frac{12^2 + 143}{12^2 + 88}$ and F in this formula becomes 1. Hence

$$M = FfS \quad \text{or} \quad M = 1 \times f \times S \quad \text{and} \quad M = fS$$

the usual form of the flexure formula.

The form factor, or depth factor, for a circular cross section is 1.18; hence, for a beam of circular cross section, $M = 1.18fS$.

The Forest Products Laboratory has developed the following formula to determine the form factor of I- and box beams:

$$F = 0.81 \left[1 + \left(\frac{h^2 + 143}{h^2 + 88} - 1\right)S\right]$$

in which F = the form factor
h = the depth of the beam, in inches
S = the support factor obtained from the formula
$S = p^2(6 - 8p + 3p^2)(1 - q) + q$
in which p = ratio of depth of compression flange to the full depth of the beam
q = ratio of thickness of web or webs to the full width of the beam

Although a form factor is unnecessary for a beam having the depth shown in the box beam in Fig. 6–3, the following example illustrates how the form factor is computed:

Example. A built-up glued box beam has the cross-sectional dimensions shown in Fig. 6–3. Determine the form factor to be used in the flexure formula for this box beam.

SOLUTION. The formula used to compute the form factor for a box beam is

$$F = 0.81\left[1 + \left(\frac{h^2 + 143}{h^2 + 88} - 1\right)S\right]$$

To determine S in this formula,

$$S = p^2(6 - 8p + 3p^2)(1 - q) + q$$

Thus

$$p = \frac{1.625}{14.75} = 0.11 \quad \text{and} \quad q = \frac{3.25}{5.625} = 0.578$$

Then

$$S = 0.11^2\,[6 - (8 \times 0.11) + (3 \times 0.11^2)](1 - 0.578) + 0.578$$

and

$$S = 0.625$$

Substituting in the first formula,

$$F = 0.81\left[1 + \left(\frac{14.75^2 + 143}{14.75^2 + 88} - 1\right)0.625\right]$$

and $F = 0.9$, the form factor

Consequently, the flexure formula to use for this box beam is

$$M = 0.9fS$$

9–14. Conversion Factors for Safe-Load Tables. Tables 9–2, 9–3 and 9–4 give safe distributed loads for extreme fiber stresses of 1200, 1400, and 1600 psi, respectively. These tables however, may also be used to determine the safe distributed loads in accordance with *any* extreme fiber stress. *To compute the safe loads for extreme fiber stresses other than those given, multiply the appropriate load in the table by the ratio of the desired stress to the stress used in the table.*

As an example, the load on a beam having a 1-in. width and of given depth *for an extreme fiber stress of 1300 psi* will be $\frac{1300}{1200}$ times the tabulated load for a stress of 1200 psi.

Example. A simple wood beam has a span of 16 ft 0 in. and a uniformly distributed load of 7300 lb. With respect to strength in bending, what size beam could be used if f, the extreme fiber stress, is 1500 psi?

SOLUTION. We shall use Table 9–3 in which the safe loads are computed on a basis of an extreme fiber stress of 1400 psi.

In this table we see that a beam 1 in. wide and 11.5 in. deep will safely support a distributed load of 1283 lb for a span of 16 ft 0 in. if the extreme fiber stress is 1400 psi.

Now let us find the safe load for a span of 16 ft, a width of 1 in., and a depth of 11.5 in. *for an extreme fiber stress of 1500 lb.*

In accordance with the rule, this safe load will be

$$\frac{1500}{1400} \times 1283 \quad \text{or} \quad 1370 \text{ lb}$$

The distributed load to be supported is 7300 lb, therefore, $7300 \div 1370 = 5.3$ in., the required width of beam that is 11.5 in. in depth. Accept, therefore, a 6 x 12 beam.

Tables 9–2, 9–3, and 9–4 are based on E, the modulus of elasticity, of 1,600,000 psi. The same procedure as explained above may be used for various moduli of elasticity. To find the load for a given span that results in a deflection that does not exceed $\frac{1}{360}$ of the span, *multiply the appropriate load given in the table by the ratio of the desired modulus of elasticity to 1,600,000.* It is convenient to remember that a greater modulus of elasticity results in a smaller deflection.

Example. A simple 6 x 12 in. beam has a span of 16 ft 0 in. and a uniformly distributed load of 6900 lb. If E, the modulus of elasticity of the timber is 1,760,000 psi, will this load result in an excessive deflection?

SOLUTION. Referring to Table 9–3, we find 1179 lb to be the load on a beam 1 in. in width and 11.5 in. in depth, for a span of 16 ft

0 in., that results in a deflection not exceeding $\frac{1}{360}$ of the span if $E = 1{,}600{,}000$ psi. Then, applying the foregoing rule,

$$\frac{1{,}760{,}000}{1{,}600{,}000} \times 1179 = 1280 \text{ lb, the load per inch of width. Since a}$$

6 x 12 in. beam has an actual width of 5.5 in., $1280 \times 5.5 = 7030$ lb, the load that produces a deflection of $\frac{1}{360}$ of the span if $E = 1{,}760{,}000$ psi. Since the load on the beam, 6900 lb, does not exceed 7030 lb, the deflection will not be greater than $\frac{1}{360}$ of the span.

CHAPTER 10

NOTCHED BEAMS

10–1. Notched Beams. It is frequently necessary to notch the ends of beams to increase clearance or to bring top surfaces level with adjacent beams or girders. Sometimes they are notched, top or bottom, at points between the supports to provide room for pipes or for framing of other beams. Notches in beams reduce the cross-sectional areas and reduce the magnitudes of the loads that the beam will properly support. Several types of notches are shown in Fig. 10–1. With the exception of the beam illustrated in Fig. 10–1 (*a*), the stiffness of a beam is almost unaffected by notches.

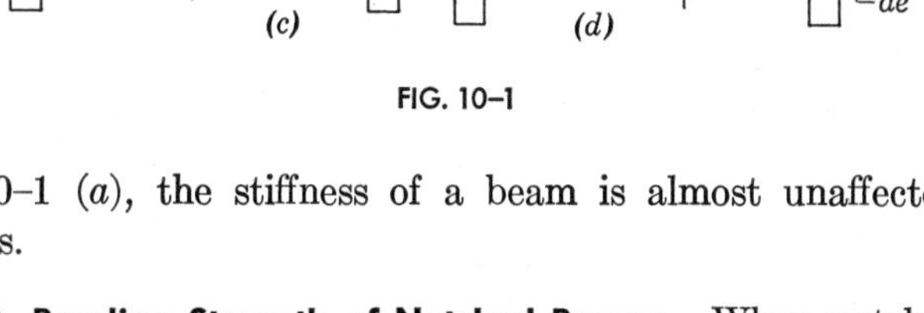

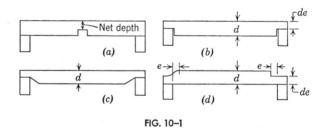

FIG. 10–1

10–2. Bending Strength of Notched Beams. When notches are cut at or near the mid-point in the open length of a beam, the net depth should be used in computing the bending strength. Suppose that an 8 x 12 in. beam is notched so that the "net depth," shown in Fig. 10–1 (*a*), is 9 in., the cross-sectional area used in computing the section modulus of such a beam is 8 x 9 in., not 8 x 12 in.

10–3. Resistance to Shear in Notched Beams. When a beam is notched on the lower side at the ends, as in Fig. 10–1 (*b*), the strength of a short, relatively deep beam is decreased by an amount depending on the shape of the notch and on the relation of the depth of the notch to the depth of the beam. The actual depth of material *above the notch* is used as the effective depth in the shear formula. In designing beams with *square-cornered* notches at the ends, the bending load should be checked for shear by the shear formula

$$V = \frac{2}{3}\left(\frac{bd_e^2q}{d}\right)$$

in which V = the vertical shear, in pounds
b = the width of the beam, in inches
d_e = the depth of the beam above the notch, in inches
d = the total depth of the beam, in inches
q = the allowable horizontal shearing unit stress. This stress is identified in Table 3–1 as H

Example. A 6 x 12 in. beam has a span length of 14 ft 0 in. with a concentrated load at the center of the span of 4400 lb. The beam has square notches at the supports similar to that shown in Fig. 10–1 (*b*) and the depth of the beam above the notch, d_e, is 8 in. The allowable horizontal shearing unit stress of the timber is 135 psi and the allowable extreme fiber stress is 1600 psi. (*a*) Is the beam safe with respect to horizontal shear? (*b*) Is the beam safe with respect to strength in bending?

SOLUTION. To find V, the maximum vertical shear, we shall use the formula

$$V = \frac{2}{3}\left(\frac{bd_e^2q}{d}\right)$$

A 6 x 12 in. timber has 5.5 x 11.5 in. actual dimensions. Therefore, in this beam, b = 5.5 in., d_e = 8 in., q = 135 psi, and d = 11.5 in. Substituting in the formula,

$$V = \frac{2}{3}\left(\frac{5.5 \times 8^2 \times 135}{11.5}\right) = 2760 \text{ lb, the maximum vertical shear}$$

The weight of the beam is $\frac{5.5 \times 11.5}{144} \times 40$ or 17.5 lb per lin ft.

Then $(2 \times V) - (\text{weight of beam}) = (2 \times 2760) - (17.5 \times 14) = 5275$ lb, the magnitude of the concentrated load that can be placed at the center of the span. Since this notched beam can safely resist a concentrated load of 5275 lb, the 4400-lb load is safe with respect to horizontal shear.

For the maximum bending moment

$$M = \frac{Pl}{4} \qquad \text{(Fig. 5–17, Case I)}$$

Then

$$M = \frac{4400 \times 14 \times 12}{4} = 184{,}800 \text{ in-lb}$$

For the distributed load

$$M = \frac{Wl}{8} \qquad \text{(Fig. 5–17, Case II)}$$

Then

$$M = \frac{(17.5 \times 14) \times 14 \times 12}{8} = 5145 \text{ in-lb}$$

Thus, $184{,}800 + 5145 = 189{,}945$ in-lb, the maximum bending moment.

Table 3–3 shows that the section modulus of a 6 x 12 in. beam is 121.23 in.^{3} Then $\frac{M}{f} = S$ and $f = \frac{M}{S} = \frac{189{,}945}{121.23} = 1560$ psi, the actual extreme fiber stress. Since 1560 psi does not exceed 1600 psi, the allowable, the beam is safe with respect to strength in bending.

Experiments show that when notches at the lower corners are cut away in order to obtain a gradual change in the cross section, as indicated in Fig. 10–1 (*c*), the loss in shearing strength is reduced. For such a condition the shearing unit stress is determined by using the actual depth of material above the notch and making no other reduction.

Example. Assume that the beam described in the foregoing example has its lower corners cut as shown in Fig. 10–1 (*c*). Compute the actual horizontal shearing unit stress.

SOLUTION. From the foregoing computations, the total weight of the beam is 14×17.5 or 245 lb. The concentrated load is 4400 lb; hence the total load is $245 + 4400$ or 4645 lb. Then each reaction and, consequently, $V = 4645 \times 0.5$ or 2323 lb. Then $q = \frac{3}{2} \times \frac{V}{bd}$ and $q = \frac{3}{2} \times \frac{2323}{5.5 \times 8} = 80$ psi, the actual horizontal shearing unit stress.

10–4. Notches on Upper Side of Beams. Refer to Fig. 10–1 (*d*), a beam notched on the upper side with two types of notches. For beams notched in either manner, the shear stress should be checked by the formula

$$V = \frac{2}{3} qb \left[d - \left(\frac{d - d_e}{d_e} \right) e \right]$$

In this formula e is the distance that the notch extends inside the inner edge of the support.

Problem 10–4–A. A 4 x 12 in. notched beam, as shown in Fig. 10–1 (*b*), has a span of 10 ft 0 in. with a uniformly distributed load, including its own weight, of 400 lb per lin ft. If $d_e = 9$ in., $H = 120$ psi, and $f = 1500$ psi, (*a*) is the beam safe with respect to horizontal shear? (*b*) Is the beam safe in bending?

Problem 10–4–B. A 4 x 12 in. beam has a span of 12 ft 0 in. and is notched as shown in Fig. 10–1 (*b*), the depth of material above the notch, d_e, being 8 in. There are two loads of 1200 lb each concentrated at the third points of span. The timber is the heart structural grade of redwood. (*a*) Is the beam safe for horizontal shear? (*b*) Is the beam safe for bending?

Problem 10–4–C. An 8 x 12 in. beam of the No. 1 SR grade of Southern pine is notched as shown in Fig. 10–1 (*b*), the distance d_e being 6 in. The span of the beam is 12 ft 0 in. Compute the magnitude of the maximum concentrated load that can be placed at the center of the span so that the allowable shearing and bending stresses will not be exceeded.

CHAPTER 11

JOISTS AND RAFTERS

11–1. Joists. Joists are the comparatively small, closely spaced beams that support floor boards. The nominal sizes commonly used are 2 x 8 in., 2 x 10 in., 2 x 12 in., 3 x 8 in., 3 x 10 in., and 3 x 12 in. The actual sizes and weights of these joists, as well as sizes and weights of other sections commonly used as joists and rafters, are given in Table 11–1. The most commonly used lengths are 12 ft 0 in., 14 ft 0 in., 16 ft 0 in., and 18 ft 0 in. Joists having lengths up to 24 ft 0 in. are obtainable in some localities but, since deflection is an important factor in their design, the longer lengths are avoided whenever possible. In designing structures the architect or engineer should have in mind the stock lengths of joists when he determines the sizes of rooms. Attention to this detail frequently avoids the use of odd lengths and the consequent waste of material.

11–2. Spacing of Joists. The spacing of joists is determined principally by the stock length of the material used for a plaster base, wood and metal lath, and plaster boards. The thickness of the flooring is also a consideration. The standard width of lath material is 48 in.; thus the usual spacings of joists are 12 in., 16 in., and 24 in., the most common spacing being 16 in. on centers. When the floor load or length of span is excessive, a 12 in. spacing is sometimes necessary.

A typical wood floor is illustrated in Fig. 11–1. The flooring consists of $\frac{7}{8}$ in. under-flooring, generally laid diagonally with the joists to stiffen the construction, and a $\frac{13}{16}$-in. finish flooring of pine, maple, or oak. A rosin-sized building paper is laid over the under-flooring before laying the top-flooring. Lath or plaster board, on which the plaster is applied, is attached to the underside of the joists.

TABLE 11-1. WEIGHTS OF FLOOR JOISTS AND ROOF RAFTERS * PER SQUARE FOOT OF FLOOR OR ROOF AREA

Nominal Size, in Inches	Actual Size, in Inches	Distance on Centers, in Inches	Weight, in Pounds
2 x 4	1⅝ x 3⅝	12	1.63
"	"	16	1.22
2 x 6	1⅝ x 5⅝	12	2.53
"	"	16	1.89
2 x 8	1⅝ x 7½	12	3.38
"	"	16	2.53
3 x 8	2⅝ x 7½	12	5.47
"	"	16	4.10
2 x 10	1⅝ x 9½	12	4.28
"	"	16	3.21
3 x 10	2⅝ x 9½	12	6.93
"	"	16	5.20
2 x 12	1⅝ x 11½	12	5.18
"	"	16	3.88
3 x 12	2⅝ x 11½	12	8.39
"	"	16	6.29
2 x 14	1⅝ x 13½	12	6.09
"	"	16	4.57
3 x 14	2⅝ x 13½	12	9.84
"	"	16	7.38

* Based on actual sizes and 40 lb per cu ft.

The purpose of *bridging* is twofold. It serves to maintain the joists in a vertical position, preventing buckling, and also aids in distributing concentrated loads to adjacent joists. Tests at the Forest Products Laboratory indicate that loads up to 400 lb concentrated on an area of $\frac{1}{3}$ sq ft of a conventional dwelling floor system are distributed laterally for a considerable distance with only 20 to 30% carried by the joist directly under the load. In the tests the load was applied at midspan. Material for cross bridging consists of ribbed metal straps, 1 x 3 in. stock for light construction, and 2 x 3 in. or 2 x 4 in. material is used for the larger joists. Joists should be bridged at intervals not exceeding 8 ft 0 in., or six times their depth, whichever is the greater. Bridging does not increase the strength of a floor in carrying distributed loads; it aids materially in preventing vibration.

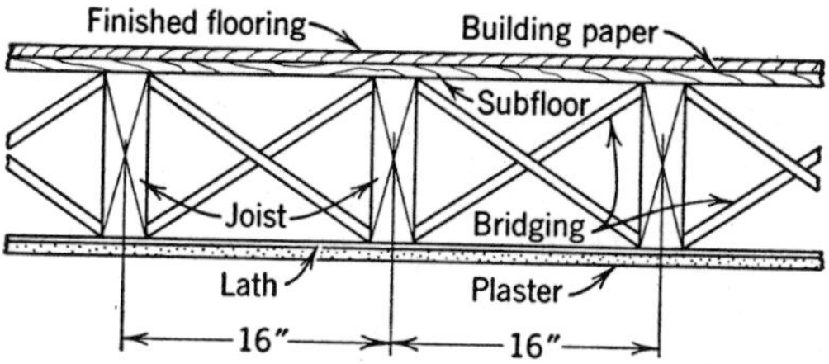

Typical Wood Floor Construction

FIG. 11–1

11–3. Joist Tables. Design of Floor Joists. The design of floor joists is generally accomplished by the use of safe load tables. In most structures it is desirable to use joists of the same depth throughout a floor, and consequently, because of the variation in span lengths, joists of sizes larger than those demanded in accordance with unit stresses must frequently be employed.

The designer should bear in mind that joists should be designed for both *strength in bending* and *deflection*. Joists that are acceptable for strength and deflection invariably have shearing stresses well within the allowable shearing stress of the material.

Many structures are designed to support live loads of either 40, 50, or 60 psf, and Tables 11–2, 11–3, and 11–4 give the maximum allowable spans for these three live loads, respectively. These tables will be found to be of great assistance in the selection of joists of the proper size.

Note particularly that each table is divided into two parts; the right-hand side gives the allowable span lengths for joist sizes and spacing for various allowable extreme fiber stresses in accordance with *strength in bending*. The left-hand side of the table gives the allowable span lengths for timbers having various moduli of elasticity when the *deflection* is limited to $\frac{1}{360}$ of the span.

TABLE 11–2. MAXIMUM SPANS FOR FLOOR JOISTS, LIVE LOAD 40 PSF

Size of Joists (Nominal), in Inches	Spacing of Joists Center to Center, in Inches	Maximum Allowable Lengths between Supports															
		Having determined from the building code or other proper authority the allowable modulus of elasticity *E* (in case the span is to be limited by deflection) or the allowable extreme fiber stress in bending *f* (in case the span is to be determined by bending) for the species and grade of lumber used, refer to the column below with the corresponding value to determine the maximum safe span for the size and spacing of joist desired. In selecting the span for deflection it should be checked with the spans for bending to see it does not exceed the length permitted for the bending stress *f* of the material used.															
		Span Limited by Deflection					Span Determined by Bending										
		E =	1,000,000	1,200,000	1,400,000	1,600,000	*f* =	900	1,000	1,100	1,200	1,300	1,400	1,500	1,600	1,700	1,800
2 x 6	12	*L*	9′ 1″	9′ 8″	10′ 2″	10′ 8″	*L*	9′ 6″	10′ 0″	10′ 5″	10′ 11″	11′ 4″	11′ 9″	12′ 3″	12′ 7″	13′ 0″	13′ 4″
"	16	*L*	8′ 4″	8′ 10″	9′ 3″	9′ 8″	*L*	8′ 3″	8′ 8″	9′ 1″	9′ 6″	9′ 11″	10′ 3″	10′ 8″	11′ 0″	11′ 4″	11′ 8″
"	24	*L*	7′ 3″	7′ 9″	8′ 2″	8′ 6″	*L*	6′ 9″	7′ 2″	7′ 6″	7′ 10″	8′ 1″	8′ 5″	8′ 9″	9′ 0″	9′ 3″	9′ 7″
2 x 8	12	*L*	12′ 1″	12′ 10″	13′ 6″	14′ 1″	*L*	12′ 6″	13′ 2″	13′ 10″	14′ 5″	15′ 0″	15′ 7″	16′ 2″	16′ 8″	17′ 2″	17′ 8″
"	16	*L*	11′ 0″	11′ 8″	12′ 4″	12′ 11″	*L*	10′ 11″	11′ 6″	12′ 1″	12′ 7″	13′ 1″	13′ 7″	14′ 1″	14′ 7″	15′ 0″	15′ 5″
"	24	*L*	9′ 8″	10′ 3″	10′ 10″	11′ 4″	*L*	9′ 0″	9′ 6″	9′ 11″	10′ 4″	10′ 9″	11′ 2″	11′ 7″	12′ 0″	12′ 4″	12′ 8″
2 x 10	12	*L*	15′ 2″	16′ 1″	17′ 0″	17′ 9″	*L*	15′ 9″	16′ 7″	17′ 5″	18′ 2″	18′ 11″	19′ 7″	20′ 4″	21′ 0″	21′ 7″	22′ 3″
"	16	*L*	13′ 11″	14′ 9″	15′ 6″	16′ 3″	*L*	13′ 9″	14′ 6″	15′ 2″	15′ 10″	16′ 6″	17′ 2″	17′ 9″	18′ 4″	18′ 11″	19′ 5″
"	24	*L*	12′ 3″	13′ 0″	13′ 8″	14′ 3″	*L*	11′ 4″	11′ 11″	12′ 6″	13′ 1″	13′ 7″	14′ 2″	14′ 7″	15′ 1″	15′ 7″	16′ 0″
2 x 12	12	*L*	18′ 4″	19′ 5″	20′ 5″	21′ 4″	*L*	18′ 11″	19′ 11″	20′ 11″	21′ 10″	22′ 9″	23′ 7″	24′ 5″	25′ 2″	26′ 0″	26′ 9″
"	16	*L*	16′ 9″	17′ 9″	18′ 9″	19′ 7″	*L*	16′ 7″	17′ 5″	18′ 3″	19′ 1″	19′ 11″	20′ 8″	21′ 4″	22′ 1″	22′ 9″	23′ 5″
"	24	*L*	14′ 9″	15′ 8″	16′ 6″	17′ 3″	*L*	13′ 8″	14′ 5″	15′ 1″	15′ 9″	16′ 5″	17′ 0″	17′ 8″	18′ 3″	18′ 9″	19′ 4″
2 x 14	12	*L*	21′ 4″	22′ 7″	23′ 10″	24′ 11″	*L*	22′ 0″	23′ 3″	24′ 4″	25′ 5″	26′ 6″	27′ 6″	28′ 5″	29′ 4″	30′ 3″	
"	16	*L*	19′ 7″	20′ 9″	21′ 10″	22′ 10″	*L*	19′ 4″	20′ 4″	21′ 4″	22′ 4″	23′ 3″	24′ 1″	24′ 11″	25′ 9″	26′ 6″	27′ 4″
"	24	*L*	17′ 3″	18′ 4″	19′ 4″	20′ 2″	*L*	16′ 0″	16′ 10″	17′ 8″	18′ 5″	19′ 2″	19′ 11″	20′ 7″	21′ 4″	21′ 11″	22′ 7″

3 x 6	12	*L*	10′ 7″	11′ 3″	11′ 10″	12′ 4″	*L*	11′ 10″	12′ 6″	13′ 1″	13′ 8″	14′ 3″	14′ 9″	15′ 4″	15′ 10″	16′ 3″	16′ 9″
"	16	*L*	9′ 8″	10′ 3″	10′ 10″	11′ 3″	*L*	10′ 4″	10′ 11″	11′ 5″	12′ 0″	12′ 5″	12′ 11″	13′ 4″	13′ 10″	14′ 3″	14′ 8″
"	24	*L*	8′ 6″	9′ 0″	9′ 6″	9′ 11″	*L*	8′ 6″	9′ 0″	9′ 5″	9′ 10″	10′ 3″	10′ 8″	11′ 0″	11′ 4″	11′ 9″	12′ 1″
3 x 8	12	*L*	13′ 11″	14′ 10″	15′ 7″	16′ 4″	*L*	15′ 7″	16′ 6″	17′ 3″	18′ 0″	18′ 9″	19′ 6″	20′ 2″	20′ 10″	21′ 6″	22′ 1″
"	16	*L*	12′ 9″	13′ 7″	14′ 4″	14′ 11″	*L*	13′ 8″	14′ 5″	15′ 2″	15′ 10″	16′ 5″	17′ 1″	17′ 8″	18′ 3″	18′ 10″	19′ 4″
"	24	*L*	11′ 3″	12′ 0″	12′ 7″	13′ 2″	*L*	11′ 4″	11′ 11″	12′ 6″	13′ 1″	13′ 7″	14′ 1″	14′ 7″	15′ 1″	15′ 6″	16′ 0″
3 x 10	12	*L*	17′ 5″	18′ 7″	19′ 7″	20′ 6″	*L*	19′ 7″	20′ 7″	21′ 8″	22′ 7″	23′ 6″	24′ 5″	25′ 3″	26′ 1″	26′ 11″	27′ 8″
"	16	*L*	16′ 1″	17′ 1″	18′ 0″	18′ 10″	*L*	17′ 2″	18′ 1″	19′ 0″	19′ 10″	20′ 8″	21′ 5″	22′ 2″	22′ 11″	23′ 7″	24′ 4″
"	24	*L*	14′ 3″	15′ 1″	15′ 11″	16′ 7″	*L*	14′ 3″	15′ 0″	15′ 9″	16′ 5″	17′ 1″	17′ 9″	18′ 5″	19′ 0″	19′ 7″	20′ 2″
3 x 12	12	*L*	21′ 0″	22′ 3″	23′ 6″	24′ 6″	*L*	23′ 5″	24′ 8″	25′ 10″	27′ 0″	28′ 1″	29′ 2″	30′ 2″			
"	16	*L*	19′ 4″	20′ 6″	21′ 7″	22′ 7″	*L*	20′ 7″	21′ 9″	22′ 9″	23′ 10″	24′ 9″	25′ 9″	26′ 7″	27′ 6″	28′ 4″	29′ 2″
"	24	*L*	17′ 1″	18′ 2″	19′ 2″	20′ 0″	*L*	17′ 1″	18′ 0″	18′ 11″	19′ 9″	20′ 7″	21′ 4″	22′ 1″	22′ 10″	23′ 6″	24′ 3″
3 x 14	12	*L*	24′ 5″	25′ 11″	27′ 4″	28′ 7″	*L*	27′ 2″	28′ 8″	30′ 0″							
"	16	*L*	22′ 6″	23′ 11″	25′ 2″	26′ 4″	*L*	24′ 0″	25′ 3″	26′ 6″	27′ 8″	28′ 10″	29′ 11′	31′ 0″			
"	24	*L*	20′ 0″	21′ 3″	22′ 4″	23′ 4″	*L*	20′ 0″	21′ 1″	22′ 1″	23′ 1″	24′ 0″	24′ 11″	25′ 10″	26′ 8″	27′ 6″	28′ 3″

NOTE: The above span lengths are based on

When limited by deflection:
Maximum allowable deflection of 1/360 of the span length
Modulus of elasticity as noted for E
Dead load—weight of joist
double thickness of flooring (5#)
weight of plaster ceiling ignored
Live load—40#/ft^2 with plastered ceiling

When limited by bending strength of piece:
Allowable stress in extreme fiber in bending as noted for f
Dead load—weight of joist
double thickness of flooring (5#)
plastered ceiling (10#)
Live load—40#/ft^2 with plastered ceiling, and
50#/ft^2 with unplastered ceiling

TABLE 11–3. MAXIMUM SPANS FOR FLOOR JOISTS, LIVE LOAD 50 PSF

Size	Spacing		Span Limited by Deflection					Span Determined by Bending									
		E =	1,000,000	1,200,000	1,400,000	1,600,000	f =	900	1,000	1,100	1,200	1,300	1,400	1,500	1,600	1,700	1,800
2 x 6	12	L	8′ 6″	9′ 1″	9′ 6″	10′ 0″	L	8′ 9″	9′ 2″	9′ 8″	10′ 1″	10′ 6″	10′ 11″	11′ 3″	11′ 8″	12′ 0″	12′ 4″
"	16	L	7′ 9″	8′ 3″	8′ 8″	9′ 1″	L	7′ 7″	8′ 0″	8′ 5″	8′ 9″	9′ 2″	9′ 6″	9′ 10″	10′ 1″	10′ 5″	10′ 9″
"	24	L	6′ 10″	7′ 3″	7′ 8″	8′ 0″	L	6′ 3″	6′ 7″	6′ 11″	7′ 2″	7′ 6″	7′ 9″	8′ 0″	8′ 4″	8′ 7″	8′ 10″
2 x 8	12	L	11′ 4″	12′ 0″	12′ 8″	13′ 3″	L	11′ 7″	12′ 2″	12′ 9″	13′ 4″	13′ 11″	14′ 5″	14′ 11″	15′ 5″	15′ 11″	16′ 4″
"	16	L	10′ 4″	11′ 0″	11′ 7″	12′ 1″	L	10′ 1″	10′ 7″	11′ 2″	11′ 8″	12′ 1″	12′ 7″	13′ 0″	13′ 5″	13′ 10″	14′ 3″
"	24	L	9′ 1″	9′ 8″	10′ 2″	10′ 7″	L	8′ 3″	8′ 9″	9′ 2″	9′ 7″	9′ 11″	10′ 4″	10′ 8″	11′ 0″	11′ 4″	11′ 8″
2 x 10	12	L	14′ 3″	15′ 2″	15′ 11″	16′ 8″	L	14′ 7″	15′ 4″	16′ 1″	16′ 10″	17′ 6″	18′ 2″	18′ 9″	19′ 5″	20′ 0″	20′ 7″
"	16	L	13′ 0″	13′ 10″	14′ 7″	15′ 3″	L	12′ 8″	13′ 5″	14′ 0″	14′ 8″	15′ 3″	15′ 10″	16′ 5″	16′ 11″	17′ 5″	17′ 11″
"	24	L	11′ 6″	12′ 2″	12′ 10″	13′ 5″	L	10′ 5″	11′ 0″	11′ 7″	12′ 1″	12′ 7″	13′ 0″	13′ 6″	13′ 11″	14′ 4″	14′ 9″
2 x 12	12	L	17′ 2″	18′ 3″	19′ 3″	20′ 1″	L	17′ 6″	18′ 5″	19′ 4″	20′ 2″	21′ 0″	21′ 10″	22′ 7″	23′ 4″	24′ 1″	24′ 9″
"	16	L	15′ 9″	16′ 9″	17′ 7″	18′ 5″	L	15′ 3″	16′ 1″	16′ 11″	17′ 8″	18′ 5″	19′ 1″	19′ 9″	20′ 5″	21′ 0″	21′ 8″
"	24	L	13′ 10″	14′ 8″	15′ 6″	16′ 2″	L	12′ 7″	13′ 3″	13′ 11″	14′ 7″	15′ 2″	15′ 9″	16′ 3″	16′ 10″	17′ 4″	17′ 10″
2 x 14	12	L	20′ 1″	21′ 4″	22′ 5″	23′ 6″	L	20′ 5″	21′ 6″	22′ 7″	23′ 7″	24′ 6″	25′ 5″	26′ 4″	27′ 3″	28′ 1″	28′ 10″
"	16	L	18′ 5″	19′ 6″	20′ 7″	21′ 6″	L	17′ 10″	18′ 10″	19′ 9″	20′ 8″	21′ 6″	22′ 3″	23′ 1″	23′ 10″	24′ 7″	25′ 3″
"	24	L	16′ 2″	17′ 3″	18′ 1″	18′ 11″	L	14′ 9″	15′ 7″	16′ 4″	17′ 0″	17′ 9″	18′ 5″	19′ 0″	19′ 8″	20′ 3″	20′ 10″
3 x 6	12	L	9′ 11″	10′ 6″	11′ 1″	11′ 7″	L	11′ 0″	11′ 7″	12′ 1″	12′ 8″	13′ 2″	13′ 8″	14′ 2″	14′ 7″	15′ 1″	15′ 6″
"	16	L	9′ 1″	9′ 8″	10′ 2″	10′ 7″	L	9′ 7″	10′ 1″	10′ 7″	11′ 0″	11′ 6″	11′ 11″	12′ 4″	12′ 9″	13′ 2″	13′ 6″
"	24	L	8′ 0″	8′ 6″	8′ 11″	9′ 4″	L	7′ 10″	8′ 3″	8′ 8″	9′ 1″	9′ 6″	9′ 10″	10′ 2″	10′ 6″	10′ 10″	11′ 2″

3 x 8	12	*L*	13′ 1″	13′ 11″	14′ 8″	15′ 4″	*L*	14′ 6″	15′ 3″	16′ 0″	16′ 9″	17′ 5″	18′ 1″	18′ 8″	19′ 4″	19′ 11″	20′ 6″
"	16	*L*	12′ 0″	12′ 9″	13′ 5″	14′ 1″	*L*	12′ 8″	13′ 4″	14′ 0″	14′ 7″	15′ 3″	15′ 9″	16′ 4″	16′ 10″	17′ 5″	17′ 11″
"	24	*L*	10′ 7″	11′ 3″	11′ 10″	12′ 4″	*L*	10′ 5″	11′ 0″	11′ 6″	12′ 1″	12′ 7″	13′ 0″	13′ 6″	13′ 11″	14′ 4″	14′ 9″
3 x 10	12	L	16′ 6″	17′ 6″	18′ 5″	19′ 3″	*L*	18′ 2″	19′ 2″	20′ 1″	21′ 0″	21′ 10″	22′ 8″	23′ 5″	24′ 2″	24′ 11″	25′ 8″
"	16	L	15′ 2″	16′ 1″	16′ 11″	17′ 8″	*L*	15′ 11″	16′ 9″	17′ 7″	18′ 4″	19′ 1″	19′ 10″	20′ 6″	21′ 3″	21′ 10″	22′ 6″
"	24	*L*	13′ 4″	14′ 2″	14′ 11″	15′ 7″	*L*	13′ 2″	13′ 10″	14′ 6″	15′ 2″	15′ 10″	16′ 5″	17′ 0″	17′ 6″	18′ 1″	18′ 7″
3 x 12	12	*L*	19′ 10″	21′ 1″	22′ 2″	23′ 2″	*L*	21′ 9″	22′ 11″	24′ 0″	25′ 1″	26′ 2″	27′ 1″	28′ 1″	29′ 0″	29′ 11″	30′ 9″
"	16	*L*	18′ 2″	19′ 4″	20′ 4″	21′ 3″	*L*	19′ 1″	20′ 2″	21′ 1″	22′ 1″	23′ 0″	23′ 10″	24′ 8″	25′ 6″	26′ 3″	27′ 0″
"	24	*L*	16′ 1″	17′ 1″	18′ 0″	18′ 10″	*L*	15′ 10″	16′ 8″	17′ 6″	18′ 3″	19′ 0″	19′ 9″	20′ 5″	21′ 1″	21′ 9″	22′ 5″
3 x 14	12	*L*	23′ 1″	24′ 6″	25′ 10″	27′ 0″	*L*	25′ 3″	26′ 8″	28′ 0″	29′ 2″	30′ 5″					
"	16	*L*	21′ 3″	22′ 7″	23′ 9″	24′ 10″	*L*	22′ 3″	23′ 6″	24′ 7″	25′ 9″	26′ 9″	27′ 9″	28′ 9″	29′ 8″	30′ 7″	
"	24	*L*	18′ 10″	20′ 0″	21′ 0″	22′ 0″	*L*	18′ 6″	19′ 6″	20′ 5″	21′ 4″	22′ 3″	23′ 1″	23′ 11″	24′ 8″	25′ 5″	26′ 2″

NOTE: The above span lengths are based on

When limited by deflection:
Maximum allowable deflection of 1/360 of the span length
Modulus of elasticity as noted for E
Dead load—weight of joist
double thickness of flooring (5#)
weight of plaster ceiling ignored
Live load—50#/ft^2 with plastered ceiling

When limited by bending strength of piece:
Allowable stress in extreme fiber in bending as noted for f
Dead load—weight of joist
double thickness of flooring (5#)
plastered ceiling (10#)
Live load—50#/ft^2 with plastered ceiling, and
60#/ft^2 with unplastered ceiling

Reproduced by permission of the National Lumber Manufacturers Association.

TABLE 11–4. MAXIMUM SPANS FOR FLOOR JOISTS, LIVE LOAD 60 PSF

Size of Joists (Nominal) in Inches	Spacing of Joists Center to Center in Inches	MAXIMUM ALLOWABLE LENGTHS BETWEEN SUPPORTS															
		Having determined from the building code or other proper authority the allowable modulus of elasticity E (in case the span is to be limited by deflection) or the allowable extreme fiber stress in bending f (in case the span is to be determined by bending) for the species and grade of lumber used, refer to the column below with the corresponding value to determine the maximum safe span for the size and spacing of joist desired. In selecting the span for deflection, it should be checked with the spans for bending to see that it does not exceed the length permitted for the bending stress f of the material used.															
		Span Limited by Deflection					Span Determined by Bending										
		E =	1,000,000	1,200,000	1,400,000	1,600,000	f =	900	1000	1100	1200	1300	1400	1500	1600	1700	1800
2 x 6	12	L	8′ 1″	8′ 7″	9′ 1″	9′ 6″	L	8′ 2″	8′ 7″	9′ 0″	9′ 5″	9′ 9″	10′ 2″	10′ 6″	10′10″	11′ 2″	11′ 6″
	16	L	7 4	7 10	8 3	8 7	L	7 1	7 6	7 10	8 2	8 6	8 10	9 2	9 5	9 9	10 0
	24	L	6 6	6 10	7 3	7 7	L	5 10	6 1	6 5	6 8	7 0	7 3	7 6	7 9	8 0	8 3
2 x 8	12	L	10 9	11 5	12 0	12 7	L	10 10	11 5	11 11	12 6	13 0	13 6	13 11	14 5	14 10	15 3
	16	L	9 9	10 5	11 0	11 5	L	9 5	9 11	10 5	10 10	11 4	11 9	12 2	12 6	12 11	13 3
	24	L	8 7	9 2	9 7	10 1	L	7 9	8 2	8 6	8 11	9 3	9 8	10 0	10 3	10 7	10 11
2 x 10	12	L	13 6	14 5	15 2	15 10	L	13 7	14 4	15 0	15 8	16 4	17 0	17 7	18 2	18 8	19 3
	16	L	12 4	13 2	13 10	14 6	L	11 10	12 6	13 1	13 8	14 3	14 9	15 4	15 10	16 4	16 9
	24	L	10 10	11 6	12 2	12 8	L	9 9	10 3	10 9	11 3	11 9	12 2	12 7	13 0	13 5	13 9
2 x 12	12	L	16 4	17 4	18 3	19 1	L	16 4	17 3	18 1	18 11	19 8	20 5	21 2	21 10	22 6	23 2
	16	L	14 11	15 10	16 8	17 5	L	14 3	15 1	15 10	16 6	17 2	17 10	18 5	19 1	19 8	20 3
	24	L	13 1	13 11	14 8	15 4	L	11 9	12 5	13 0	13 7	14 2	14 8	15 2	15 8	16 2	16 8

2 x 14	12	*L*	19 1	20 3	21 4	22 4	*L*	19 1	20 2	21 2	22 1	23 0	23 10	24 8	25 6	26 3	27 0
	16	*L*	17 6	18 7	19 6	20 5	*L*	16 9	17 7	18 6	19 3	20 1	20 10	21 7	22 3	23 0	23 8
	24	*L*	15 4	16 4	17 2	18 0	*L*	13 9	14 6	15 3	15 11	16 7	17 2	17 9	18 4	18 11	19 6
3 x 6	12	*L*	9 5	10 0	10 6	11 0	*L*	10 3	10 10	11 4	11 10	12 4	12 9	13 3	13 8	14 1	14 6
	16	*L*	8 7	9 2	9 7	10 1	*L*	8 11	9 5	9 10	10 4	10 9	11 2	11 6	11 11	12 3	12 8
	24	*L*	7 7	8 0	8 5	8 10	*L*	7 4	7 9	8 1	8 6	8 10	9 2	9 6	9 10	10 1	10 5
3 x 8	12	*L*	12 6	13 3	13 11	14 7	*L*	13 6	14 3	15 0	15 8	16 3	16 11	17 6	18 1	18 7	19 2
	16	*L*	11 5	12 1	12 9	13 4	*L*	11 10	12 6	13 1	13 8	14 3	14 9	15 3	15 9	16 3	16 9
	24	*L*	10 0	10 8	11 3	11 9	*L*	9 9	10 3	10 9	11 3	11 9	12 2	12 7	13 0	13 5	13 9
3 x 10	12	*L*	15 8	16 8	17 7	18 4	*L*	17 0	17 11	18 10	19 8	20 5	21 3	22 0	22 8	23 4	24 1
	16	*L*	14 4	15 3	16 1	16 10	*L*	14 11	15 8	16 6	17 2	17 11	18 7	19 3	19 10	20 6	21 1
	24	*L*	12 8	13 5	14 2	14 10	*L*	12 3	12 11	13 7	14 2	14 9	15 4	15 10	16 5	16 11	17 5
3 x 12	12	*L*	18 10	20 1	21 1	22 1	*L*	20 5	21 6	22 7	23 7	24 6	25 5	26 4	27 2	28 0	28 10
	16	*L*	17 4	18 5	19 4	20 3	*L*	17 11	18 10	19 9	20 8	21 6	22 4	23 1	23 10	24 7	25 4
	24	*L*	15 3	16 3	17 1	17 10	*L*	14 10	15 7	16 4	17 1	17 9	18 6	19 1	19 9	20 4	20 11
3 x 14	12	*L*	22 0	23 5	24 7	25 9	*L*	23 9	25 0	26 3	27 5	28 7	29 7	30 8			
	16	*L*	20 3	21 6	22 7	23 8	*L*	20 10	22 0	23 1	24 1	25 1	26 0	26 11	27 10	28 8	29 6
	24	*L*	17 10	19 0	20 0	20 11	*L*	17 4	18 3	19 2	20 0	20 9	21 7	22 4	23 1	23 9	24 6

NOTE: The above span lengths are based on the following:

When limited by deflection,

Maximum allowable deflection of $\frac{1}{360}$ of the span length.

Modulus of elasticity as noted for E.

Dead load—weight of joist.

double thickness of flooring (5#)

weight of plaster ceiling ignored.

Live load—60 psf with plastered ceiling.

When limited by bending strength of piece,

Allowable stress in extreme fiber in bending as noted for f.

Dead load—weight of joist.

double thickness of flooring (5#).

plastered ceiling (10#).

Live load—60 psf with plastered ceiling, and

70 psf with unplastered ceiling.

Be sure to read the footnotes to the table. For instance, we read for Table 11–2 that in the determination of the span lengths for bending the dead load consists of the weight of the joists, 5 psf for a double thickness of flooring, and a plastered ceiling for which there is an allowance of 10 psf. The table may be used for a live load of 40 psf with a plastered ceiling or 50 psf with an unplastered ceiling.

In Tables 11–2, 11–3, and 11–4 the limiting spans for deflection are computed by ignoring the weight of the plastered ceiling, the assumption being that the initial deflection from the dead load occurs before the plaster sets.

Example. Joists 2 x 10 in., spaced 16 in. on centers, are to be used in a building for which the live load is 40 psf. There will be the usual double thickness of flooring and a plastered ceiling. If f, the allowable extreme fiber stress of the timber, is 1000 psi and E, the modulus of elasticity, is 1,000,000 psi, what is the maximum allowable span for the joists if the deflection is not to exceed $\frac{1}{360}$ of the span?

SOLUTION. Referring to Table 11–2, we find under the column headed $f = 1000$ psi that the maximum allowable span for 2 x 10 in., 16 in. on centers, is 14 ft 6 in. This is the maximum span length determined by strength in bending. Now refer to the left-hand side of the table under the column headed $E = 1{,}000{,}000$ psi. Here we find that the limiting span for 2 x 10 in., 16 in. on centers, *if the deflection is not to exceed* $\frac{1}{360}$ *of the span*, is 13 ft 11 in. Thus 13 ft 11 in. is the maximum allowable span for the joists and, in this instance, it is determined in accordance with deflection.

It should be noted that floor joists are in reality simple beams designed, usually, to support uniformly distributed loads. The methods of beam design previously discussed may be used in designing joists. As an illustration, consider the following example.

Example. What size joists should be used for a span of 19 ft 0 in. with a spacing of 16 in. on centers? The dead load will consist of the weight of the joists, double flooring, and a plastered ceiling. The live load is 40 psf. For these joists, $f = 1200$ psi, $H = 95$ psi, and $E = 1{,}200{,}000$ psi.

SOLUTION. The first step in the design is to compute the load *a single joist* will support.

Finished flooring	= 2.5	
Rough flooring	= 2.5	
Plastered ceiling	= 10.0	(Table 9–5)
Weight of joists (estimated)	= 3.88	(Table 11–1)
Live load	= 40.0	
Total	58.88 psf	

Since the joists are to be spaced 16 in. on centers, each linear foot of joist will support $\frac{16}{12}$ or 1.33 sq ft. Hence the load on each linear foot of joist will be 58.88 × 1.33 or 78.5 lb, and the total uniformly distributed load on one joist will be 78.5 × 19 or 1490 lb.

$$M = \frac{Wl}{8} \qquad \text{(Fig. 5–17, Case II)}$$

$$M = \frac{1490 \times 19 \times 12}{8} = 42{,}600 \text{ in-lb, the maximum bending moment}$$

$$\frac{M}{f} = S = \frac{42{,}600}{1200} = 35.5 \text{ in.}^3\text{, the required section modulus}$$

On referring to Table 3–3 we find that a 2 x 12 in. cross section has a section modulus of 35.82 in.^{3}, and therefore 2 x 12 in. joists are acceptable *with respect to strength in bending.* Note that this is the same information given in Table 11–2. Here we find that the allowable span, determined by bending, for 2 x 12 in., 16 in. on centers, for an allowable extreme fiber stress of 1200 psi is 19 ft 1 in. Actually, no computations were required.

In accordance with Art. 6–2,

$$V = \frac{78.5 \times (19 - 2)}{2} = 668 \text{ lb}$$

$$q = \frac{3}{2} \times \frac{V}{bh} = \frac{3}{2} \times \frac{668}{18.69} = 54 \text{ psi}$$

the actual horizontal shearing unit stress. As the allowable shearing unit stress is 95 psi, the joists are acceptable with respect to shear.

Now let us investigate the deflection of the 2 x 12 in. joists for a span of 19 ft 0 in. As noted previously, the weight of the plastered ceiling will be ignored in computing the deflection; thus the floor load will be 58.88 − 10 or 48.88 psf.

The load per linear foot on each joist will be $\frac{16}{12} \times 48.88$ or 65 lb per lin ft; $65 \times 19 = 1235$ lb, the total load on one joist.

$$\text{Span length} = 19 \text{ ft } 0 \text{ in.} = 228 \text{ in.}$$

I, the moment of inertia of a 2 x 12 in., = 205.95 in.^{4} (Table 3–3).

$$D = \frac{5}{384} \times \frac{Wl^3}{EI} \qquad \text{(Fig. 5–17, Case II)}$$

$$D = \frac{5}{384} \times \frac{1235 \times 228 \times 228 \times 228}{1{,}200{,}000 \times 205.95} = 0.77 \text{ in., the actual deflection}$$

$$\frac{19 \times 12}{360} = 0.63 \text{ in., the allowable deflection}$$

Since the actual deflection exceeds 0.63 in., the allowable, the 2 x 12 in. joists are not acceptable with respect to deflection.

This, too, is verified in Table 11–2. We find that 2 x 12 in. joists spaced 16 in. on centers, for a timber whose modulus of elasticity is 1,200,000 psi, have a limiting span of only 17 ft 9 in.

By continued use of the table we find that 3 x 12 in. joists, 16 in. on centers, have an allowable span, determined by bending, of 23 ft 10 in.; the allowable span determined by deflection is 20 ft 6 in. Thus 3 x 12 in. joists spaced 16 in. on centers meet the requirements for both strength in bending and deflection and therefore are acceptable.

Example. Floor joists in a building have a span of 15 ft 0 in. and support a live load of 40 psf. There is a double thickness of flooring and a plastered ceiling below. In addition to the live load, the joists support a plastered 4 in. stud partition, 8 ft 6 in. in height, running across the joists at 5 ft 0 in. from one end of the span. See Fig. 11–2 (*a*). What should the size of the joists be if they are spaced 16 in. on centers? The allowable unit stresses for the timber that is to be used are $f = 1200$ psi, $H = 95$ psi, and $E = 1{,}200{,}000$ psi.

SOLUTION. This is a problem in which there is a uniformly distributed load as well as a concentrated load acting on the joists.

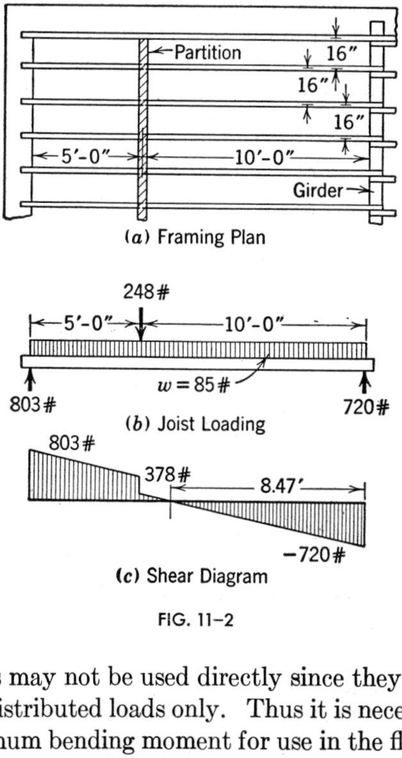

(a) Framing Plan

(b) Joist Loading

(c) Shear Diagram

FIG. 11–2

The joist tables may not be used directly since they are to be used for uniformly distributed loads only. Thus it is necessary to determine the maximum bending moment for use in the flexure formula.

The first step is to compute the loads.

Finished flooring	=	2.5
Rough flooring	=	2.5
Plastered ceiling	=	10.0
Joists (estimated)	=	9.0
Live load	=	40.0
Total		64.0 psf

As the joists are 16 in. on centers, $64 \times \frac{16}{12} = 85$ lb, the load per linear foot *on a single joist.*

Now let us consider the concentrated load exerted by the partition. Bear in mind that we are computing the load on a single joist. The joists are spaced 16 in. (1.33 ft) on centers, and, as the partition is 8 ft 6 in. in height, $1.33 \times 8.5 = 11.3$ sq ft, the area of the partition that bears on one joist. We note in Table 9–5 that the weight of the partition is 22 psf; thus $11.3 \times 22 = 248$ lb, the concentrated load on a single joist. The load diagram is shown in Fig. 11–2 (*b*).

Computing the reactions,

$$15R_1 = (85 \times 15 \times 7.5) + (248 \times 10)$$

$$R_1 = 803 \text{ lb}$$

$$15R_2 = (85 \times 15 \times 7.5) + (248 \times 5)$$

$$R_2 = 720 \text{ lb}$$

The shear diagram is drawn as shown in Fig. 11–2 (*c*). We note that the shear passes through zero at some point between the concentrated load and the right reaction, let us call it x ft from R_2. (See the second example under Art. 5–4.) Then, considering the forces to the right, $720 - (85 \times x) = 0$ and $x = 8.47$ ft. This is the section of the beam at which the bending moment is maximum. Its magnitude is, taking the forces to the right,

$$M_{(x=8.47)} = (720 \times 8.47) - (85 \times 8.47 \times 4.235)$$

$= 3049$ ft-lb or 36,588 in-lb, the maximum bending moment

$$\frac{M}{f} = S = \frac{36{,}588}{1200} = 30.49 \text{ in.}^3, \text{ the required section modulus}$$

Table 3–3 shows that a 2 x 12 in. joist has a section modulus of 35.82 in.^{3}, hence this joist is acceptable with respect to strength in bending.

Testing this section for horizontal shear,

$$V = 803 \text{ lb}$$

$$q = \frac{3}{2} \times \frac{V}{bh} = \frac{3}{2} \times \frac{803}{1.625 \times 11.5} = 65 \text{ psi}$$

As the allowable horizontal shearing unit stress is 95 psi, the 2 x 12 in. joist is acceptable for shear.

To investigate the deflection, the actual extreme fiber stress is first determined.

$$\frac{M}{f} = S$$

$$f = \frac{M}{S} = \frac{36{,}588}{35.82} = 1021 \text{ psi}$$

The deflection coefficient for $E = 1{,}200{,}000$ psi, and a span of 15 ft 0 in. is found in Table 9–1 to be 5.62. The footnote to the table directs that we multiply the coefficient by 0.92 for irregular loading; thus

$$\frac{1021}{1000} \times \frac{5.62}{11.5} \times 0.92 = 0.46 \text{ in., the actual deflection}$$

$$\frac{15 \times 12}{360} = 0.5 \text{ in., the allowable deflection}$$

Hence the 2 x 12 in. joists, having an actual deflection not exceeding the allowable, are acceptable.

In practice it is seldom necessary to perform the computations given in this example. Joist tables similar to Tables 11–2, 11–3, and 11–4 are employed, and experience soon enables the designer to select the proper sizes for most of the conditions that occur. For unusual cases, or for cases in which there may be a doubt, this example illustrates the method of procedure.

For the data given in the following problems determine by the use of Tables 11–2, 11–3, or 11–4 the proper joist sizes and spacings. In each instance there is a double thickness of flooring and a plastered ceiling.

Problem 11–3–A. Live load = 40 psf, span = 13 ft 0 in., f = 1000 psi, and E = 1,000,000 psi.

Problem 11–3–B. Live load = 40 psf, span = 11 ft 0 in., f = 1000 psi, and E = 1,000,000 psi.

Problem 11–3–C. Live load = 40 psf, span = 17 ft 6 in., f = 1200 psi, and E = 1,200,000 psi.

Problem 11–3–D. Live load = 50 psf, span = 18 ft 0 in., f = 1000 psi, and E = 1,200,000 psi.

Problem 11–3–E. Live load = 60 psf, span = 20 ft 0 in., f = 1200 psi, and E = 1,200,000 psi.

Problem 11–3–F. Floor joists having a span of 16 ft 0 in. support a double thickness of flooring, a plastered ceiling, and a live load of 50 psf. In addition, the joists support a plastered 4-in. stud partition 9 ft 0 in. in height, at 4 ft 0 in. from one end of the span. For the timber used, f = 1300 psi, H = 95 psi, and E = 1,200,000 psi. What size joists should be used if they are spaced 16 in. on centers?

11–4. Ceiling Joists and Attic Floor Joists.

The joists used for ceilings or for attic floors are designed for relatively small or no live loads. Computations show, therefore, that the size of the members is determined by deflection requirements rather than by strength in bending.

Table 11–5 gives the maximum allowable spans for ceiling joists based on $\frac{1}{360}$ of the span as the maximum allowable deflection. These spans are computed for a dead load composed of the weight of the joists and a plastered ceiling. There is no live load.

Table 11–5 also gives the maximum allowable spans for attic floor joists. For these joists the dead load consists of the weight of the joists, the weight of a plastered ceiling, and a single thickness of flooring. The live load is 20 psf.

Example. The timber used for ceiling joists has a modulus of elasticity of 1,000,000 psi and the span is 17 ft 0 in. What should be the size of the joists?

SOLUTION. Refer to Table 11–5 and note the span lengths given in the column for E = 1,000,000 psi. We find that 2 x 8 in. joists spaced 16 in. on centers have an allowable span of 17 ft 2 in. and thus are acceptable.

Example. Attic floor joists with a single thickness of flooring, a plastered ceiling, and a live load of 20 psf have a span of 16 ft 0 in. If the timber has a modulus of elasticity of 1,200,000 psi, what should be the size of the joists?

SOLUTION. Under the column heading E = 1,200,000 psi, Table 11–5, we find that 2 x 10 in. joists spaced 16 in. on centers have an allowable span of 16 ft 4 in.; therefore they are acceptable.

TABLE 11–5. CEILING JOISTS AND ATTIC FLOOR JOISTS

Size of Joists (Nominal), in Inches	Spacing of Joists, Center to Center, in Inches	Maximum Allowable Lengths between Supports				
Ceiling Joists						
		Span Limited by Deflection				
		$E=$	1,000,000	1,200,000	1,400,000	1,600,000
2 x 4	12	L	9′ 4″	10′ 0″	10′ 6″	11′ 0″
"	16	L	8′ 7″	9′ 2″	9′ 8″	10′ 1″
"	24	L	7′ 7″	8′ 1″	8′ 6″	8′ 11″
2 x 6	12	L	14′ 2″	15′ 1″	15′ 10″	16′ 7″
"	16	L	13′ 1″	13′ 11″	14′ 8″	15′ 4″
"	24	L	11′ 8″	12′ 5″	13′ 1″	13′ 8″
2 x 8	12	L	18′ 6″	19′ 8″	20′ 8″	21′ 7″
"	16	L	17′ 2″	18′ 3″	19′ 3″	20′ 1″
"	24	L	15′ 4″	16′ 4″	17′ 2″	17′ 11″
2 x 10	12	L	22′ 11″	24′ 4″	25′ 7″	26′ 9″
"	16	L	21′ 5″	22′ 9″	23′ 11″	25′ 0″
"	24	L	19′ 2″	20′ 5″	21′ 6″	22′ 5″
2 x 12	12	L	27′ 2″	28′ 11″	30′ 5″	
"	16	L	25′ 5″	27′ 1″	28′ 6″	29′ 9″
"	24	L	23′ 0″	24′ 5″	25′ 8″	26′ 10″
Attic Floor Joists						
2 x 4	12	L	6′ 6″	6′ 11″	7′ 4″	7′ 8″
"	16	L	6′ 0″	6′ 4″	6′ 8″	7′ 0″
"	24	L	5′ 3″	5′ 7″	5′ 10″	6′ 1″
2 x 6	12	L	10′ 1″	10′ 8″	11′ 3″	11′ 9″
"	16	L	9′ 2″	9′ 9″	10′ 4″	10′ 9″
"	24	L	8′ 1″	8′ 7″	9′ 1″	9′ 6″
2 x 8	12	L	13′ 4″	14′ 2″	14′ 11″	15′ 7″
"	16	L	12′ 2″	13′ 0″	13′ 8″	14′ 3″
"	24	L	10′ 9″	11′ 5″	12′ 0″	12′ 7″
2 x 10	12	L	16′ 9″	17′ 9″	18′ 8″	19′ 7″
"	16	L	15′ 4″	16′ 4″	17′ 2″	17′ 11″
"	24	L	13′ 6″	14′ 5″	15′ 2″	15′ 10″
2 x 12	12	L	20′ 1″	21′ 4″	22′ 5″	23′ 6″
"	16	L	18′ 6″	19′ 7″	20′ 8″	21′ 7″
"	24	L	16′ 4″	17′ 4″	18′ 3″	19′ 1″

Limited by Deflection of 1/360 of the Span

Having determined by reference to the building code or to other proper authority the allowable modulus of elasticity for the species of timber used, refer to the column below with the corresponding value to determine maximum safe span.

NOTE: The span lengths are based on

Ceiling joists:
- Maximum allowable deflection of 1/360 of span length
- Modulus of elasticity as noted for E
- Dead load—weight of joists plus plaster ceiling (10#/ft²)
- Live load—none

NOTE. The span lengths are based on

Attic floor joists:
- Maximum allowable deflection of 1/360 of span length
- Modulus of elasticity as noted for E
- Dead load—weight of joist weight of lath and plaster ceiling (10#/ft²) single thickness of flooring (2.5#/ft²)
- Live load—20#/ft² of floor area

Reproduced by permission of the National Lumber Manufacturers Association

By the use of Table 11–5 select the proper joist sizes for the following conditions:

Problem 11–4–A. Ceiling joists, E = 1,000,000 psi, span = 13 ft 0 in.

Problem 11–4–B. Ceiling joists, E = 1,200,000 psi, span = 18 ft 0 in.

Problem 11–4–C. Attic floor joists, E = 1,000,000 psi, span = 12 ft 0 in.

Problem 11–4–D. Attic floor joists, E = 1,200,000 psi, span = 19 ft 0 in.

11–5. Rafters and Roof Joists. The dead load to be supported by roof rafters consists of the weight of the rafters, the sheathing, and the roof covering. The live load is the load that results from snow and wind. Tables 11–6 and 11–7 give the maximum allowable *horizontal* lengths between supports for rafters of various sizes and spacings. For both tables the live load is 30 psf.

Because there is a wide variety of materials used for roof coverings, two separate tables have been prepared. Table 11–6 is for roofs in which the roof covering has been taken as 2.5 psf.

Group I:

Shingles	2.5 psf
Copper sheets	1.5 psf
Copper tile	1.75 psf
Three-ply ready roofing	1.00 psf

In Table 11–7, Group II, the assumed weight of the roof covering is 8 psf.

Group II:

Five-ply felt and gravel	7 psf
Slate, $\frac{3}{16}$	7.25 psf
Roman tile	8 psf
Spanish tile	8 psf
Ludowici tile	8 psf

These rafter tables are used in the manner described for floor joists in Art. 11–3. The size of the rafter may be determined either by strength in bending or by deflection. The shearing stresses are invariable within the allowable stresses of the timber used.

To verify the span lengths given in Tables 11–6 and 11–7 consider the following example.

Example. The dead load on roof rafters consists of the weight of the roof sheathing (2.5 psf), a Spanish tile roof (8.0 psf) and the weight of the rafters. The live load is 30 psf, the span of the rafters is 12 ft 0 in., and the lumber used is the 1200 *f* structural grade of eastern spruce. If the rafters are spaced 24 in. on centers, determine their size with respect to strength in bending by computing the required section modulus.

SOLUTION. The loads to be supported are the following:

Sheathing	= 2.5	
Spanish tile roofing	= 8.0	(Art. 11–5)
Live load	= 30.0	
Total	= 40.5 psf	

not including the weight of the rafter. Since the rafters are to be spaced 24 in. on centers, $40.5 \times 2 = 81$ lb, the load on one rafter. The span of the rafters is 12 ft 0 in. Note that this is the *horizontal* distance between supports, as shown in Fig. 11–3. Then $81 \times 12 = 972$ lb, the load on one rafter not including its own weight.

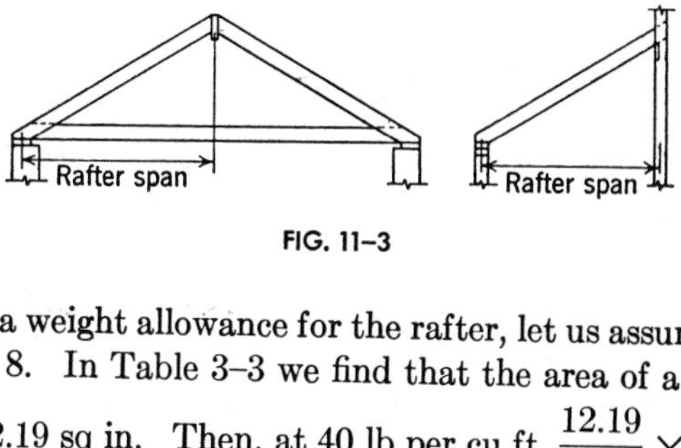

FIG. 11–3

To make a weight allowance for the rafter, let us assume that the size is a 2 x 8. In Table 3–3 we find that the area of a 2 x 8 cross section is 12.19 sq in. Then, at 40 lb per cu ft, $\frac{12.19}{144} \times 40 = 3.38$ lb, the weight of one rafter per linear foot. Therefore, $12 \times 3.38 = 40.56$ lb, the weight allowance for the rafter, and $972 + 40.56 = 1012$ lb, the rafter load to be used in computing the maximum bending moment.

The flexure formula is

$$S = \frac{M}{f} \quad \text{and} \quad S = \frac{1012 \times 12 \times 12}{8 \times 1200} = 15.2 \text{ in.}^3$$

the required section modulus. Referring to Table 3–3, we find

TABLE 11–6. RAFTERS AND ROOF JOISTS—LIVE LOAD 30 POUNDS PER SQUARE FOOT—GROUP I ROOF COVERING

Size of Joists (Nominal), in Inches	Spacing of Joists, Center to Center, in Inches	Maximum Allowable Lengths between Supports															
		Having determined from the building code or other proper authority the allowable modulus of elasticity E (in case the span is to be limited by deflection) or the allowable extreme fiber stress in bending f (in case the span is to be determined by bending) for the species and grade of lumber used, refer to the column below with the corresponding value to determine the maximum safe span for the size and spacing of rafter and roof joist desired. In selecting the span for deflection it should be checked with the spans for bending to see it does not exceed the length permitted for the bending stress f of the material used.															
		Span Limited by Deflection					Span Determined by Bending										
		$E=$	1,000,000	1,200,000	1,400,000	1,600,000	$f=$	900	1,000	1,100	1,200	1,300	1,400	1,500	1,600	1,700	1,800
2 x 4	12	L	6′ 5″	6′ 9″	7′ 2″	7′ 6″	L	7′ 8″	8′ 1″	8′ 5″	8′ 10″	9′ 2″	9′ 6″	9′ 10″	10′ 2″	10′ 6″	10′ 10″
"	16	L	5′ 10″	6′ 2″	6′ 6″	6′ 10″	L	6′ 8″	7′ 0″	7′ 4″	7′ 8″	8′ 0″	8′ 3″	8′ 7″	8′ 10″	9′ 2″	9′ 5″
"	24	L	5′ 1″	5′ 5″	5′ 9″	6′ 0″	L	5′ 6″	5′ 9″	6′ 0″	6′ 4″	6′ 7″	6′ 10″	7′ 1″	7′ 3″	7′ 6″	7′ 9″
2 x 6	12	L	9′ 10″	10′ 5″	11′ 0″	11′ 6″	L	11′ 9″	12′ 4″	12′ 11″	13′ 6″	14′ 1″	14′ 7″	15′ 1″	15′ 7″	16′ 1″	16′ 7″
"	16	L	9′ 0″	9′ 7″	10′ 1″	10′ 6″	L	10′ 3″	10′ 9″	11′ 4″	11′ 10″	12′ 3″	12′ 9″	13′ 2″	13′ 8″	14′ 1″	14′ 6″
"	24	L	7′ 11″	8′ 5″	8′ 10″	9′ 3″	L	8′ 5″	8′ 11″	9′ 4″	9′ 9″	10′ 1″	10′ 6″	10′ 10″	11′ 3″	11′ 7″	11′ 11″
2 x 8	12	L	13′ 0″	13′ 10″	14′ 7″	15′ 3″	L	15′ 5″	16′ 3″	17′ 1″	17′ 10″	18′ 6″	19′ 3″	19′ 11″	20′ 7″	21′ 2″	21′ 10″
"	16	L	11′ 11″	12′ 8″	13′ 4″	13′ 11″	L	13′ 6″	14′ 3″	14′ 11″	15′ 7″	16′ 3″	16′ 10″	17′ 5″	18′ 0″	18′ 7″	19′ 1″
"	24	L	10′ 6″	11′ 2″	11′ 9″	12′ 3″	L	11′ 2″	11′ 9″	12′ 4″	12′ 11″	13′ 5″	13′ 11″	14′ 5″	14′ 11″	15′ 4″	15′ 9″
2 x 10	12	L	16′ 4″	17′ 5″	18′ 4″	19′ 2″	L	19′ 4″	20′ 4″	21′ 4″	22′ 4″	23′ 3″	24′ 1″	24′ 11″	25′ 9″	26′ 7″	27′ 4″
"	16	L	15′ 0″	15′ 11″	16′ 9″	17′ 6″	L	17′ 0″	17′ 10″	18′ 9″	19′ 7″	20′ 5″	21′ 2″	21′ 11″	22′ 7″	23′ 4″	24′ 0″
"	24	L	13′ 3″	14′ 1″	14′ 10″	15′ 6″	L	14′ 1″	14′ 10″	15′ 6″	16′ 3″	16′ 11″	17′ 6″	18′ 2″	18′ 9″	19′ 4″	19′ 10″

2 x 12	12	*L*	19′ 8″	20′ 11″	22′ 0″	23′ 0″	*L*	23′ 1″	24′ 4″	25′ 7″	26′ 8″	27′ 9″	28′ 10″	29′ 10″	30′ 10″		
"	16	*L*	18′ 1″	19′ 2″	20′ 2″	21′ 1″	*L*	20′ 4″	21′ 5″	22′ 6″	23′ 6″	24′ 6″	25′ 5″	26′ 3″	27′ 2″	28′ 0″	28′ 9″
"	24	*L*	15′ 11″	16′ 11″	17′ 10″	18′ 8″	*L*	16′ 11″	17′ 10″	18′ 8″	19′ 6″	20′ 4″	21′ 1″	21′ 10″	22′ 6″	23′ 3″	23′ 11″
2 x 14	12	*L*	22′ 11″	24′ 4″	25′ 7″	26′ 9″	*L*	26′ 10″	28′ 4″	29′ 8″	31′ 0″						
"	16	*L*	21′ 1″	22′ 5″	23′ 7″	24′ 8″	*L*	23′ 8″	25′ 0″	26′ 2″	27′ 4″	28′ 6″	29′ 6″	30′ 7″			
"	24	*L*	18′ 8″	19′ 10″	20′ 10″	21′ 10″	*L*	19′ 9″	20′ 9″	21′ 10″	22′ 9″	23′ 9″	24′ 7″	25′ 6″	26′ 4″	27′ 1″	27′ 11″
3 x 6	12	*L*	11′ 5″	12′ 1″	12′ 9″	13′ 4″	*L*	14′ 7″	15′ 4″	16′ 1″	16′ 10″	17′ 6″	18′ 2″	18′ 10″	19′ 5″	20′ 0″	20′ 7″
"	16	*L*	10′ 5″	11′ 1″	11′ 8″	12′ 2″	*L*	12′ 9″	13′ 6″	14′ 2″	14′ 9″	15′ 4″	15′ 11″	16′ 6″	17′ 1″	17′ 7″	18′ 1″
"	24	*L*	9′ 2″	9′ 9″	10′ 3″	10′ 9″	*L*	10′ 7″	11′ 2″	11′ 8″	12′ 3″	12′ 9″	13′ 2″	13′ 8″	14′ 1″	14′ 7″	15′ 0″
3 x 8	12	*L*	15′ 0″	15′ 11″	16′ 9″	17′ 7″	*L*	19′ 1″	20′ 2″	21′ 1″	22′ 1″	22′ 11″	23′ 10″	24′ 8″	25′ 6″	26′ 3″	27′ 0″
"	16	*L*	13′ 9″	14′ 8″	15′ 5″	16′ 1″	*L*	16′ 10″	17′ 9″	18′ 7″	19′ 5″	20′ 3″	21′ 0″	21′ 9″	22′ 5″	23′ 1″	23′ 9″
"	24	*L*	12′ 2″	12′ 11″	13′ 8″	14′ 3″	*L*	14′ 0″	14′ 9″	15′ 6″	16′ 2″	16′ 10″	17′ 5″	18′ 1″	18′ 8″	19′ 3″	19′ 9″
3 x 10	12	*L*	18′ 9″	20′ 0″	21′ 0″	22′ 0″	*L*	23′ 9″	25′ 1″	26′ 3″	27′ 6″	28′ 7″	29′ 8″	30′ 8″			
"	16	*L*	17′ 4″	18′ 5″	19′ 4″	20′ 3″	*L*	21′ 0″	22′ 2″	23′ 3″	24′ 3″	25′ 3″	26′ 3″	27′ 2″	28′ 0″	28′ 11″	29′ 9″
"	24	*L*	15′ 4″	16′ 4″	17′ 2″	17′ 11″	*L*	17′ 7″	18′ 6″	19′ 5″	20′ 3″	21′ 1″	21′ 11″	22′ 8″	23′ 5″	24′ 1″	24′ 10″

NOTE: The above span lengths are based on

When limited by deflection:
Maximum allowable deflection of 1/360 of the span length
Modulus of elasticity as noted for *E*
When determined by bending strength of the piece:
Allowable stress in extreme fiber in bending as noted for *f*

Dead load—weight of roof joist or rafter
weight of roof sheathing (2.5#/ft²)
weight of roof coverings (2.5#/ft²) (Group I)
Live load—30#/ft² of roof surface considered as acting normal to the surface

Reproduced by permission of the National Lumber Manufacturers Association.

TABLE 11–7. RAFTERS AND ROOF JOISTS—LIVE LOAD 30 POUNDS PER SQUARE FOOT—GROUP II ROOF COVERING

Size	Spacing	Span Limited by Deflection					Span Determined by Bending										
		E =	1,000,000	1,200,000	1,400,000	1,600,000	f =	900	1,000	1,100	1,200	1,300	1,400	1,500	1,600	1,700	1,800
2 x 4	12	L	6' 1"	6' 6"	6' 10"	7' 2"	L	7' 1"	7' 6"	7' 10"	8' 3"	8' 7"	8' 11"	9' 2"	9' 6"	9' 9"	10' 1"
"	16	L	5' 7"	5' 11"	6' 3"	6' 6"	L	6' 2"	6' 6"	6' 10"	7' 2"	7' 5"	7' 9"	8' 0"	8' 3"	8' 6"	8' 9"
"	24	L	4' 10"	5' 2"	5' 5"	5' 8"	L	5' 1"	5' 4"	5' 7"	5' 10"	6' 1"	6' 4"	6' 7"	6' 9"	7' 0"	7' 2"
2 x 6	12	L	9' 5"	10' 0"	10' 6"	11' 0"	L	10' 11"	11' 6"	12' 1"	12' 8"	13' 2"	13' 8"	14' 1"	14' 7"	15' 0"	15' 6"
"	16	L	8' 7"	9' 1"	9' 7"	10' 0"	L	9' 6"	10' 1"	10' 7"	11' 0"	11' 6"	11' 11"	12' 4"	12' 9"	13' 1"	13' 6"
"	24	L	7' 6"	8' 0"	8' 5"	8' 10"	L	7' 10"	8' 3"	8' 8"	9' 1"	9' 5"	9' 9"	10' 2"	10' 6"	10' 9"	11' 1"
2 x 8	12	L	12' 5"	13' 3"	13' 11"	14' 7"	L	14' 5"	15' 3"	15' 11"	16' 8"	17' 4"	18' 0"	18' 8"	19' 3"	19' 10"	20' 5"
"	16	L	11' 5"	12' 1"	12' 9"	13' 4"	L	12' 7"	13' 4"	13' 11"	14' 7"	15' 2"	15' 9"	16' 3"	16' 10"	17' 4"	17' 10"
"	24	L	10' 0"	10' 8"	11' 2"	11' 9"	L	10' 5"	11' 0"	11' 6"	12' 0"	12' 6"	13' 0"	13' 5"	13' 10"	14' 4"	14' 9"
2 x 10	12	L	15' 8"	16' 8"	17' 6"	18' 4"	L	18' 1"	19' 1"	20' 0"	20' 11"	21' 9"	22' 7"	23' 4"	24' 1"	24' 10"	25' 7"
"	16	L	14' 4"	15' 3"	16' 0"	16' 9"	L	15' 10"	16' 9"	17' 6"	18' 4"	19' 1"	19' 9"	20' 6"	21' 2"	21' 10"	22' 5"
"	24	L	12' 8"	13' 5"	14' 2"	14' 9"	L	13' 1"	13' 10"	14' 6"	15' 2"	15' 9"	16' 4"	16' 11"	17' 6"	18' 0"	18' 6"
2 x 12	12	L	18' 10"	20' 0"	21' 1"	22' 0"	L	21' 8"	22' 10"	24' 0"	25' 0"	26' 1"	27' 1"	28' 0"	28' 11"	29' 10"	30' 8"
"	16	L	17' 3"	18' 4"	19' 4"	20' 2"	L	19' 1"	20' 1"	21' 1"	22' 0"	22' 11"	23' 9"	24' 7"	25' 5"	26' 2"	26' 11"
"	24	L	15' 3"	16' 2"	17' 1"	17' 10"	L	15' 9"	16' 8"	17' 6"	18' 3"	19' 0"	19' 8"	20' 5"	21' 1"	21' 8"	22' 4"
2 x 14	12	L	22' 0"	23' 4"	24' 7"	25' 8"	L	25' 2"	26' 7"	27' 10"	29' 1"	30' 4"					
"	16	L	20' 2"	21' 5"	22' 7"	23' 7"	L	22' 2"	23' 5"	24' 6"	25' 8"	26' 8"	27' 8"	28' 8"	29' 7"	30' 6"	
"	24	L	17' 10"	18' 11"	19' 11"	20' 10"	L	18' 5"	19' 5"	20' 5"	21' 3"	22' 2"	23' 0"	23' 1J"	24' 7"	25' 4"	26' 1"

3 x 6	12	L	10′ 11″	11′ 7″	12′ 2″	12′ 9″	L	13′ 8″	14′ 5″	15′ 1″	15′ 9″	16′ 5″	17′ 0″	17′ 7″	18′ 2″	18′ 9″	19′ 4″
"	16	L	10′ 0″	10′ 7″	11′ 2″	11′ 8″	L	12′ 0″	12′ 7″	13′ 3″	13′ 10″	14′ 4″	14′ 11″	15′ 5″	15′ 11″	16′ 5″	16′ 11″
"	24	L	8′ 9″	9′ 4″	9′ 10″	10′ 3″	L	9′ 11″	10′ 5″	10′ 11″	11′ 5″	11′ 10″	12′ 4″	12′ 9″	13′ 2″	13′ 7″	14′ 0″
3 x 8	12	L	14′ 5″	15′ 3″	16′ 1″	16′ 10″	L	17′ 11″	18′ 11″	19′ 10″	20′ 8″	21′ 6″	22′ 4″	23′ 2″	23′ 11″	24′ 8″	25′ 4″
"	16	L	13′ 2″	14′ 0″	14′ 9″	15′ 5″	L	15′ 9″	16′ 7″	17′ 5″	18′ 2″	18′ 11″	19′ 8″	20′ 4″	21′ 0″	21′ 8″	22′ 3″
"	24	L	11′ 8″	12′ 5″	13′ 0″	13′ 7″	L	13′ 1″	13′ 9″	14′ 5″	15′ 1″	15′ 8″	16′ 3″	16′ 10″	17′ 5″	18′ 0″	18′ 6″
3 x 10	12	L	18′ 0″	19′ 2″	20′ 2″	21′ 1″	L	22′ 4″	23′ 7″	24′ 9″	25′ 10″	26′ 10″	27′ 11″	28′ 10″	29′ 10″	30′ 9″	
"	16	L	16′ 7″	17′ 7″	18′ 6″	19′ 5″	L	19′ 9″	20′ 9″	21′ 10″	22′ 9″	23′ 8″	24′ 7″	25′ 6″	26′ 3″	27′ 1″	27′ 11″
"	24	L	14′ 8″	15′ 7″	16′ 5″	17′ 2″	L	16′ 5″	17′ 4″	18′ 2″	19′ 0″	19′ 9″	20′ 6″	21′ 2″	21′ 11″	22′ 7″	23′ 3″
3 x 12	12	L	21′ 7″	22′ 11″	24′ 2″	25′ 3″	L	26′ 8″	28′ 1″	29′ 6″	30′ 9″						
"	16	L	19′ 11″	21′ 2″	22′ 3″	23′ 3″	L	23′ 7″	24′ 10″	26′ 1″	27′ 3″	28′ 4″	29′ 5″	30′ 5″			
"	24	L	17′ 8″	18′ 9″	19′ 9″	20′ 8″	L	19′ 8″	20′ 9″	21′ 9″	22′ 9″	23′ 8″	24′ 7″	25′ 5″	26′ 3″	27′ 1″	27′ 10″
3 x 14	12	L	25′ 1″	26′ 8″	28′ 1″	29′ 4″	L	30′ 10″									
"	16	L	23′ 2″	24′ 8″	26′ 0″	27′ 2″	L	27′ 5″	28′ 10″	30′ 3″							
"	24	L	20′ 8″	21′ 11″	23′ 1″	24′ 2″	L	22′ 11″	24′ 2″	25′ 5″	26′ 6″	27′ 7″	28′ 8″	29′ 8″	30′ 7″		

NOTE: The above span lengths are based on

When limited by deflection:
Maximum allowable deflection of 1/360 of the span length
Modulus of elasticity as noted for E
When determined by bending strength of the piece:
Allowable stress in extreme fiber in bending as noted for f

Dead load—weight of roof joist or rafter
weight of roof sheathing (2.5#/ft^2)
weight of roof coverings (8#/ft^2) (Group II)
Live load—30#/ft^2 of roof surface considered as acting normal to the surface

Reproduced by permission of the National Lumber Manufacturers Association.

that a 2 x 8-in. rafter has a section modulus of 15.23 in.^{3} and, therefore, is accepted.

Refer to Table 11–7. Note that this same rafter size could have been selected without computations.

Example. The covering of a roof consists of wood shingles, and the horizontal length between supports of the rafters is 10 ft 0 in. If the allowable extreme fiber stress of the timber and modulus of elasticity are 1000 psi and 1,000,000 psi, respectively, the live load is 30 psf, and the rafters are spaced 24 in. on centers, what should be the size of the rafters?

SOLUTION. As shingles are included in Group I, we shall use Table 11–6. For $f = 1000$ psi we find that 2 x 8 in. rafters, 24 in. on centers, have an allowable span of 11 ft 9 in. Under the column headed $E = 1{,}000{,}000$ psi we note that the allowable span for the same rafters and spacing is 10 ft 6 in. Therefore, the 2 x 8 in. rafters spaced 24 in. on centers are acceptable.

Example. The timber to be used for roof rafters has an allowable extreme fiber stress of $f = 1200$ psi and $E = 1{,}200{,}000$ psi. The span between supports is 15 ft 0 in., the rafter spacing is 16 in., the roof covering consists of $\frac{3}{16}$-in. slate, and the live load is 30 psf. What should be the size of the rafters?

SOLUTION. Slate $\frac{3}{16}$-in. thick is included in the roof coverings in Group II; therefore we use Table 11–7. Under $E = 1{,}200{,}000$ psi we note that 2 x 10 in. rafters with 16 in. spacing have an allowable span of 15 ft 3 in., and in the column $f = 1200$ psi the allowable span for these rafters is 18 ft 4 in. Therefore the 2 x 10 in. rafters spaced 16 in. on centers are accepted.

By the use of Tables 11–6 and 11–7 select the roof rafter sizes in accordance with the following data:

Problem 11–5–A. Live load = 30 psf, $f = 900$ psi, $E = 1{,}000{,}000$ psi, span = 7 ft 6 in., and roof covering is copper tile.

Problem 11–5–B. Live load = 30 psf, $f = 1000$ psi, $E = 1{,}000{,}000$ psi, span = 11 ft 6 in., and roof covering is wood shingles.

Problem 11–5–C. Live load = 30 psf, $f = 1200$ psi, $E = 1{,}200{,}000$ psi, span = 18 ft 0 in., and roof covering is Spanish tile.

Problem 11–5–D. Live load = 30 psf, $f = 1400$ psi, $E = 1{,}600{,}000$ psi, span = 16 ft 6 in., and roof covering is $\frac{3}{16}$-in. slate.

CHAPTER 12

PLANK AND LAMINATED FLOORS

12–1. Plank and Laminated Floors. The structural flooring of *mill construction* consists of floor planks. Plank floors or decks consist of lumber laid with the wide faces bearing on the supports securely nailed to the supporting members. Generally, for floors, the planks are covered with a $\frac{13}{16}$ in. top floor of maple or other hardwood to afford a wearing surface.

Plank floors consist of material square-edged, *tongued and grooved*, or *splined* with the material laid flat, as indicated in Figs. 12–1 (*a*) and (*b*). Material 4 in. and more in thickness should be splined. The spacing of the beams on which the planks are laid usually varies from 6 ft 0 in. to 11 ft 0 in., depending on the magnitude and type of the live load to be supported. The planks are nailed directly to the floor beams. A *laminated floor* consists of planks set on edge side by side and nailed together at the ends and at frequent intervals, approximately 18 in., alternating at top and bottom.

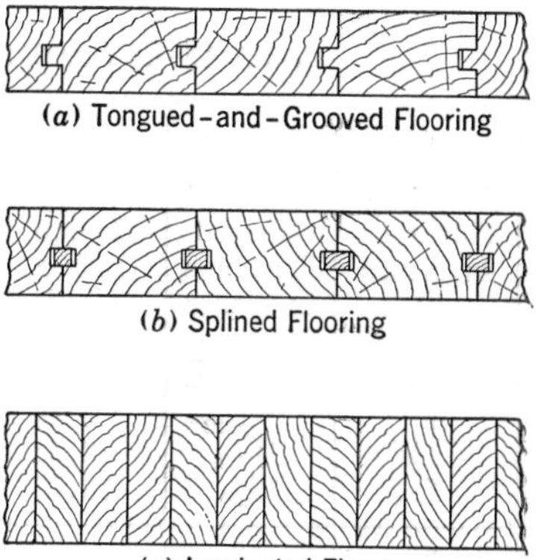

(*a*) Tongued-and-Grooved Flooring

(*b*) Splined Flooring

(*c*) Laminated Floor

FIG. 12–1

Whenever possible, plank and laminated floors should have the planks two or more bays in length, breaking joints about every 4 ft 0 in. This results in a stiffer floor than a system in which the planks act as simple beams terminating at supports. For the longer spans it is difficult to obtain planks two bays in length, and a common method of breaking joints is indicated in Fig. 12–2. When this method is used, the ends of the planks should not occur in the middle third of the span between the beams.

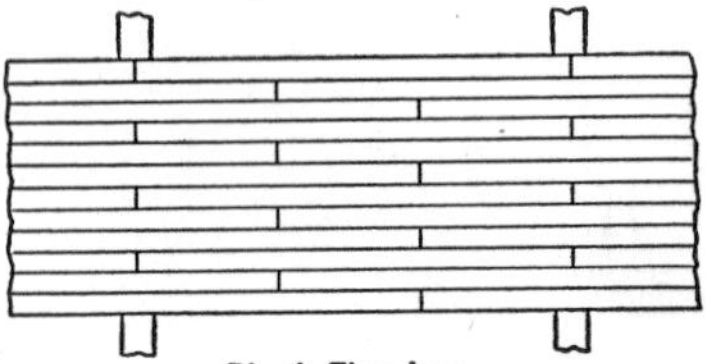

Plank Flooring

FIG. 12–2

12–2. Design of Plank Floors. In practice, the design of plank floors is accomplished by the use of safe load tables. Such tables are prepared by application of the principles previously explained in the design of beams. Table 12–1 gives the various properties of floors and may be used directly in design. It should be noted that in computing the properties a 12-in. breadth of flooring is considered; this is indicated by b in the table. Likewise, the thickness of the flooring is indicated by t.

TABLE 12–1. PROPERTIES OF FLOOR MATERIAL *

Nominal Thickness, in Inches	American Standard Dressed Thickness, in Inches	Area of Section, in Square Inches $A = bt$	Weight per Square Foot, in Pounds	Moment of Inertia, in Inches^4 $I = \frac{bt^3}{12}$	Section Modulus, in Inches^3 $S = \frac{bt^2}{6}$
1	25/32	9.38	2.6	0.48	1.22
1¼	11/16	12.75	3.5	1.20	2.26
1½	15/16	15.75	4.4	2.26	3.45
2	1⅝	19.5	5.4	4.29	5.28
2½	2⅛	25.5	7.1	9.60	9.03
3	2⅝	31.5	8.8	18.09	13.78
3½	3⅛	37.5	10.4	30.52	19.53
4	3⅝	43.5	12.1	47.63	26.28
5	4⅝	55.5	15.4	98.93	42.78
6	5⅝	67.5	18.8	177.98	63.28
8	7½	90.0	25.0	421.88	112.50
10	9½	114.0	31.7	857.38	180.50

* Horizontal breadth, $b = 12''$ and t = thickness of floor, in inches.

Table 12–2 gives the maximum spans of mill or plank floors, and Table 12–3 gives the maximum spans for laminated floors. Both tables are based on a timber having a modulus of elasticity of 1,760,000 psi. Therefore both tables can be used for either Southern pine or Douglas fir. As in the design of joists and rafters, deflection may be an important consideration, and these two tables give the maximum spans for both deflection and strength in bending. Shearing stresses are invariably well within the allowable stresses.

In certain types of buildings a deflection exceeding $\frac{1}{360}$ of the span is not objectionable. Before determining the thickness of the planks the designer must decide the maximum allowable deflection.

Example. A mill (plank) floor is to be designed to support a live load of 50 psf. The span between beams is 13 ft 0 in., the allowable extreme fiber stress of the timber is 1600 psi, and $E = 1{,}760{,}000$ psi. What should be the thickness of the planks?

SOLUTION. In order to make an allowance for the weight of the material, let us assume the thickness to be $2\frac{1}{2}$ in. Table 12–1 shows that the actual thickness of $2\frac{1}{2}$-in. planks is $2\frac{1}{8}$ in. and that its weight *per square foot* is 7.1 lb.

$$\begin{aligned} \text{Weight of flooring} &= 7.1 \\ \text{Live load} &= 50.0 \\ \hline \text{Total} &= 57.1 \text{ psf} \end{aligned}$$

As the span is 13 ft 0 in., $57.1 \times 13 = 742.3$ lb, the total load on a strip of floor 12 in. wide and 13 ft 0 in. in length.

Since these planks may be two spans in length, they are not simple beams; they are continuous beams having uniformly distributed loads two spans in length as indicated in Fig. 5–17, Case VII. On referring to this figure, we note that the negative bending moment is the greater and its magnitude is $\frac{Wl}{8}$. Although not given in the figure, the maximum positive bending moment is $\frac{Wl}{14.2}$. Attention is called to the maximum moment for Cases II and VII

TABLE 12–2. MAXIMUM SPANS FOR SOUTHERN PINE MILL FLOORS

Nominal Thickness	Actual Thickness	Fiber Stress, Pounds per Square Inch	Span in Feet — Live Load in Pounds Per Square Foot					
			50#	100#	125#	150#	175#	200#
2"	1⅝"	1200	8' 9"	6' 4"	5' 8"	5' 3"	4' 10"	4' 6"
2"	1⅝"	1400	9' 5"	6' 10"	6' 2"	5' 8"	5' 3"	4' 11"
2"	1⅝"	1500	9' 9"	7' 1"	6' 4"	5' 10"	5' 5"	5' 1"
2"	1⅝"	1600	10' 1"	7' 4"	6' 7"	6' 0"	5' 7"	5' 3"
2"	1⅝"	1750	10' 6"	7' 8"	6' 10"	6' 4"	5' 10"	5' 6"
2"	1⅝"	1800	10' 8"	7' 9"	7' 0"	6' 5"	5' 11"	5' 7"
2"	1⅝"	2050	11' 5"	8' 3"	7' 5"	6' 10"	6' 4"	5' 11"
2"	1⅝"	Deflection	5' 10"	4' 9"	4' 5"	4' 2"	3' 11"	3' 9"
2½"	2⅛"	1200	11' 3"	8' 2"	7' 5"	6' 9"	6' 4"	5' 11"
2½"	2⅛"	1400	12' 2"	8' 10"	8' 0"	7' 4"	6' 10"	6' 5"
2½"	2⅛"	1500	12' 7"	9' 2"	8' 3"	7' 7"	7' 0"	6' 7"
2½"	2⅛"	1600	13' 0"	9' 6"	8' 6"	7' 10"	7' 3"	6' 10"
2½"	2⅛"	1750	13' 7"	9' 11"	8' 11"	8' 2"	7' 7"	7' 2"
2½"	2⅛"	1800	13' 10"	10' 1"	9' 1"	8' 4"	7' 8"	7' 3"
2½"	2⅛"	2050	14' 8"	10' 9"	9' 8"	8' 10"	8' 3"	7' 9"
2½"	2⅛"	Deflection	7' 7"	6' 2"	5' 9"	5' 5"	5' 2"	4' 11"
3"	2⅝"	1200	13' 8"	10' 1"	9' 1"	8' 4"	7' 9"	7' 3"
3"	2⅝"	1400	14' 10"	10' 11"	9' 10"	9' 0"	8' 4"	7' 10"
3"	2⅝"	1500	15' 4"	11' 3"	10' 2"	9' 4"	8' 8"	8' 2"
3"	2⅝"	1600	15' 10"	11' 8"	10' 6"	9' 7"	8' 11"	8' 4"
3"	2⅝"	1750	16' 6"	12' 2"	11' 0"	10' 1"	9' 4"	8' 9"
3"	2⅝"	1800	16' 9"	12' 4"	11' 2"	10' 3"	9' 6"	8' 11"
3"	2⅝"	2050	17' 11"	13' 2"	11' 10"	10' 11"	10' 1"	9' 6"
3"	2⅝"	Deflection	9' 3"	7' 7"	7' 1"	6' 8"	6' 4"	6' 1"
4"	3⅝"	1200	18' 5"	13' 8"	12' 4"	11' 5"	10' 7"	10' 0"
4"	3⅝"	1400	19' 11"	14' 10"	13' 5"	12' 4"	11' 5"	10' 9"
4"	3⅝"	1500	20' 7"	15' 4"	13' 10"	12' 9"	11' 10"	11' 2"
4"	3⅝"	1600	21' 3"	15' 10"	14' 4"	13' 2"	12' 3"	11' 6"
4"	3⅝"	1750	22' 3"	16' 6"	14' 11"	13' 9"	12' 10"	12' 0"
4"	3⅝"	1800	22' 7"	16' 9"	15' 2"	13' 11"	13' 0"	12' 2"
4"	3⅝"	2050	24' 1"	17' 11"	16' 2"	14' 11"	13' 10"	13' 0"
4"	3⅝"	Deflection	12' 7"	10' 4"	9' 8"	9' 2"	8' 9"	8' 4"
5"	4⅝"	1200	22' 10"	17' 8"	15' 7"	14' 5"	13' 5"	12' 7"
5"	4⅝"	1400	24' 9"	18' 7"	16' 10"	15' 6"	14' 5"	13' 7"
5"	4⅝"	1600	26' 5"	19' 11"	18' 0"	16' 7"	15' 6"	14' 7"
5"	4⅝"	1800	28' 0"	21' 1"	19' 1"	17' 7"	16' 5"	15' 5"
5"	4⅝"	Deflection	15' 10"	13' 1"	12' 3"	11' 7"	11' 1"	10' 7"

Reproduced by permission of the Southern Pine Association.

TABLE 12–3. MAXIMUM SPANS FOR SOUTHERN PINE LAMINATED FLOORS

Nominal Thickness	Actual Thickness	Fiber Stress "f" Pounds Per Sq. Inch	SPAN IN FEET				
			Live Load in Pounds Per Square Foot				
			100	125	150	175	200
4″	3⅝″	1200	13′ 8″	12′ 4″	11′ 5″	10′ 7″	10′ 0″
4″	3⅝″	1400	14′ 10″	13′ 5″	12′ 4″	11′ 5″	10′ 9″
4″	3⅝″	1500	15′ 4″	13′ 10″	12′ 9″	11′ 10″	11′ 2″
4″	3⅝″	1750	16′ 6″	14′ 11″	13′ 9″	12′ 10″	12′ 0″
4″	3⅝″	Deflection	11′ 10″	11′ 1″	10′ 6″	10′ 0″	9′ 7″
6″	5⅝″	1200	20′ 8″	18′ 9″	17′ 4″	16′ 2″	15′ 3″
6″	5⅝″	1400	22′ 4″	20′ 3″	18′ 9″	17′ 6″	16′ 5″
6″	5⅝″	1500	23′ 1″	21′ 0″	19′ 4″	18′ 1″	17′ 0″
6″	5⅝″	1750	24′ 11″	22′ 8″	20′ 11″	19′ 6″	18′ 4″
6″	5⅝″	Deflection	18′ 2″	16′ 11″	16′ 0″	15′ 4″	14′ 9″
8″	7½″	1200	26′ 10″	24′ 6″	22′ 8″	21′ 2″	20′ 0″
8″	7½″	1400	29′ 0″	26′ 6″	24′ 6″	22′ 11″	21′ 7″
8″	7½″	1500	30′ 0″	27′ 5″	25′ 4″	23′ 9″	22′ 4″
8″	7½″	1750	32′ 5″	29′ 7″	27′ 5″	25′ 7″	24′ 2″
8″	7½″	Deflection	23′ 8″	22′ 3″	21′ 1″	20′ 3″	19′ 5″
			Live Load in Pounds Per Square Foot				
			225	250	275	300	350
4″	3⅝″	1200	9′ 5″	9′ 0″	8′ 7″	8′ 3″	7′ 7″
4″	3⅝″	1400	10′ 2″	9′ 8″	9′ 3″	8′ 10″	8′ 3″
4″	3⅝″	1500	10′ 6″	10′ 0″	9′ 7″	9′ 2″	8′ 6″
4″	3⅝″	1750	11′ 4″	10′ 10″	10′ 4″	9′ 11″	9′ 2″
4″	3⅝″	Deflection	9′ 3″	8′ 11″	8′ 8″	8′ 5″	8′ 0″
6″	5⅝″	1200	14′ 5″	13′ 9″	13′ 2″	12′ 8″	11′ 9″
6″	5⅝″	1400	15′ 7″	14′ 10″	14′ 2″	13′ 7″	12′ 8″
6″	5⅝″	1500	16′ 1″	15′ 4″	14′ 8″	14′ 1″	13′ 1″
6″	5⅝″	1750	17′ 5″	16′ 7″	15′ 10″	15′ 3″	14′ 2″
6″	5⅝″	Deflection	14′ 2″	13′ 9″	13′ 4″	13′ 0″	12′ 4″
8″	7½″	1200	19′ 0″	18′ 1″	17′ 4″	16′ 7″	15′ 6″
8″	7½″	1400	20′ 6″	19′ 6″	18′ 9″	18′ 0″	16′ 9″
8″	7½″	1500	21′ 2″	20′ 3″	19′ 4″	18′ 7″	17′ 4″
8″	7½″	1750	22′ 11″	21′ 10″	20′ 11″	20′ 1″	18′ 9″
8″	7½″	Deflection	18′ 9″	18′ 2″	17′ 8″	17′ 2″	16′ 5″

Reproduced by permission of the Southern Pine Association.

in Fig. 5–17; for each of the two types of beams, it is $\frac{Wl}{8}$. Thus

$$M = \frac{Wl}{8} = \frac{742.3 \times 13 \times 12}{8} = 14{,}474 \text{ in-lb}$$

$$\frac{M}{f} = S = \frac{14{,}474}{1600} = 9.03 \text{ in.}^3, \text{ the required section modulus}$$

Again referring to Table 12–1, we find that a section of plank flooring 12 in. wide and $2\frac{1}{2}$ in. deep has a section modulus of 9.03 in.^{3} Hence this thickness of flooring is acceptable for strength in bending.

Now refer to Table 12–2. We find that for a live load of 50 psf and an extreme fiber stress of 1600 psi the maximum span for $2\frac{1}{2}$-in. planking is 13 ft 0 in. This is the same result found by computation. However, this table shows that the maximum span for $2\frac{1}{2}$-in. planking for a live load of 50 psf is only 7 ft 7 in. if the *deflection* is not to exceed $\frac{1}{360}$ of the span. Hence, if we wish the deflection to be within the limit of $\frac{1}{360}$ of the span, the $2\frac{1}{2}$-in. planks are not acceptable. Further investigation of Table 12–2 shows that 5-in. planking may be used for spans up to 15 ft 10 in. and thus is accepted.

Example. By the use of Table 12–2 determine the thickness of plank flooring for a span of 7 ft 0 in., a live load of 100 psf, an allowable extreme fiber stress of 1400 psi, and $E = 1{,}760{,}000$ psi.

SOLUTION. Table 12–2 shows that 3-in. planking has an allowable span of 10 ft 11 in. if the allowable extreme fiber stress is 1400 psi and that the maximum span is 7 ft 7 in. if the deflection is not to exceed $\frac{1}{360}$ of the span. Thus planking 3 in. in thickness is accepted; its thickness is determined in accordance with the requirements for deflection.

Problem 12–2–A. Select, by the use of Table 12–2, the required thickness of a mill floor, the timber having an allowable extreme fiber stress of 1200 psi and a modulus of elasticity of 1,760,000 psi. The live load is 100 psf, and the span is 10 ft 0 in. The deflection is not to be excessive.

Problem 12–2–B. The live load on a mill floor is 125 psf, and the span is 9 ft 0 in. By the use of Table 12–2 select the proper thickness of planking if the timber has an allowable extreme fiber stress of 1400 psi and the modulus of elasticity is 1,760,000 psi. The deflection is not to be excessive.

12–3. Deflection of Mill and Laminated Floors. In Table 12–2 the spans in the line marked *deflection* are the spans that will result in deflections of $\frac{1}{30}$ in. per foot of span. This is a deflection of $\frac{1}{360}$ of the span.

Actually, the deflections of mill and laminated floors have been found to be considerably less than the deflections computed by the usual deflection formulas. This is due to the facts that the planking usually acts as a continuous beam, that the finished flooring adds to the stiffness of the plank flooring, and that the live load used in computations is seldom attained in reality. Because of this, limiting the actual deflection to $\frac{1}{360}$ of the span is probably too severe a requirement and quite often $\frac{1}{240}$ or even $\frac{1}{180}$ is set as the allowable limit. Table 12–3 gives the maximum spans for laminated floors for various loads and stresses. The spans opposite *deflection* in this table are those that will produce deflections of $\frac{1}{20}$ in. per foot of span which is, of course, $\frac{1}{240}$ of the span.

Example. The wood used for a laminated floor has an allowable extreme fiber stress of 1400 psi and a modulus of elasticity of 1,760,000 psi. By the use of Table 12–3, select the required thickness of flooring for a live load of 100 psf and a span of 11 ft 6 in.

SOLUTION. Table 12–3 shows that for a 4-in. nominal thickness and an extreme fiber stress of 1400 psi, the maximum span is 14 ft 10 in. But opposite *deflection* the maximum allowable span is only 11 ft 10 in. Therefore, we accept a nominal thickness of 4 in. for the laminated floor.

Problem 12–3–A. It is desired to construct a laminated floor for a span of 12 ft 0 in. and a live load of 125 psf. The timber has an allowable extreme fiber stress of 1400 psi, and the modulus of elasticity is 1,760,000 psi. What should be the thickness of the flooring if deflection is an important consideration?

Problem 12–3–B. A building to be used solely for storage purposes has a laminated floor on which there is a live load of 125 psf. The span of the structural flooring is 12 ft 0 in., the allowable extreme fiber stress is 1200 psi, and $E = 1{,}760{,}000$ psi. Assuming that deflection is not a governing factor in the design, what should be the thickness of the flooring?

CHAPTER 13

WOOD COLUMNS

13–1. Wood Columns. The type of wood column that is used most frequently is a *simple solid column.* It consists of a single piece of wood, rectangular in cross section. A type of column also considered as a simple solid column is a solid member of circular cross section; it is used less frequently than a column having a rectangular cross section. Now that timber connectors are available, *spaced columns* are used constantly. They consist of an assembly of wood pieces and are commonly used for the compression members in trusses. *Built-up columns* are made by gluing or bolting together planks and square members. They lack efficiency in load capacity. In all types of columns the load capacity depends on the slenderness ratio.

13–2. Slenderness Ratio. The *slenderness ratio* of a solid timber column is the ratio of the unsupported length of the column to the dimension of its least side. This side is the narrowest of the two faces, and the slenderness ratio is $\frac{l}{d}$, in which l = the unsupported column length, in inches and d = the dimension of the least side, in inches.

All formulas used for the design of timber columns include the ratio $\frac{l}{d}$. For simple solid columns $\frac{l}{d}$ is limited to 50; most columns are well within this limit. For spaced columns, the limiting ratio is 80.

13–3. Allowable Loads on Simple Solid Columns. In Table 3–1 we find a column of stresses giving c, the allowable compressive unit stress parallel to the grain, for the various grades and species of wood. Column loads are parallel to the direction of the grain in the columns, and, regardless of the unit stress found by the column formula, the allowable compressive stress used in determining the allowable column load must never exceed the magnitude of c.

The formula to use in the design of timber columns of rectangular cross section, as recommended by the National Lumber Manufacturers Association, is

$$\frac{P}{A} = \frac{0.3 \times E}{(l/d)^2}$$

in which P = the total axial load on the column, in pounds
A = the cross-sectional area of the column, in square inches
$\frac{P}{A}$ = the allowable unit stress, in pounds per square inch
E = the modulus of elasticity of the wood, in pounds per square inch
l = the unsupported length of the column, in inches
d = the dimension of the least side, in inches

This formula gives $\frac{P}{A}$, the allowable compressive unit stress, but *the maximum unit stress must never exceed c, the allowable compressive unit stress parallel to the grain, as given in Table 3–1.*

The formula applies to restrained and square-end columns as well as to the pin-end condition from which it was derived. It is appropriate for a timber column to be used in a dry location and that it be at least surface seasoned before the maximum load is applied.

13–4. Safe Loads for Wood Columns. The procedure to follow in finding the safe load that a wood column will support is to substitute the known data in the foregoing formula to determine $\frac{P}{A}$, the allowable unit stress. If this quantity does not exceed c, it is multiplied by A, the number of square inches in the column cross section and the result is the allowable or safe column load. If the computed $\frac{P}{A}$ exceeds c, c is the allowable unit stress for this particular column and it is multiplied by A to find the safe load. To find the safe axial load that a solid column of a given cross section and length will support, the following steps may be taken:

Step 1. Consult a table, such as Table 3–1, of allowable unit stresses for timber and find the values of E, the modulus of elasticity of the species, and c, the allowable compressive unit stress parallel to the grain, *for the particular species and grade of timber.*

Step 2. Compute $\frac{l}{d}$, the slenderness ratio. It should not exceed 50.

Step 3. Substitute the values of E, l, and d in the formula $\frac{P}{A} = \frac{0.30E}{(l/d)^2}$ and determine the value of $\frac{P}{A}$, the allowable compressive stress.

Step 4. If the value of $\frac{P}{A}$, found in Step 3, does not exceed c, multiply the value of $\frac{P}{A}$ by the number of square inches in the column cross section. The product will be the allowable axial load that the column will support.

Step 5. If the value of $\frac{P}{A}$, found in Step 3, exceeds the magnitude of c, multiply the value of c by the number of square inches in the column cross section. This determines the safe axial load the column will support.

Example. An 8 x 10 in. Douglas fir column made of the construction grade has an unsupported length of 14 ft 0 in. Compute its allowable axial load.

SOLUTION. Following the foregoing steps:

Step 1. Referring to Table 3–1, we find, for this grade of Douglas fir, that $c = 1200$ psi and $E = 1{,}760{,}000$ psi.

Step 2. Computing $\frac{l}{d}$, $l = 14 \times 12$ or 168 in. and, from Table 3–3, $d = 7.5$ in. Note that the cross-sectional dimensions are 7.5 x 9.5 and that 7.5 is *the dimension of the least side.* Then

$\frac{l}{d} = \frac{168}{7.5} = 22.4$, the slenderness ratio; it is within the limit of 50.

Step 3. $\frac{P}{A} = \frac{0.3 \times E}{(l/d)^2} = \frac{0.3 \times 1{,}760{,}000}{22.4 \times 22.4} = 1052$ psi, the unit stress.

Step 4. We find that $\frac{P}{A}$, 1052 psi, does not exceed c, which we know to be 1200 psi. Thus, since $A = 7.5 \times 9.5$ or 71.25 sq in. (see Table 3–3), $P = 1052 \times 71.25$ or $P = 74{,}955$ lb, the allowable axial load on the 8 x 10 in. column. (See Table 13–2.)

Example. A Southern pine column of the No. 1 SR grade has 10 x 10 in. for the nominal dimensions of its cross section. If its unsupported length is 14 ft 0 in., compute its allowable axial load.

Step 1. For this grade of Southern pine, Table 3–1 gives c as 1300 psi and $E = 1{,}760{,}000$ psi.

Step 2. To compute the slenderness ratio, $\frac{l}{d}$, $l = 14 \times 12 = 168$ in., and, from Table 3–3, $d = 9.5$ in. Then $\frac{l}{d} = \frac{168}{9.5} = 17.7$, less than 50.

Step 3. $\frac{P}{A} = \frac{0.3 \times E}{(l/d)^2} = \frac{0.3 \times 1{,}760{,}000}{17.7 \times 17.7} = 1685$ psi. (Note that Table 13–1 gives this stress for $\frac{P}{A}$.)

Step 4. In this problem $\frac{P}{A}$, or 1685 psi, *exceeds* c, 1300 psi; therefore we proceed to the next step.

Step 5. $A = 9.5 \times 9.5 = 90.25$ sq in. Then $1300 \times 90.25 = 117{,}325$ lb, the allowable axial load. (See Table 13–2.)

Problem 13–4–A. An 8 x 8 in. redwood column of the dense structural grade has an unsupported length of 10 ft 0 in. Compute its allowable axial load.

Problem 13–4–B. A white oak column of the 1325 c grade has 6 x 8 in. for its nominal cross-sectional dimensions. If its length is 10 ft 0 in., compute its allowable axial load.

Problem 13–4–C. Compute the allowable axial load for an 8 x 8 in. Southern pine column of the No. 1 Dense SR grade, whose unsupported length is 10 ft 0 in.

Problem 13–4–D. A 6 x 6 in. Eastern hemlock column of the select structural grade has an unsupported length of 10 ft 0 in. Compute its allowable axial load.

13–5. Design of Wood Columns. The architect or engineer makes use of safe-load tables to determine the proper column sizes. Actually, the procedure is to select a certain cross section and, by the use of tables, determine the allowable load it will support. Because of the number of factors that must be considered, care must be taken in using safe-load column tabulations. Table 13–1 is a safe-load column table that has been compiled in accordance with the formula $\frac{P}{A} = \frac{0.3 \times E}{(l/d)^2}$. Attention is called to the four columns of various values of E, the moduli of elasticity. Note especially that *values of c do not appear in this table.*

Consider an 8 x 8 in. Southern pine column that has a length of 12 ft 0 in. Table 13–1 shows that $\frac{P}{A}$, the unit stress computed by the column formula, is 1432 psi. If the grade of Southern pine is No. 1 Dense SR ($c = 1500$ psi), 1432 does not exceed c; hence, since $A = 56.25$ sq in., $1432 \times 56.25 = 80{,}550$ lb, the allowable axial load. This is the value of P given in the table.

Suppose, however, the grade of Southern pine is No. 1 SR. Table 3–1 shows that the value of c for this grade is 1300 psi. Note that $\frac{P}{A}$ found by use of the formula is 1432 psi. *Since 1432 exceeds c, 1300, the allowable unit stress permitted, is only 1300 psi* and $P = 1300 \times 56.25$ or 73,125 lb, the allowable axial load. This magnitude is not given in the table.

Example. A wood column of the 1075 c grade of white oak has an unsupported length of 14 ft 0 in. What should be its size if the axial load is 50,000 lb?

SOLUTION. For this grade of wood Table 3–1 shows that $c =$ 1075 psi and $E = 1{,}650{,}000$ psi. Since $c = 1075$ psi, the actual unit stress must not exceed this value. Therefore, in order to select a trial section, let us estimate that the unit compressive stress will be about 1000 psi. Then $50{,}000 \div 1000 = 50$ sq in.,

TABLE 13–1. ALLOWABLE AXIAL LOADS ON TIMBER COLUMNS IN POUNDS

BASED ON $\frac{P}{A} = \frac{0.30\,E}{(l/d)^2}$. *Note:* $\frac{P}{A}$ IS NOT TO EXCEED c

Nominal Size	Actual Size	Area	Length	$E = 1{,}210{,}000$ Eastern Hemlock		$E = 1{,}320{,}000$ Cypress, Redwood, Spruce		$E = 1{,}650{,}000$ Oak		$E = 1{,}760{,}000$ Douglas Fir, Southern Pine	
in.	in.	in.^{2}	ft	$\frac{P}{A}$ psi	P lb	$\frac{P}{A}$ psi	P lb	$\frac{P}{A}$ psi	P lb	$\frac{P}{A}$ psi	P lb
6 x 6	5.5 x 5.5	30.25	8	1185	35846	1293	39113	1616	48884	1723	52121
			10	764	23111	833	25198	1042	31521	1111	33608
			12	529	16002	577	17454	721	21810	769	23262
8 x 8	7.5 x 7.5	56.25	8	2216	124650	2418	136013	3022	169988	3223	181294
			10	1418	79763	1547	87019	1934	108789	2063	116044
			12	985	55406	1074	60413	1343	75544	1432	80550
			14	723	40669	789	44381	986	55463	1052	59175
			16	554	31163	604	33975	755	42469	806	45338
			18	438	24638	477	26831	597	33581	637	35831
10 x 10	9.5 x 9.5	90.25	8	3559	321200	3882	350351	4853	437983	5176	467134
			10	2286	206312	2494	225084	3117	281309	3325	300081
			12	1571	141783	1714	154689	2143	193406	2286	206312
			14	1159	104600	1264	114076	1580	142595	1685	152071
			16	890	80323	971	87633	1213	109473	1294	116784
			18	704	63536	768	69312	961	86730	1025	92506
			20	567	51172	619	55865	773	69763	825	74456
12 x 12	11.5 x 11.5	132.25	9	4106	543019	4480	592480	5600	740600	5973	789929
			10	3355	443699	3660	484035	4575	605044	4880	645380
			12	2322	307085	2534	335122	3167	418836	3378	446741
			14	1703	225222	1857	245588	2322	307085	2477	327583
			16	1302	172190	1420	187795	1775	234744	1893	250349
			18	1027	135821	1121	148252	1401	185282	1494	197582
			20	831	109900	907	119951	1133	149839	1209	159890
14 x 14	13.5 x 13.5	182.25	12	3170	577733	3459	630403	4323	787867	4611	840355
			13	2697	491528	2942	536180	3678	670316	3923	714967
			14	2360	430110	2575	469294	3218	586481	3433	625664
			15	2052	373977	2239	408058	2798	509936	2985	544016
			16	1801	328232	1964	357939	2455	447424	2619	477313
			18	1418	258431	1547	281941	1934	352472	2063	375982
			20	1146	208859	1250	227813	1563	284857	1667	303811

Compiled by permission from data furnished by the National Lumber Manufacturers Association.

the estimated required area. In Table 13–1 we see that an 8 x 8 in. column has 56.25 sq in. in its cross section, and we select an 8 x 8 in. for a trial column section. In Table 13–1, under $E = 1{,}650{,}000$ psi, we find that $\frac{P}{A}$ (for an 8 x 8 in., 14 ft 0 in. in length) is 986 psi. This is less than the value of c, 1075 psi; hence $P = 986 \times 56.25 = 55{,}463$ lb, the allowable load. Accept an 8 x 8 in. column. Note that all this information is given in Table 13–1; no computations are necessary.

In the following problems determine the proper column size in accordance with these data:

Problem 13–5–A. Axial load = 57,000 lb, length = 12 ft 0 in., heart structural grade of redwood.

Problem 13–5–B. Axial load = 140,000 lb, length = 16 ft 0 in., select structural grade of Douglas fir.

Problem 13–5–C. Axial load = 20,000 lb, length = 10 ft 0 in., select structural grade of Eastern hemlock.

Problem 13–5–D. Axial load = 100,000 lb, length = 16 ft 0 in., 1325 c grade of white oak.

Problem 13–5–E. Axial load = 70,000 lb, length = 12 ft 0 in., No. 1 SR grade of Southern pine.

13–6. Safe-Load Table for Wood Columns. Table 13–2 is another safe-load table. It is a special table for use in determining the proper size of wood columns. It is special because it is applicable only for woods having $E = 1{,}760{,}000$ psi, Southern pine, and Douglas fir. It is based on the column formula $\frac{P}{A} = \frac{0.3 \times E}{(l/d)^2}$ and, in addition, takes into consideration various values of c as shown at the head of the table. It is readily used.

Example. A Southern pine column, for which $c = 1500$ psi, has an unsupported length of 14 ft 0 in. and an axial load of 70,000 lb. What size column should be used?

SOLUTION. Referring to Table 13–2, we see, without computations, that an 8 x 8 in. for a length of 14 ft will support 59,175 lb and that an 8 x 10 in. will support 74,955 lb. Accept an 8 x 10 in. column.

TABLE 13–2. ALLOWABLE AXIAL LOADS ON SOUTHERN PINE COLUMNS IN POUNDS

$E = 1{,}760{,}000$ PSI

BASED ON $\frac{P}{A} = \frac{0.30\,E}{(l/d)^2}$

Nominal Size, Inches	Length, Feet	Compression Parallel to Grain c, Pounds per Square Inch						
		900	1050	1300	1400	1500	1550	1800
6 x 6	8	28476	33222	41132	44296	47460	49042	56952
6 x 6	10	28476	33222	36829	36829	36829	36829	36829
6 x 6	12	25502	25502	25502	25502	25502	25502	25502
6 x 6	14	17529	18699	18699	18699	18699	18699	18699
6 x 8	8	37971	44300	54847	59066	63285	65394	75942
6 x 8	10	37971	44300	49109	49109	49109	49109	49109
6 x 8	12	34005	34005	34005	34005	34005	34005	34005
6 x 8	14	24934	24934	24934	24934	24934	24934	24934
8 x 8	8	50625	59062	73125	78750	84375	87188	101250
8 x 8	10	50625	59062	73125	78750	84375	87188	101250
8 x 8	12	50625	59062	73125	78750	80550	80550	80550
8 x 8	14	50625	59062	59175	59175	59175	59175	59175
8 x 8	16	45338	45338	45338	45338	45338	45338	45338
8 x 8	18	35831	35831	35831	35831	35831	35831	35831
8 x 8	20	29025	29025	29025	29025	29025	29025	29025
8 x 10	8	64125	74812	92625	99750	106875	110438	128250
8 x 10	10	64125	74812	92625	99750	106875	110438	128250
8 x 10	12	64125	74812	92625	99750	102030	102030	102030
8 x 10	14	64125	74812	74955	74955	74955	74955	74955
8 x 10	16	57428	57428	57428	57428	57428	57428	57428
8 x 10	18	45386	45386	45386	45386	45386	45386	45386
8 x 10	20	36765	36765	36765	36765	36765	36765	36765
10 x 10	8	81225	94762	117325	126350	135375	139888	162450
10 x 10	10	81225	94762	117325	126350	135375	139888	162450
10 x 10	12	81225	94762	117325	126350	135375	139888	162450
10 x 10	14	81225	94762	117325	126350	135375	139888	152071
10 x 10	16	81225	94762	116784	116784	116784	116784	116784
10 x 10	18	81225	92506	92506	92506	92506	92506	92506
10 x 10	20	74456	74456	74456	74456	74456	74456	74456
10 x 12	8	98325	114712	142025	152950	163875	169338	196650
10 x 12	10	98325	114712	142025	152950	163875	169338	196650
10 x 12	12	98325	114712	142025	152950	163875	169338	196650
10 x 12	14	98325	114712	142025	152950	163875	169338	184086
10 x 12	16	98325	114712	141370	141370	141370	141370	141370
10 x 12	18	98325	111981	111981	111981	111981	111981	111981
10 x 12	20	90131	90131	90131	90131	90131	90131	90131
12 x 12	8	119025	138862	171925	185150	198375	204988	238050
12 x 12	10	119025	138862	171925	185150	198375	204988	238050
12 x 12	12	119025	138862	171925	185150	198375	204988	238050
12 x 12	14	119025	138862	171925	185150	198375	204988	238050
12 x 12	16	119025	138862	171925	185150	198375	204988	238050
12 x 12	18	119025	138862	171925	185150	197582	197582	197582
12 x 12	20	119025	138862	159890	159890	159890	159890	159890

13–7. Round Columns. A solid wood column that has a circular cross section is used infrequently as a structural member. As for load-bearing capacity, round and square wood columns of the same cross-sectional area will support the same loads and have the same degree of stiffness.

In designing a wood column of circular cross section, a simple procedure is to design a square column first and then select a round column with an equivalent cross-sectional area. The round column will have a diameter approximately 1.1284 times the side of the square column.

Example. A Douglas fir column, circular in cross section, of the select structural grade, has an unsupported length of 12 ft 0 in. What should be its diameter if the axial load is 135,000 lb?

SOLUTION. For this wood Table 3–1 shows that $E = 1{,}760{,}000$ psi and $c = 1500$ psi. In Table 13–2 we see that a 10 x 10 in. column will safely support 135,375 lb. The side of the square cross section is 9.5 in. Therefore, $1.1284 \times 9.5 = 10.7$ in., the minimum diameter of a round column to support the 135,000-lb load.

13–8. Spaced Columns. *Spaced columns* are formed of two or more individual members with their longitudinal axes parallel, separated at the ends and middle points of their length by blocking, and joined at their ends by timber connectors and bolts capable of developing the required shear resistance. Spaced columns are used for the compression members of trusses in which timber connectors are employed.

A single spacer block should be located within the middle 10% of the column length l, and, if so located, connectors are not necessary for this block. See Fig. 13–1. If more than one spacer block is used, the distance between any two blocks should not exceed one half the distance (l_1) between centers of connectors in the end blocks. The requirements for connectors in spacer blocks under the latter condition are the same as for end blocks.

End condition a, as shown in Fig. 13–1, requires that connectors be placed within $\frac{l}{20}$ from the column end. End condition b relates to connectors placed $\frac{l}{20}$ to $\frac{l}{10}$ from the column end; this also is shown in Fig. 13–1.

13–9. Spaced Column Formulas. A spaced column is made up of two or more individual members. Figure 13–1 shows a spaced column having two members. For each member, $\frac{l}{d}$ shall not exceed 80, nor shall $\frac{l_2}{d}$ exceed 40.

For end condition *a*, in which the connectors are placed within $\frac{l}{20}$ from the column end, the allowable load on *the individual mem-*

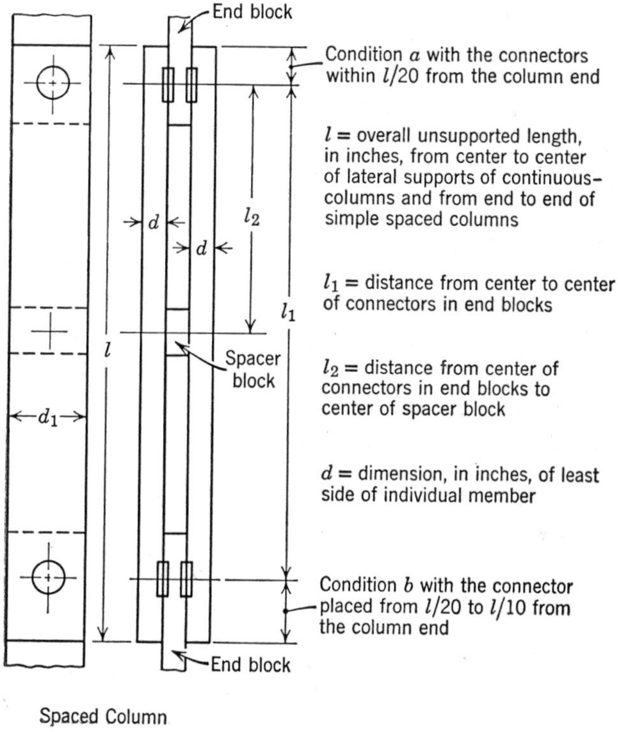

FIG. 13–1

bers of a spaced column is determined by the formula

$$\frac{P}{A} = \frac{0.75 \times E}{(l/d)^2}$$

For end condition *b*,

$$\frac{P}{A} = \frac{0.90 \times E}{(l/d)^2}$$

The terms in these formulas have the significance given in Art. 13–3. Bear in mind that in using either of these two column formulas $\frac{P}{A}$, the unit stress, must not exceed the magnitude of c, as given in Table 3–1.

13–10. Safe Loads for Spaced Columns. The safe load on a spaced column is determined by use of either of the two column formulas given in Art. 13–9. The design of a spaced column consists in taking trial sizes and computing their safe loads.

Example. A spaced column, of the dense construction grade of Douglas fir, is composed of two 3 x 8 in. members. Its length is 7 ft 0 in. Compute its safe axial load if the end conditions comply with condition *a*.

SOLUTION. The dressed dimensions of a 3 x 8 are 2.625 x 7.5 in. and its cross-sectional area is 19.69 sq in. (Table 3–3). The slenderness ratio of an individual member is $\frac{l}{d} = \frac{7 \times 12}{2.625} = 32$. In Table 3–1 we find, for the dense construction grade of Douglas fir, that $E = 1{,}760{,}000$ psi and $c = 1400$ psi. Then

$$\frac{P}{A} = \frac{0.75 \times E}{(l/d)^2} = \frac{0.75 \times 1{,}760{,}000}{(84/2.625)^2} = 1289 \text{ psi}$$

Since 1289 psi does not exceed c, 1400 psi, the allowable axial load on one of the two 3 x 8 in. members is 1289 × 19.69 or 25,300 lb. For the two 3 x 8 in. members P, the safe axial load, is 2 × 25,300 or 50,600 lb, the safe load on the spaced column.

Example. The axial load on a spaced column of the No. 2 SR grade of Southern pine is 25,000 lb. The column is composed of two 3 x 10 in. members, the length of column is 12 ft 0 in., and the connectors in the end blocks comply with condition *b*. Is this spaced column large enough to support the 25,000 lb load?

SOLUTION. For this species and grade of lumber Table 3–1 shows that $E = 1{,}760{,}000$ psi and $c = 900$ psi. In Table 3–3 we see that the dressed size of a 3 x 10 is 2.625 x 9.5 in. and that its cross-sectional area is 24.94 sq in. The slenderness ratio $\frac{l}{d} = \frac{12 \times 12}{2.625} = 54.6$. Then

$$\frac{P}{A} = \frac{0.90 \times E}{(l/d)^2} = \frac{0.90 \times 1{,}760{,}000}{54.6^2} = 532 \text{ psi}$$

Since this does not exceed 900 psi, then, as the cross-sectional area of one 3 x 10 is 24.94 sq in., $24.94 \times 532 = 13{,}300$ lb, the allowable load on one of the individual members. As there are two 3 x 10 in. members, $2 \times 13{,}300 = 26{,}600$ lb, the safe load on the spaced column. This load exceeds 25,000 lb and therefore this spaced column is accepted.

Problem 13–10–A. A spaced column of the dense structural grade of redwood has a length of 8 ft 0 in. and is made up of two 2 x 6 members. If the restraint at the ends agrees with condition *b*, compute the allowable axial load.

Problem 13–10–B. Compute the allowable axial load on a spaced column composed of two 3 x 6 in. members made up of the 1200 *c* grade of cypress. The length of the column is 6 ft 0 in. and the end restraint agrees with condition *a*.

13–11. Built-Up Columns with Mechanical Fastenings. Timber columns are sometimes constructed with pieces joined together with spikes, bolts, or other mechanical fastenings. No arrangement of pieces with any kind of mechanical fastenings will make a built-up column fully equal in strength to a one-piece solid column of the same dimensions and material. Arrangements of parallel planks and cover plates or planks boxed around a solid core are shown in Fig. 13–2. It is customary to use planks

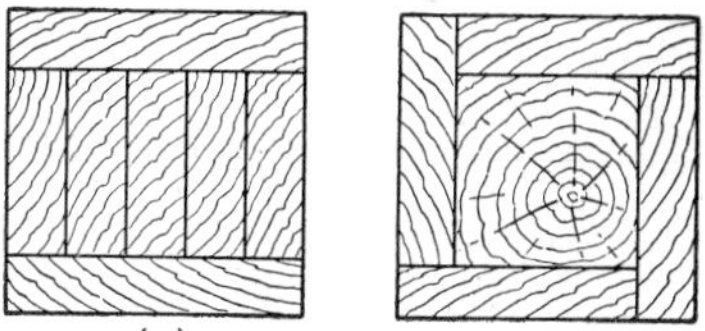

(*a*) (*b*)
Built-Up Columns

FIG. 13–2

not wider than five times their thickness, and, when spiked together, the spikes should extend through two pieces and well into the third. The spikes should not be spaced farther apart longitudinally than six times the plank thickness.

When the individual pieces are arranged as shown in Fig. 13–2, the percentage of solid column strength that may be expected for various $\frac{l}{d}$ ratios is given in Table 13–3.

TABLE 13–3. PERCENTAGE OF SOLID COLUMN STRENGTH FOR BUILT-UP COLUMNS

l/d Ratios	Percentage of Solid Column Strength	l/d Ratios	Percentage of Solid Column Strength
6	82	18	65
10	77	22	74
14	71	26	82

Reproduced by permission of the U. S. Forest Products Laboratory.

Example. A built-up column, well spiked together, is constructed as shown in Fig. 13–2 (*b*). The core is a solid 8 x 8 and the planks are 2 x 10's, forming a 12 x 12 in. cross section. If the unsupported length of the column is 14 ft 0 in. and the timber is the construction grade of Douglas fir, compute the maximum allowable load on the built-up column, using nominal or rough sizes.

SOLUTION. Referring to Table 3–1 we find that $E = 1{,}760{,}000$ psi and $c = 1200$ psi. The slenderness ratio, $\frac{l}{d} = \frac{12 \times 14}{12} = 14.$

The solid timber column formula given in Art. 13–3 is

$$\frac{P}{A} = \frac{0.3 \times E}{(l/d)^2}$$

Thus

$$\frac{P}{A} = \frac{0.3 \times 1{,}760{,}000}{14 \times 14} = 2690 \text{ psi}$$

Since $\frac{P}{A}$, 2690 psi, exceeds c, 1200 psi, the maximum compressive unit stress permitted on the cross section of the column is c, 1200 psi. Then, as the column cross section contains 12×12 or 144 sq in., $144 \times 1200 = 172{,}800$ lb, the allowable axial load *if the column is a solid piece.*

For a slenderness ratio of 14, Table 13–3 gives the percentage of solid column strength to be 0.71. Hence $172{,}800 \times 0.71 = 122{,}600$ lb, the allowable axial load on the built-up column.

Problem 13–11–A. Four enclosed planks of a built-up column, as indicated in Fig. 13–2 (*a*), are each 3 x 8 in. pieces and the cover planks are each 3 x 12, thus forming a 12 x 14 in. cross section. The unsupported length of the column is 10 ft 0 in., and the timber is the heart structural grade of redwood. Using nominal or rough sizes, compute the maximum allowable axial load on the built-up column.

13–12. Glued Laminated Columns. The allowable axial loads on glued laminated columns are determined by the column formula given in Art. 13–3. In using this formula, however, the value of c, the allowable compressive stress parallel to the grain, may be higher than is permitted for solid wood columns. See Art. 23–4.

CHAPTER 14

COMBINED BENDING AND AXIAL LOADING

14–1. Axial Compression and Bending Combined. The great majority of roof trusses are constructed in such a manner that the roof loads are transferred to the truss only at the panel points. This results in the truss members being in tension or compression. Usually the purlins transfer roof loads to the truss at the panel points and the upper chord is subjected to compressive stresses only. Imagine a truss with the purlins omitted and with roof rafters, extending from truss to truss, resting on the upper chord, as shown in Fig. 14–1. Such an arrangement would result in the

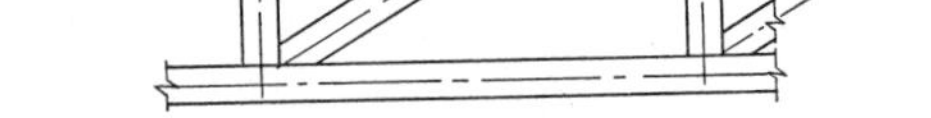

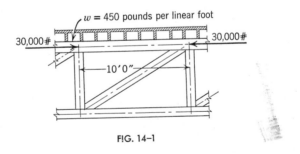

FIG. 14–1

upper-chord members being subjected to axial compressive stresses, due to the truss action, and also to the bending stresses that result from the loads transferred by the roof rafters.

When a member is subjected to both axial compression and bending, it should be proportioned so that the quantities $\frac{P/A}{c} + \frac{M/S}{f}$ do not exceed 1, in which P = the axial compressive force, in pounds

A = the cross-sectional area of the member, in square inches

$\frac{P}{A}$ = the compressive stress induced by the axial load, that is, the total axial load divided by the cross-sectional area of the member

c = the allowable stress in compression parallel to the grain that would be permitted for the column if only axial stress existed, in pounds per square inch (the term c represents the allowable compressive stress in accordance with the $\frac{l}{d}$ ratio)

M = the maximum bending moment that results from the loads producing bending, in inch-pounds,

S = the section modulus of the cross section, in inches^3

$\frac{M}{S}$ = the flexural stress induced by the bending load

f = the allowable extreme fiber stress in bending that would be permitted if only bending stresses existed, in pounds per square inch

For spaced columns the combined stress formula may be applied only when the bending is in a direction parallel to the mutually contacting surfaces of the blocks and individual pieces.

Example. An upper-chord member of a parallel-chord roof truss has a span of 10 ft 0 in. and an axial compressive force of 30,000 lb. In addition to this axial load, a uniformly distributed roof load of 450 lb per lin ft produces bending. See Fig. 14–1. The lumber is Southern pine, No. 1 SR grade, which has an allowable extreme fiber stress of 1400 psi, an allowable compressive stress parallel to the grain of 1300 psi, and a modulus of elasticity of 1,760,000 psi. What should be the size of the member?

SOLUTION. The design of such a member is accomplished by investigating trial sections. In this instance let us assume that the member is a 6 x 10 with the long axis placed in a vertical position. Referring to Table 3–3, we note that $A = 52.25$ sq in., $S = 82.73$ in.^{3}, and the actual width of the member is 5.5 in.

Then

$$\frac{l}{d} = \frac{10 \times 12}{5.5} = 21.8$$

Substituting the known quantities in the column formula,

$$\frac{P}{A} = \frac{0.3 \times E}{(l/d)^2}, \qquad \frac{P}{A} = \frac{0.3 \times 1{,}760{,}000}{21.8 \times 21.8} = 1110 \text{ psi}$$

This compressive stress is less than c, 1400 psi. The cross-sectional area of the member is 5.5×9.5 or 52.25 sq in., the value of A. Then

$$\frac{P/A}{c} = \frac{30{,}000/52.25}{1110} = 0.516$$

The upper chord of the truss in bending is somewhat similar to the end span of a continuous beam. For an end span with a distributed load $M = \dfrac{wl^2}{10}$. Thus

$$M = \frac{450 \times 10 \times 10 \times 12}{10} = 54{,}000 \text{ in-lb}$$

the maximum bending moment. The section modulus, S, of a 6 x 10 in. section is 82.73 in.^{3} Then

$$\frac{M/S}{f} = \frac{54{,}000/82.73}{1400} = 0.466$$

Thus $\dfrac{P/A}{c} + \dfrac{M/S}{f} = 0.516 + 0.466 = 0.982$. This quantity does not exceed 1; therefore the 6 x 10 in. section is accepted.

Problem 14–1–A. An upper-chord member of a parallel-chord roof truss has a span of 9 ft 0 in. It is subjected to an axial compressive force of 45,000 lb and a uniformly distributed load of 850 lb per lin ft that produces bending stresses. The allowable unit stresses for the lumber to be used are $f = 1500$ psi, $c = 1400$ psi, and $E = 1{,}760{,}000$ psi. What should be the size of the member?

14–2. Axial Tension and Bending Combined. Sometimes a member is subjected to both axial tension and bending stresses. A lower chord of a roof truss with bending stresses that result from ceiling rafters is an example. Such a member should be proportioned so that $\frac{P/A}{t} + \frac{M/S}{f}$ do not exceed 1. In the quantity $\frac{P/A}{t}$ the term t is the allowable tensile unit stress parallel to the grain in pounds per square inch, as given in Table 3–1. The other terms in the two quantities are given in Art. 14–1.

Example. A member of the lower chord of a truss has a length of 8 ft 0 in., an axial tensile load of 30,000 lb, and, in addition, a uniformly distributed load of 300 lb per lin ft producing bending. Assuming that the timber has both t and f equal to 1200 psi, design the truss member.

SOLUTION. Assume that the member is a 6 x 8 in. From Table 3–3, $A = 41.25$ sq in. and $S = 51.56$ in.^{3} Then

$$\frac{P/A}{t} = \frac{30{,}000/41.25}{1200} = 0.606$$

$$M = \frac{wl^2}{10} = \frac{300 \times 8 \times 8 \times 12}{10} = 23{,}040 \text{ in-lb}$$

$$\frac{M/S}{f} = \frac{23{,}040/51.56}{1200} = 0.37$$

Then

$$\frac{P/A}{t} + \frac{M/S}{f} = 0.606 + 0.37 = 0.976$$

Since this quantity does not exceed 1, the 6 x 8 in. section is acceptable.

Problem 14–2–A. A lower-chord member of a roof truss is 10 ft 0 in. in length. This member has a load of 400 lb per lin ft producing bending stresses, and, also, there is an axial tensile load of 40,000 lb that results from the truss action. Design the member, assuming f and t to be 1400 psi.

14–3. Eccentric Loads. Columns with Loads on Side Brackets.

A condition that sometimes occurs in the design of structural timber members is a column with an axial load and, in addition, a load on a side bracket attached to the column. An exact analysis of combined end and bracket loads is extremely complex. The National Lumber Manufacturers Association gives a simple procedure to use in the design of such members. It is appropriate when brackets are in the upper quarter of the height of the column. This procedure is safe and sufficiently accurate. The following steps may be used:

Step 1. Assume that the eccentric bracket load P is acting as a concentric end load and that a side load P' is acting at the mid-height of the column. Figure 14–2 (*a*) indicates the load P on the side bracket, and Fig. 14–2 (*b*) shows the assumed loading.

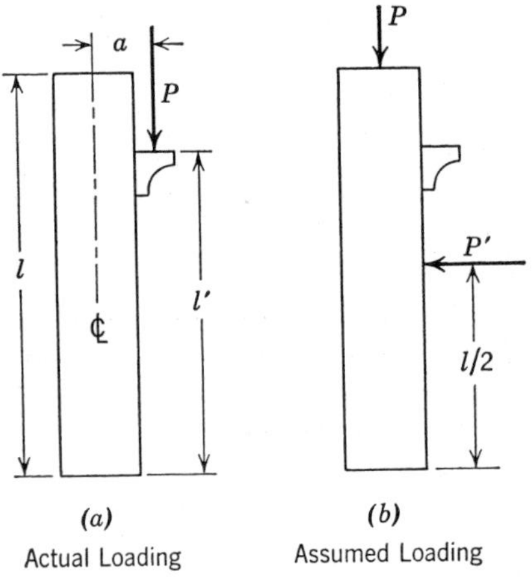

FIG. 14–2

Step 2. Compute the magnitude of P', the side load, assumed to be acting at the center of the length of the column. It is determined by the empirical formula:

$$P' = \frac{3al'P}{l^2}$$

in which P = the actual load on the bracket, in pounds
P' = the assumed horizontal side load, in pounds

a = the horizontal distance from the load on the bracket to the center of the column, in inches
l = the total length of the column, in inches
l' = the vertical distance from the point of application of the bracket load to the base of the column, in inches

Step 3. Take a trial cross section and add the *assumed* concentric load P' to any other axial column loads. Solve $\frac{P}{A}$ in the column formula and compute $\frac{P/A}{c}$.

Step 4. Use P' to determine the induced flexural stress, $\frac{M}{S}$, as though the column were a beam with the concentrated load at its midspan, and compute the value of $\frac{M/S}{f}$.

Step 5. Apply the combined stress formula given in Art. 14–1.

Example. A Southern pine column, of the No. 1 dense SR grade, has a length of 12 ft 0 in. and an axial load of 30,000 lb. A side bracket, the top of which is 11 ft 0 in. from the base of the column, supports an eccentric load of 20,000 lb. This eccentric load is 10 in. from the center line of the column. What should be the size of this wood column?

SOLUTION. Referring to Table 3–1 we find, for this species and grade of lumber, that E = 1,760,000 psi, c = 1500 psi, and f = 1600 psi.

Step 1. The bracket load in this problem is 20,000 lb. We shall assume that it is an axial load and proceed to compute P'.

Step 2. To determine P', we use the formula $P' = \frac{3al'P}{l^2}$. Then

$$P' = \frac{3 \times 10 \times (11 \times 12) \times 20{,}000}{(12 \times 12)^2} = 3820 \text{ lb}$$

the assumed horizontal side load.

Step 3. For a trial section, let us take a 10 x 10 in. column.

From Table 3–3, $A = 9.5 \times 9.5$ or 90.25 sq in. and $S = 142.90$ in.^{3} If we add the 20,000 lb eccentric load to the 30,000-lb axial load, $20{,}000 + 30{,}000 = 50{,}000$ lb. Then $\frac{l}{d} = \frac{12 \times 12}{9.5} = 15.15$, the slenderness ratio. Thus

$$\frac{P}{A} = \frac{0.3 \times E}{(l/d)^2} = \frac{0.3 \times 1{,}760{,}000}{15.15 \times 15.15} = 2300 \text{ psi}$$

Note that this stress exceeds c, 1500 psi. Then

$$\frac{P/A}{c} = \frac{50{,}000/90.25}{1500} = 0.369$$

Step 4. $M = \frac{P'l}{4} = \frac{3820 \times (12 \times 12)}{4} = 137{,}500$ in-lb. Then

$$\frac{M/S}{f} = \frac{137{,}500/142.90}{1600} = 0.602$$

Step 5. Substituting, the quantities

$$\frac{P/A}{c} + \frac{M/S}{f} = 0.369 + 0.602 = 0.971$$

This quantity does not exceed 1; consequently the 10 x 10 in. column is accepted for this loading.

CHAPTER 15

BOLTED JOINTS

15–1. Bolted Joints. Bolts provide a strong, efficient, and economical method of fastening wood members together. They are used for wood-to-wood fastenings and also for fastening steel plates to wood members. Bolts are available in almost any size and can be used with all sizes of lumber.

15–2. Allowable Loads for Bolts. The allowable loads for bolts, given in Table 15–1, are for common bolts and are the maximum for normal loading. These tabulated loads are for bolts in lumber seasoned to a moisture content approximately equal to that to which it will eventually attain in service. The loads are for bolted joints used under conditions continuously dry, as in most covered structures. When joints are exposed to weather or when always wet, 75 and 67%, respectively, of the tabulated loads apply. A washer or metal plate must be placed between the wood and the bolt head and between the wood and the nut.

The loads given in Table 15–1 apply when side members of wood are each one half the thickness of the main (enclosed) member, as shown in Fig. 15–1 (*a*).

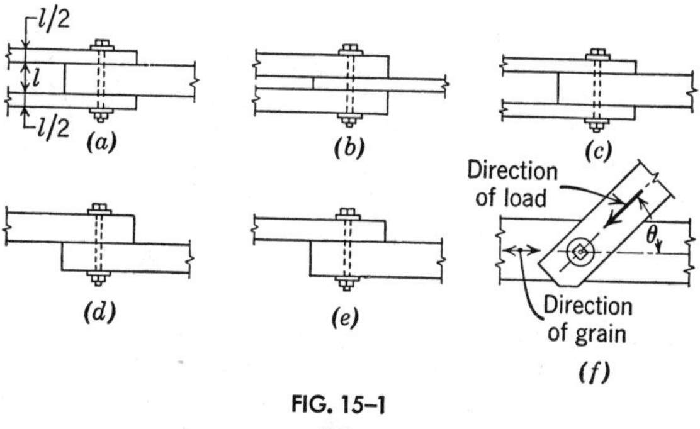

FIG. 15–1

TABLE 15–1. ALLOWABLE LOADS ON ONE BOLT LOADED AT BOTH ENDS, IN POUNDS

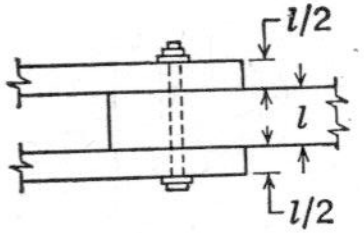

Length of bolt in main member, inches l	Diameter of bolt, inches d	l/d	Projected area of bolt, Sq. In. $A = l \times d$	Cypress Southern: Parallel to grain P	Cypress Southern: Perpendicular to grain Q	Southern Pine and Douglas Fir, Coast Region: Parallel to grain P	Southern Pine and Douglas Fir, Coast Region: Perpendicular to grain Q	Hemlock, Eastern: Parallel to grain P	Hemlock, Eastern: Perpendicular to grain Q	Oak, Red and White: Parallel to grain P	Oak, Red and White: Perpendicular to grain Q	Redwood: Parallel to grain P	Redwood: Perpendicular to grain Q	Spruce, Eastern: Parallel to grain P	Spruce, Eastern: Perpendicular to grain Q
$1\frac{5}{8}$	$\frac{1}{2}$	3.3	0.8125	1010	450	1010	480	680	450	940	750	940	380	750	380
	$\frac{5}{8}$	2.6	1.0156	1290	510	1290	540	850	510	1200	850	1200	420	930	420
	$\frac{3}{4}$	2.2	1.2188	1550	570	1550	600	1010	570	1450	950	1450	470	1120	470
	$\frac{7}{8}$	1.9	1.4219	1810	620	1810	670	1190	620	1690	1040	1690	520	1310	520
	1	1.6	1.625	2070	680	2070	730	1360	680	1930	1140	1930	570	1500	570
2	$\frac{1}{2}$	4.0	1.00	1180	550	1180	590	840	550	1100	920	1100	460	900	460
	$\frac{5}{8}$	3.2	1.25	1560	630	1560	670	1050	630	1460	1050	1460	520	1160	520
	$\frac{3}{4}$	2.7	1.50	1910	700	1910	740	1250	700	1780	1160	1780	580	1390	580
	$\frac{7}{8}$	2.3	1.75	2230	770	2230	820	1470	770	2080	1280	2080	640	1620	640
	1	2.0	2.00	2550	840	2550	890	1670	840	2380	1400	2380	700	1850	700
$2\frac{5}{8}$	$\frac{1}{2}$	5.3	1.3125	1280	730	1280	780	1010	730	1180	1210	1180	610	1030	610
	$\frac{5}{8}$	4.2	1.6406	1890	820	1890	880	1360	820	1760	1370	1760	690	1460	690
	$\frac{3}{4}$	3.5	1.9688	2430	920	2430	980	1650	920	2250	1530	2250	760	1810	760
	$\frac{7}{8}$	3.0	2.2969	2900	1010	2900	1080	1920	1010	2700	1680	2700	840	2120	840
	1	2.6	2.625	3340	1100	3340	1170	2190	1100	3110	1830	3110	920	2430	920
3	$\frac{1}{2}$	6.0	1.50	1290	830	1290	890	1070	830	1200	1330	1200	690	1050	690
	$\frac{5}{8}$	4.8	1.875	1980	940	1980	1000	1510	940	1850	1570	1850	780	1560	780
	$\frac{3}{4}$	4.0	2.25	2660	1050	2660	1120	1870	1050	2470	1740	2470	870	2030	870
	$\frac{7}{8}$	3.4	2.625	3250	1150	3250	1230	2190	1150	3020	1920	3020	960	2420	960
	1	3.0	3.00	3790	1260	3790	1340	2510	1260	3530	2100	3530	1050	2770	1050

$3\frac{5}{8}$	$\frac{1}{2}$	7.3	1.8125	1290	950	1290	1020	1070	950	1200	1390	1200	830	1050	830
	$\frac{5}{8}$	5.8	2.2656	2010	1140	2010	1210	1660	1140	1860	1850	1860	950	1640	950
	$\frac{3}{4}$	4.8	2.7188	2860	1270	2860	1350	2190	1270	2680	2110	2680	1050	2280	1050
	$\frac{7}{8}$	4.1	3.1719	3680	1390	3680	1490	2630	1390	3450	2320	3450	1160	2840	1160
	1	3.6	3.625	4430	1520	4430	1620	3030	1520	4120	2530	4120	1270	3320	1270
4	$\frac{1}{2}$	8.0	2.00	1290	980	1290	1040	1070	980	1200	1390	1200	890	1050	890
	$\frac{5}{8}$	6.4	2.50	2010	1250	2010	1330	1670	1250	1870	1950	1870	1050	1640	1050
	$\frac{3}{4}$	5.3	3.00	2890	1400	2890	1490	2330	1400	2690	2310	2690	1160	2340	1160
	$\frac{7}{8}$	4.6	3.50	3830	1540	3830	1640	2850	1540	3570	2560	3570	1280	3000	1280
	1	4.0	4.00	4720	1680	4720	1790	3330	1680	4400	2790	4400	1400	3600	1400
$4\frac{1}{2}$	$\frac{1}{2}$	9.0	2.25	1290	960	1290	1020	1070	960	1200	1340	1200	900	1050	900
	$\frac{5}{8}$	7.2	2.8125	2010	1350	2010	1440	1670	1350	1870	1980	1870	1170	1640	1170
	$\frac{3}{4}$	6.0	3.375	2890	1570	2890	1680	2420	1570	2690	2520	2690	1310	2360	1310
	$\frac{7}{8}$	5.1	3.9375	3920	1730	3920	1840	3110	1730	3670	2880	3670	1440	3160	1440
	1	4.5	4.50	4980	1890	4980	2010	3670	1890	4660	3140	4660	1570	3900	1570
	$1\frac{1}{8}$	4.0	5.0625	5980	2050	5980	2190	4210	2050	5560	3420	5560	1710	4560	1710
5	$\frac{1}{2}$	10.0	2.50	1290	930	1290	990	1070	930	1200	1280	1200	800	1050	800
	$\frac{5}{8}$	8.0	3.125	2010	1380	2010	1470	1670	1380	1870	1960	1870	1260	1640	1260
	$\frac{3}{4}$	6.7	3.75	2890	1720	2890	1840	2420	1720	2690	2620	2690	1450	2360	1450
	$\frac{7}{8}$	5.7	4.375	3940	1920	3940	2050	3260	1920	3670	3140	3670	1600	3210	1600
	1	5.0	5.00	5100	2100	5100	2240	3990	2100	4750	3490	4750	1750	4080	1750
	$1\frac{1}{8}$	4.4	5.625	6280	2280	6280	2440	4610	2280	5910	3810	5910	1900	4910	1900
$5\frac{1}{2}$	$\frac{5}{8}$	8.8	3.4375	2010	1360	2010	1450	1670	1360	1870	1910	1870	1270	1640	1270
	$\frac{3}{4}$	7.3	4.125	2890	1820	2890	1940	2420	1820	2690	2660	2690	1590	2380	1590
	$\frac{7}{8}$	6.3	4.8125	3940	2100	3940	2250	3310	2100	3670	3310	3670	1760	3230	1760
	1	5.5	5.50	5120	2300	5120	2460	4180	2300	4770	2800	4770	1920	4170	1920
	$1\frac{1}{8}$	4.9	6.1875	6440	2510	6440	2680	4960	2510	6000	4190	6000	2090	5110	2090
6	$\frac{5}{8}$	9.6	3.75	2010	1340	2010	1420	1670	1340	1870	1840	1870	1250	1650	1250
	$\frac{3}{4}$	8.0	4.50	2890	1840	2890	1970	2420	1840	2690	2620	2690	1680	2380	1680
	$\frac{7}{8}$	6.9	5.25	3940	2250	3940	2410	3310	2250	3670	3380	3670	1920	3230	1920
	1	6.0	6.00	5140	2510	5140	2680	4290	2510	4790	4040	4790	2100	4210	2100
	$1\frac{1}{8}$	5.3	6.75	6500	2740	6500	2920	5240	2740	6050	4540	6050	2280	5270	2280
$6\frac{1}{2}$	$\frac{5}{8}$	10.4	4.0625	2010	1300	2010	1390	1670	1300	1870	1800	1870	1230	1650	1230
	$\frac{3}{4}$	8.7	4.875	2890	1820	2890	1940	2420	1820	2690	2560	2690	1700	2380	1700
	$\frac{7}{8}$	7.4	5.6875	3940	2350	3940	2510	3310	2350	3670	3410	3670	2070	3230	2070
	1	6.5	6.50	5140	2700	5140	2880	4290	2700	4790	4180	4790	2270	4210	2270
	$1\frac{1}{8}$	5.8	7.3125	6500	2970	6500	3170	5370	2970	6050	4820	6050	2470	5290	2470
7	$\frac{5}{8}$	11.2	4.375	2010	1270	2010	1350	1670	1270	1870	1720	1870	1210	1650	1210
	$\frac{3}{4}$	9.3	5.25	2890	1800	2890	1910	2420	1800	2690	2510	2690	1690	2380	1690
	$\frac{7}{8}$	8.0	6.125	3940	2370	3940	2530	3310	2370	3670	3360	3670	2150	3230	2150
	1	7.0	7.00	5140	2850	5140	3040	4290	2850	4790	4250	4790	2440	4210	2440
	$1\frac{1}{8}$	6.2	7.875	6500	3190	6500	3410	5450	3190	6050	5050	6050	2660	5340	2660

TABLE 15–1. ALLOWABLE LOADS ON ONE BOLT LOADED AT BOTH ENDS, IN POUNDS (Continued)

Length of bolt in main member, inches l	Diameter of bolt, inches d	l/d	Projected area of bolt, Sq. In. $A = l \times d$	Cypress Southern: Parallel to grain P	Cypress Southern: Perpendicular to grain Q	Southern Pine and Douglas Fir, Coast Region: Parallel to grain P	Southern Pine and Douglas Fir, Coast Region: Perpendicular to grain Q	Hemlock, Eastern: Parallel to grain P	Hemlock, Eastern: Perpendicular to grain Q	Oak, Red and White: Parallel to grain P	Oak, Red and White: Perpendicular to grain Q	Redwood: Parallel to grain P	Redwood: Perpendicular to grain Q	Spruce, Eastern: Parallel to grain P	Spruce, Eastern: Perpendicular to grain Q
7½	⅝	12.0	4.6875	2010	1220	2010	1300	1670	1220	1870	1670	1870	1200	1650	1200
	¾	10.0	5.625	2890	1760	2890	1880	2420	1760	2690	2420	2690	1660	2380	1660
	⅞	8.6	6.5625	3940	2340	3940	2500	3310	2340	3670	3300	3670	2180	3230	2180
	1	7.5	7.50	5140	2940	5140	3130	4290	2940	4790	4230	4790	2590	4210	2590
	1⅛	6.7	8.4375	6500	3370	6500	3610	5450	3370	6050	5140	6050	2850	5340	2850
8	⅝	12.8	5.00	2010	1180	2010	1260	1670	1180	1870	1600	1870	1180	1650	1180
	¾	10.7	6.00	2890	1720	2890	1840	2420	1720	2690	2360	2690	1630	2380	1630
	⅞	9.1	7.00	3940	2320	3940	2470	3310	2320	3670	3260	3670	2180	3230	2180
	1	8.0	8.00	5140	2950	5140	3150	4290	2950	4790	4190	4790	2680	4210	2680
	1⅛	7.1	9.00	6500	3530	6500	3750	5450	3530	6050	5210	6050	3040	5340	3040
	1¼	6.4	10.00	8040	3900	8040	4170	6780	3900	7480	6090	7480	3270	6570	3270
9½	¾	12.7	7.125	2890	1580	2890	1690	2420	1580	2690	2150	2690	1570	2380	1570
	⅞	10.9	8.3125	3940	2190	3940	2350	3310	2190	3670	2980	3670	2080	3230	2080
	1	9.5	9.50	5140	2860	5140	3050	4290	2860	4790	3960	4790	2680	4210	2680
	1⅛	8.4	10.6875	6500	3630	6500	3830	5450	3630	6050	5120	6050	3350	5340	3350
	1¼	7.6	11.875	8040	4310	8040	4590	6780	4310	7480	6190	7480	3820	6570	3820
10	⅞	11.4	8.75	3940	2160	3940	2290	3310	2160	3670	2940	3670	2080	3230	2080
	1	10.0	10.00	5140	2820	5140	3000	4290	2820	4790	3870	4790	2660	4210	2660
	1⅛	8.9	11.25	6500	3560	6500	3790	5450	3560	6050	4990	6050	3330	5340	3330
	1¼	8.0	12.50	8040	4320	8040	4610	6780	4320	7480	6140	7480	3930	6570	3930
11½	1	11.5	11.50	5140	2680	5140	2850	4290	2680	4790	3640	4790	2580	4210	2580
	1⅛	10.2	12.9375	6500	3440	6500	3660	5450	3440	6050	4710	6050	3260	5340	3260
	1¼	9.2	14.375	8040	4210	8040	4490	6780	4210	7480	5890	7480	3950	6570	3950
12	1	12.0	12.00	5140	2610	5140	2790	4290	2610	4790	3560	4790	2560	4210	2560
	1⅛	10.7	13.50	6500	3370	6500	3600	5450	3370	6050	4640	6050	3200	5340	3200
	1¼	9.6	15.00	8040	4180	8040	4450	6780	4180	7480	5770	7480	3920	6570	3920

Compiled by permission from data furnished by the National Lumber Manufacturers Association.

If the side members are more than one half the thickness of the main member, no increase in the tabulated loads is permitted. See Fig. 15–1 (*b*).

When the side members are less than one half the thickness of the main member, the tabulated loads indicated for a main member that is twice the thickness of the thinnest side member used shall apply. For example, with 3-in. side members and an 8-in. main (center) member, the tabulated loads for a 6-in. main member shall apply. See Fig. 15–1 (*c*).

The loads in Table 15–1 are for a joint consisting of three members as shown in Fig. 15–1 (*a*). The bolts are in double shear. The length of the bolt, l, is the thickness of the main member.

When the joint consists of two members of equal thickness (the bolt being in single shear), one half the tabulated load for a piece twice the thickness of one of the members shall apply. See Fig. 15–1 (*d*).

When members of a two-member joint are of unequal thickness, one half the tabulated load for a piece twice the thickness of the thinner member shall apply. See Fig. 15–1 (*e*).

When *steel plates* are used for side members, the tabulated loads for parallel-to-grain loading shall be increased by 25% but no increase shall be made for the perpendicular-to-grain loads.

15–3. Direction of Load on Grain of Wood. The direction of the bolt pressure on the grain of the wood must be taken into consideration. Figure 15–2 shows a spliced tension member. For such a condition the bolt pressure is parallel to the grain of the wood. In Fig. 15–4 the bolts exert pressure parallel to the grain of the vertical member but the bolt pressure is perpendicular to the grain of the horizontal member. Note, in Table 15–1, that the allowable pressures for both parallel and perpendicular to grain are given. They are identified as P and Q. In Fig. 15–1 (*f*) the bolt pressure is parallel to the grain of the inclined member, but in the horizontal member the load is neither parallel nor perpendicular to the grain. To find the allowable bolt load on the horizontal member, we use the Hankinson formula given in Art. 3–6. This formula, with the aid of Table 3–2, affords a ready solution for finding the allowable bolt load for any angle between the direction of the load and the direction of the grain.

15–4. Bolt-Design Requirements. Consider two tension members connected by bolts, as indicated in Fig. 15–2. First of all, the allowable load that the joint will support must not exceed the allowable bolt load of one bolt multiplied by the number of bolts. The net section of a member, taken at right angles to the direction of the load, is the gross cross-sectional area of the member minus the area of the bolt holes in the section. For any bolted joint the allowable tensile joint load must not exceed the net cross-sectional area multiplied by t, the allowable tensile unit stress of the lumber, as shown in Table 3–1. In addition to these two requirements, the net area for softwoods at the critical section, for parallel to grain loading, must be at least 80% of the total area in bearing under all bolts in the member. For hardwoods the net section must be at least 100%.

15–5. Design of Bolted Joints. Data for the design of a bolted joint includes the species and sizes of the members to be joined. The procedure is to assume a bolt size and then to find the allowable load for one bolt. This bolt load divided into total load on the joint determines the required number of bolts.

Example. A 6 x 10 in. Southern pine main member, of the No. 2 SR grade, is spliced with 4 x 10 in. side pieces. How many $\frac{3}{4}$-in. bolts are required on each side of this three-member splice if the tensile load to be resisted is 25,000 lb? See Fig. 15–2.

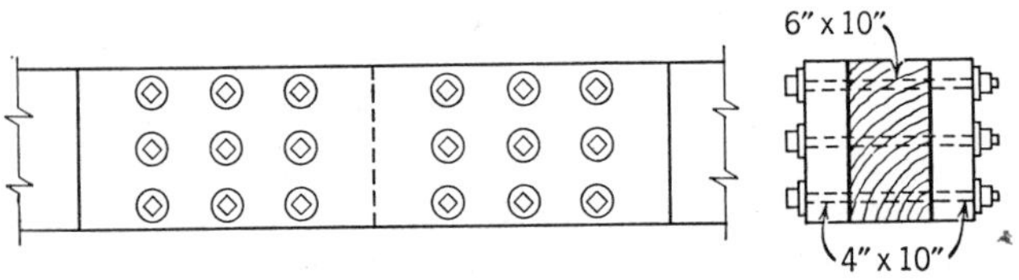

FIG. 15–2

SOLUTION. Since the thicknesses of the side pieces are greater than one half the thickness of the main member, the main member controls the joint load. The length of the bolt in the main member is 5.5 in.; hence, referring to Table 15–1, $P = 2890$ lb, the allowable load on one bolt with parallel to the grain loading. Then 25,000 ÷

2890 = 8+, and we shall use nine bolts in three rows on each side of the splice.

The area of a 6 x 10 in. member is found in Table 3–3 to be 52.25 sq in. The area to be deducted for one bolt hole is (0.75 x 5.5) sq in. Therefore, the net area at a critical section is 52.25 − (3 × 0.75 × 5.5) or 39.87 sq in.

The bolt-bearing area of one bolt is (0.75 x 5.5) sq in. and for nine bolts it is (9 × 0.75 × 5.5) or 37.12 sq in.; 80% of 37.12 = 29.7 sq in. This is acceptable, since the net area, 39.87 sq in. is a greater magnitude. Table 3–1 shows that t, the allowable tensile stress for this grade of Southern pine, is 1200 psi. Then, since the net area is 39.87 sq in., 39.87 × 1200 = 47,800 lb, the allowable tensile load for the splice. This load is greater than the required 25,000 lb; hence nine $\frac{3}{4}$-in. bolts on each side of the splice are accepted. See Fig. 15–2.

Example. Two 2 x 6 in. side members are used to splice a 4 x 6 in. tension member. The lumber is the heart structural grade of redwood, and there are four $\frac{5}{8}$-in. bolts on each side of this three-member splice. See Fig. 15–3. Compute the maximum load that the splice will support.

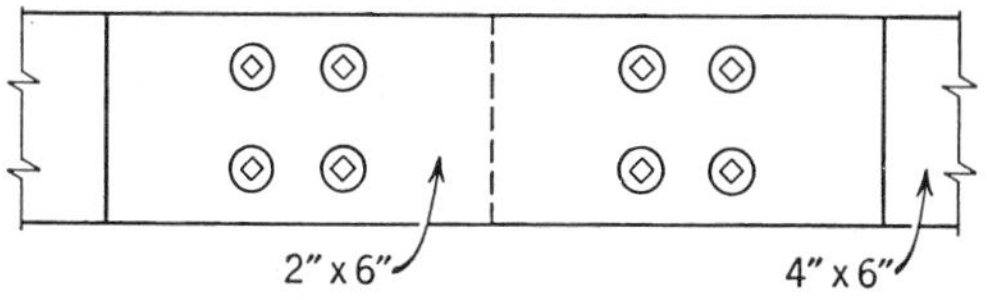

FIG. 15–3

SOLUTION. The side members are less than one half the thickness of the main member and, therefore, control the joint load. See Fig. 15–1 (c). Then, 2 × 1.625 = 3.25 in., and we base the bolt load on a 3.25-in. thick main member. By interpolating, Table 15–1 gives P = 1854-lb bolt load for a 3.25-in. length bolt. For four bolts, 4 × 1854 = 7416 lb, the total bolt load.

The area of a 2 x 6 in. member is 9.14 sq in.; hence the net area is (2 × 9.14) − (2 × 0.625 × 3.25) = 14.22 sq in.

The bolt bearing area is $4 \times 0.625 \times 3.25 = 8.12$ sq in.; 80% of $8.12 = 6.49$ sq in., less than the net area, 14.22 sq in.

In Table 3–1 we see that t, the allowable tensile stress for the heart structural grade of redwood, is 1300 psi. Then, since the net area is 14.22 sq in., $1300 \times 14.22 = 18{,}500$ lb, the allowable tension in the wood.

Thus the maximum load the splice will support is 7416 lb, the total bolt load.

Example. A two-member joint consists of a short 3 x 6 in. vertical member exerting a compressive force of 1600 lb on a 2 x 6 in. horizontal member, as indicated in Fig. 15–4. If the lumber is the construction grade of Douglas fir and the bolts are $\frac{1}{2}$ in., how many bolts are required for the joint?

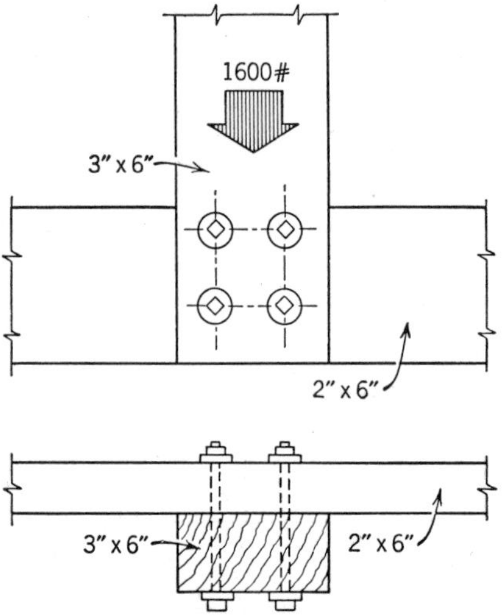

FIG. 15–4

SOLUTION. This is a two-member joint, Fig. 15–1 (*e*), and the 2 x 6 in. piece is the controlling member. For this condition, "one-half the tabulated load for a piece twice the thickness of the thinner member shall apply." Then, $2 \times 1.625 = 3.25$ in. For a member having a bolt length of 3.25 in., Table 15–1, by interpolating, gives Q, the bolt load *perpendicular to the grain*, to be 942 lb. This is the bolt load for a three-piece joint, but for this joint we have only two pieces. Hence the allowable bolt load is $\frac{1}{2} \times 942$ or 471 lb. The number of bolts required is $1600 \div 471 = 3+$, and we shall use four $\frac{1}{2}$-in. bolts. See Fig. 15–4.

Example. Two 3 x 8 in. members are bolted to a 4 x 10 in. horizontal member, as shown in Fig. 15–5, with four $\frac{3}{4}$-in. bolts. The

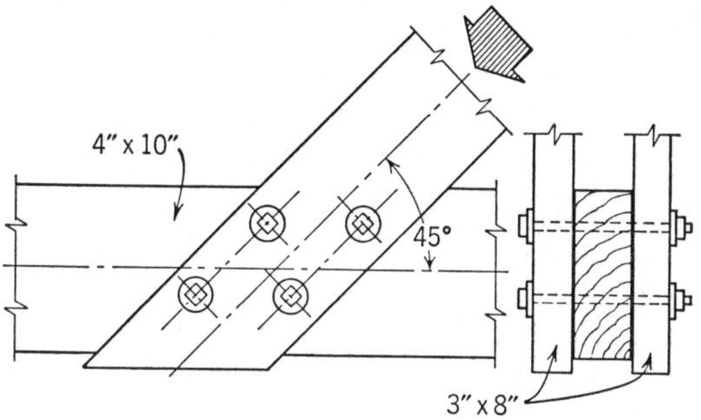

FIG. 15–5

angle between the members is 45°, the sloping member transmits a compressive force to the horizontal member and the wood is the 1300 f grade of cypress. Compute the maximum total bolt load for the joint.

SOLUTION. The thicknesses of the outside pieces are greater than one half the thickness of the center member; consequently the center piece is the controlling member and the length of bolt is 3.625 in.

Note that the bolts exert pressure parallel to the grain of the inclined pieces and that the pressure they transmit to the horizontal member is neither parallel nor perpendicular to the grain. Referring to Table 15–1, we find that $P = 2860$ lb and $Q = 1270$ lb., the allowable pressures of one bolt parallel and perpendicular to the grain, respectively. To find the allowable pressure on the inclined surface, we use the Hankinson formula and Table 3–2 in Art. 3–6. Then

$$N = \frac{P \times Q}{P \sin^2 \theta + Q \cos^2 \theta}$$

$$= \frac{2860 \times 1270}{(2860 \times 0.5) + (1270 \times 0.5)} = 1760 \text{ lb}$$

the allowable load for one $\frac{3}{4}$-in. bolt. Since there are four bolts, $4 \times 1760 = 7040$ lb, the maximum total bolt load.

Problem 15–5–A. A 4 x 6 in. tension member is spliced with 3 x 6 in. side pieces and four $\frac{7}{8}$-in. bolts. The wood is the 1300 *f* grade of white oak. What is the maximum load the joint will support?

Problem 15–5–B. A two-member joint is composed of a 2 x 6 in. and a 3 x 6 in. member. The members are in tension, and the wood is the 1300 *f* grade of Southern cypress. If there are four $\frac{5}{8}$-in. bolts in the joint, what is the maximum load for the splice?

Problem 15–5–C. A three-member joint consists of a 4 x 6 in. main member with two 2 x 6 in. side pieces. The wood is the No. 2 SR grade of Southern pine. If there are four $\frac{7}{8}$-in. bolts, what is the maximum load the splice will support?

Problem 15–5–D. If metal side plates are used instead of the two 3 x 6 in. side pieces for the joint described in Problem 15–5–A, compute the maximum load for the joint.

Problem 15–5–E. A 4 x 10 in. horizontal member is bolted to two 3 x 8 in. outside pieces, as indicated in Fig. 15–5. The angle between the two members is 60°. Four $\frac{3}{4}$-in. bolts are used, and the sloping member exerts a compressive force on the 4 x 10 in. horizontal member. If the wood is the No. 2 SR grade of Southern pine, compute the maximum bolt load for the joint.

15–6. Placement of Bolts in Joints. Figure 15–6 shows the terms used in connection with placement dimensions in bolted joints. The two conditions shown are (*a*) loads parallel to grain and (*b*) loads perpendicular to grain. The spacings, end distances, and edge distances in a bolted joint must be sufficient to develop the full strength of each bolt. The following are some of the placement requirements. All spacings and distances are measured from the center of the bolts.

Spacings of bolts in a row. For parallel-to-grain loading the minimum spacing is four times the bolt diameter. For perpendicular-to-grain loading use the same spacing as parallel-to-grain loading

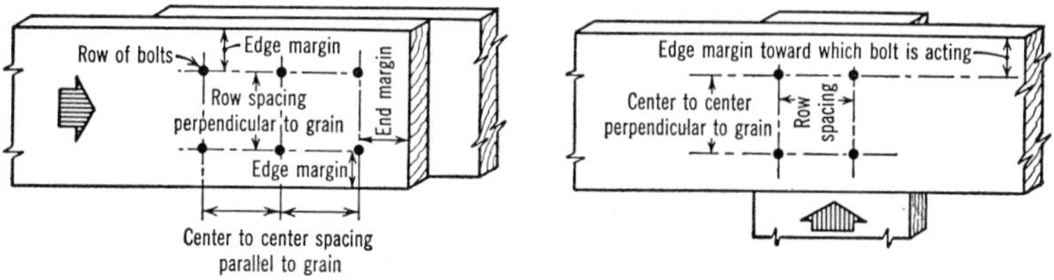

(*a*) Parallel To Grain Loading (*b*) Perpendicular To Grain Loading

FIG. 15–6

if the design load approaches bolt-bearing capacity of side members. If the design load is less, the spacing may be reduced.

Spacing between rows. For parallel-to-grain loading the spacing is controlled by the bolt-bearing and net-section requirements. For perpendicular-to-grain loading the spacing shall be at least two and one half times the bolt diameter for an $\frac{l}{d}$ ratio of 2, and five times the bolt diameter for $\frac{l}{d}$ ratios of 6 or more.

End distance. For parallel-to-grain loading (*a*) in tension, seven times the bolt diameter for softwoods and five times for hardwoods, (*b*) in compression, four times the bolt diameter.

Edge distance. For parallel-to-grain loading in tension or compression the edge distance shall be at least one and one half times the bolt diameter, except that for $\frac{l}{d}$ ratios more than 6 one half the distance between rows of bolts is used. For perpendicular-to-grain loading the edge distance nearest the edge toward which the load is acting shall be at least four times the bolt diameter.

CHAPTER 16

TIMBER CONNECTORS

16–1. Timber Connectors. In the design of timber trusses, as well as of other timber structures in which loads are transferred from one member to another, the design of the joints demands particular attention. In the past the size of truss members was frequently determined by the type of joint and the reduced cross-sectional area that resulted from the notches and bolts. Intensive investigation by the U. S. Forest Products Laboratory, the Timber Engineering Company (a subsidiary of the National Lumber Manufacturers Association), and numerous colleges and universities has resulted in invaluable technical information pertaining to the use of *timber connectors.*

Basically, timber connectors are metal rings or fabricated plates that are imbedded partly in each face of adjacent members to transmit the loads from one member to another, with bolts of relatively small diameter. The result is greater joint efficiency which permits the use of shorter timbers and smaller cross sections. In the methods used in the past truss joints were often the weakest part of the structure. With timber connectors it is possible to develop the full permissible working stress of the timber.

16–2. Types of Connectors. Numerous types of connectors have been patented here and abroad. Figure 16–1 illustrates types of Teco connectors, manufactured by the Timber Engineering Company, and Fig. 16–2 shows typical joints in which timber connectors are used.

Probably the most commonly used connector is the *split-ring connector*. Its purpose is to transmit loads between two pieces of timber. The split rings are placed in precut grooves and are thus imbedded partly in the face of each timber. The tongue-and-groove split in the ring permits simultaneous bearing of the inner

(a) Split Ring Joint
Portion of one member cut away to show position of rings

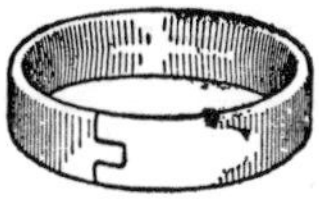

(b) Split Ring

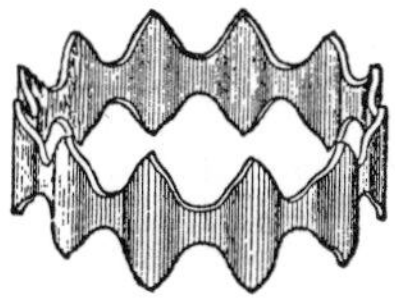

(c) Toothed Ring

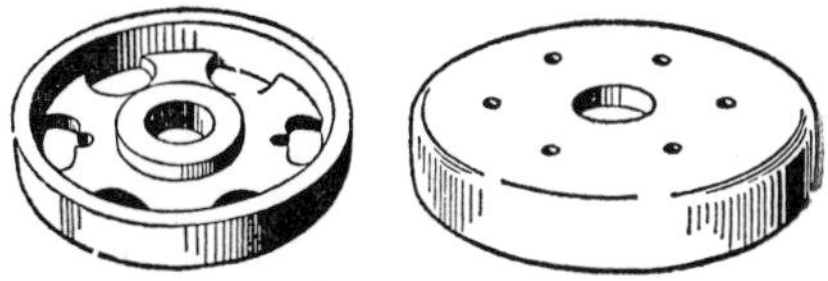

(d) Shear Plates

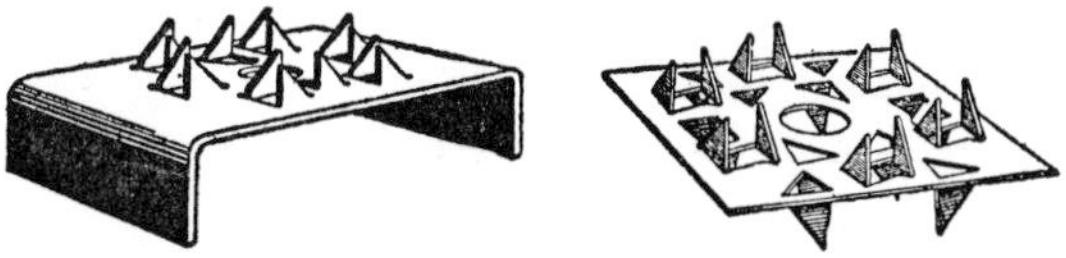

(e) Clamping Plates

(f) Spike Grids

FIG. 16–1

surface of the ring against the core left in the grooving and of the outer face of the ring against the outer wall of the groove. The wedge-fit split ring affords ease of assembly. After the split ring has been inserted in the grooves, the two pieces of timber are held together with bolts and washers, the bolts being placed in holes that are concentric with the rings. The $2\frac{1}{2}$-in. split ring is used in lumber with a minimum width of $3\frac{5}{8}$ in. The 4-in. split ring is

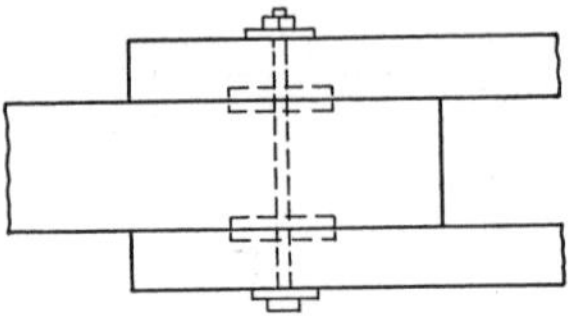

(a) Multiple Split Ring Joint Assembly

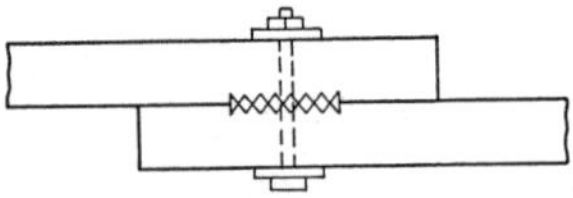

(b) Single-Toothed Ring Joint Assembly

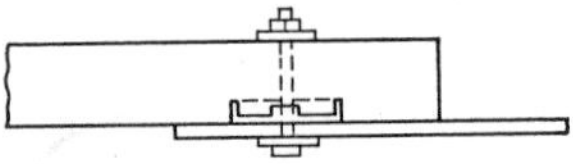

(c) Shear Plate Wood-to-Steel Joint

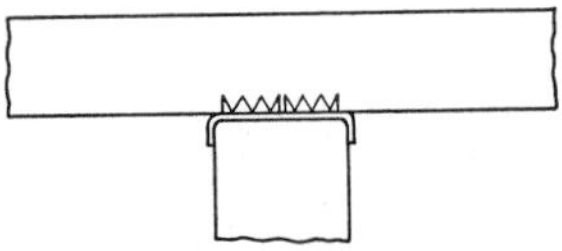

(d) Clamping Plate

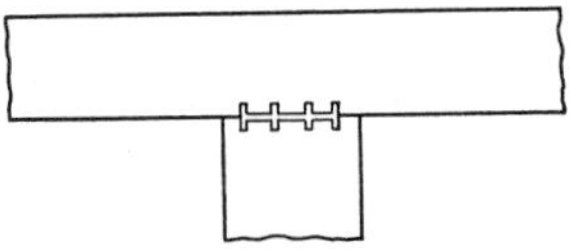

(e) Spike Grid

FIG. 16–2

probably the most common timber connector. It is used in lumber that has a minimum width of $5\frac{1}{2}$ in.

The *toothed-ring connector* transfers loads between two timber members, particularly in relatively light timber framing. No grooves are required for installing toothed rings, since they are imbedded in the faces of the timbers by pressure. The 2-, $2\frac{5}{8}$-, $3\frac{3}{8}$-, and 4-in. toothed rings are used in lumber having minimum widths of 3, $3\frac{5}{8}$, $4\frac{5}{8}$, and $5\frac{1}{2}$ in., respectively.

The *shear plate* is intended primarily for wood-to-steel and wood-to-wood connections in demountable structures when used in pairs. The plates are flush with the surface of the timber, and they fit into precut daps in the timber faces. They are used to attach wood columns to footings with the addition of steel straps and for various steel-to-wood connections in timber structures.

The *clamping plate* is used principally for maintaining the spacing of ties on open-deck railroad structures or wherever timbers overlap at right angles. They are seated by means of a maul and protecting plate.

The *spike grid* is used with piles and poles in trestle construction, piers and wharves, and in transmission lines. They are imbedded in the wood surfaces by pressure. The *circular grid* is used between the top of a pile and the cap to prevent lateral movement.

16–3. Split-Ring Connectors. Split-ring connectors are made in two sizes, the $2\frac{1}{2}$-in. split ring and the 4-in. split ring, the dimensions being the inside diameters at the center when the ring is closed. Because of the number of types of timber connectors and their various sizes, it is impractical to include specific data concerning all of them in a book of this scope. The 4-in. split-ring connector is probably the most widely used, and the following discussions are limited to this particular connector. Data pertaining to the $2\frac{1}{2}$-in. and 4-in. split rings are given in Table 16–1.

TABLE 16–1. SPLIT RING DATA

	$2\frac{1}{2}''$	$4''$
Split ring—dimensions		
Inside diameter at center when closed	$2\frac{1}{2}''$	$4''$
Depth	$\frac{3}{4}''$	$1''$
Lumber, minimum dimensions allowed		
Width	$3\frac{5}{8}''$	$5\frac{1}{2}''$
Thickness, rings in one face	$1''$	$1''$
Thickness, rings opposite in both faces	$1\frac{5}{8}''$	$1\frac{5}{8}''$
Bolt, diameter	$\frac{1}{2}''$	$\frac{3}{4}''$
Bolt hole, diameter	$\frac{9}{16}''$	$\frac{13}{16}''$
Projected area for portion of one ring within a member, in square inches	1.10	2.24
Washers, minimum		
Round, cast or malleable iron, diameter	$2\frac{1}{8}''$	$3''$
Square plate		
Length of side	$2''$	$3''$
Thickness	$\frac{1}{8}''$	$\frac{3}{16}''$
(For trussed rafters and similar light construction standard wrought washers may be used.)		

Reproduced by permission of the Timber Engineering Company.

16–4. Timber Species Groups. The species and density of timber are factors used in determining the allowable loads for connectors. For use in presenting connector loads the species have been divided into three groups, A, B, and C, as shown in Table 16–2. In using

TABLE 16–2. CONNECTOR LOAD SPECIES GROUPS

Group A	Group B	Group C
Douglas fir (dense) Oak, red and white Pine, southern (dense)	Douglas fir (coast region) Larch, western Pine, southern	Cypress, southern and tidewater red Hemlock, West Coast Pine, Norway Redwood

Reproduced by permission of the Timber Engineering Company.

Fig. 16–3 to determine allowable loads, note that the chart is divided vertically into three parts, each part relating to one of the three species groups.

TABLE 16–3. PERMISSIBLE PERCENTAGE INCREASES FOR DURATION OF MAXIMUM LOAD

Two months loading, as for snow	115%
Seven days loading	125%
Wind or earthquake loading	$133\frac{1}{3}$%
Impact loading	200%
Permanent loading	90%

Reproduced by permission of the Timber Engineering Company.

16–5. Permissible Stress Increases for Load Duration. As noted in Art. 3–2, a timber may properly support a load for a relatively short period, whereas a load of the same magnitude applied for a longer or permanent period may cause failure. Table 16–3 gives permissible stress increases to be used for split rings for various load durations. The allowable connector loads given in the chart shown in Fig. 16–3 are for loadings of *normal duration.* Normal duration of loading contemplates the joint being fully loaded for approximately 10 years, either continuously or cumulatively.

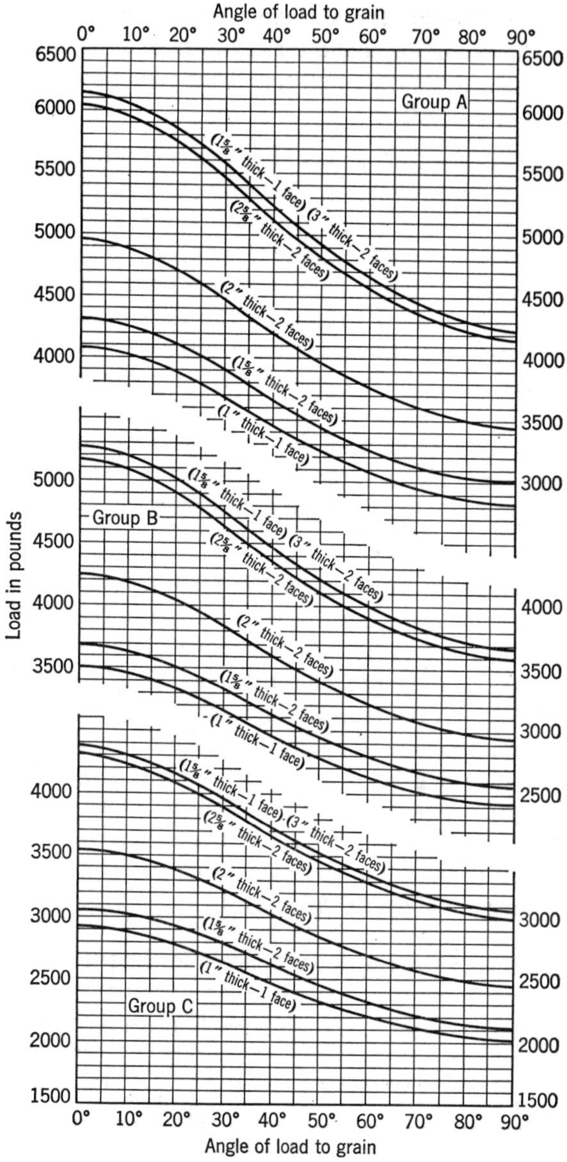

FIG. 16–3. Load chart for normal loading one 4-in. split ring and bolt in single shear. (Reproduced by permission of the Timber Engineering Company.)

Example. Determine the allowable load acting parallel to the grain for a 4-in. split-ring connector in two faces of $2\frac{5}{8}$-in. material. The timber is dense Southern pine, and the condition of loading is "two months' loading."

SOLUTION. Table 16–2 shows that dense Southern pine is included in the Group A species. Referring to Fig. 16–3, note that the upper third of the chart gives allowable 4-in. split-ring connector loads for woods classified under Group A species. As the load on the connectors is acting parallel to the grain, this indicates a zero-degree angle of load to grain. The second curve from the top of the chart gives the loads for a connector in two faces of $2\frac{5}{8}$-in. material and the curve shows that the allowable connector load is 6030 lb.

Table 16–3 shows the load for "two months' loading" to be 115% of the loads given in the chart shown in Fig. 16–3. Hence $6030 \times 1.15 = 6935$ lb, the allowable connector load for a two months' loading period.

16–6. Decreases in Connector Loads for Moisture Content. The allowable loads for split-ring connectors given in the chart in Fig. 16–3 are for connectors used in "seasoned" lumber, lumber seasoned to approximately 15% moisture content to a depth of $\frac{3}{4}$ in. from the surface. If the lumber is unseasoned when fabricated and used under conditions in which it has seasoned or will season, only 80% of the allowable loads given in the chart may be used. If connectors are used in unseasoned lumber under conditions in which it will remain wet, only 67% of the loads given in the chart may be used. These decreases in allowable loads for various moisture conditions are given in Table 16–4.

TABLE 16–4. DECREASES FOR MOISTURE CONTENT CONDITIONS FOR SPLIT RINGS

Condition when fabricated.........	Seasoned	Unseasoned	Unseasoned
Condition when used..............	Seasoned	Seasoned	Unseasoned or wet
	0%	20%	33%

Reproduced by permission of the Timber Engineering Company.

Example. A 4-in. split-ring connector, acting parallel to the grain, in one face of $1\frac{5}{8}$-in. group A material is to be used in lumber unseasoned when fabricated in a position in which it is seasoned when used. What is the allowable load for one connector?

SOLUTION. On referring to the chart in Fig. 16–3, we find that the allowable load for one connector when used in seasoned lumber with a 0° angle of load to grain is 6140 lb. Referring to Table 16–4, we find the decrease in allowable load to be 20%. Then $6140 \times 0.20 = 1228$ and $6140 - 1228 = 4912$ lb, the allowable load for one connector.

16–7. Allowable Connector Loads. The chart shown in Fig. 16–3 gives the allowable normal loads for one 4-in. split-ring connector unit and bolt in single shear. Note that the chart is divided vertically into three parts according to the species, groups A, B, and C, as shown in Table 16–2. In each group are several curves pertaining to specific lumber thicknesses and the number of loaded faces, one or two.

Since lumber has a greater compression strength parallel to the grain than perpendicular to the grain, the allowable load of a connector varies with the angle at which it bears with respect to direction of the grain of the piece on which it bears. Consequently, each curve in Fig. 16–3 is plotted in accordance with the Hankinson formula given in Art. 3–6, the two variables being the load and the "angle of load to grain." Therefore, to determine the allowable load for one connector, select the proper "angle of load to the grain" at the top or bottom of the chart and proceed vertically to the intersection of the curve corresponding to the species group and to the desired thickness of lumber and the number of loaded faces. From this point of intersection proceed horizontally to the edge of the chart and read the allowable normal load.

16–8. Angle of Load to Grain. Owing to the fact that lumber has a greater bearing value parallel to the grain than perpendicular to it, the angle at which the load acts is a factor in determining the allowable connector load. The "angle of load to grain" is the angle between the direction of the load exerted by the connector acting on the member and the longitudinal axis of the member. See Fig. 16–4 (*a*). The angle of load to grain is angle θ.

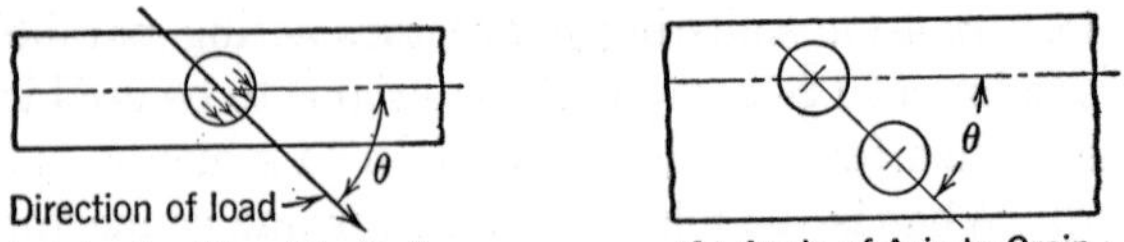

(a) Angle of Load to Grain (b) Angle of Axis to Grain

FIG. 16–4

Figures 16–5 (*a*) and (*b*) indicate the heel joint of a truss. The upper chord is composed of the two outer pieces and the lower chord of a single inner piece. Note that two connectors are used. In considering the various forces in equilibrium at a joint, it is

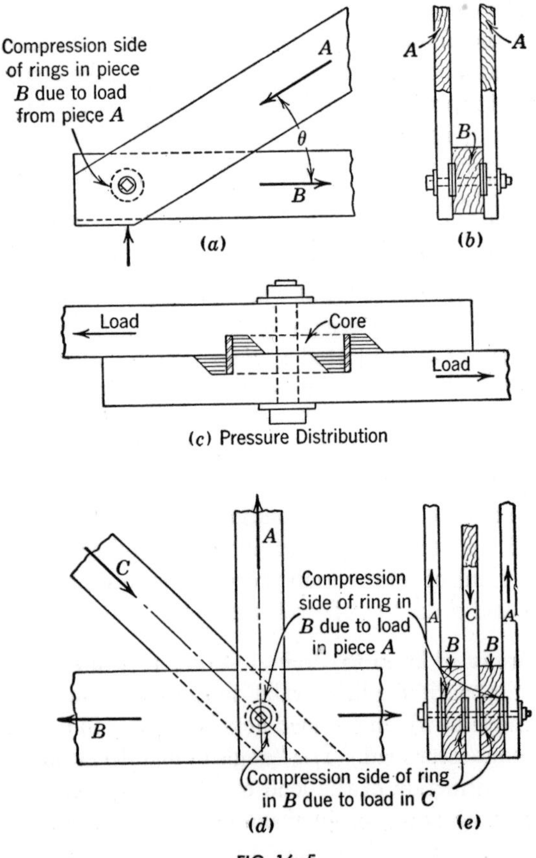

FIG. 16–5

important to recognize the compression side of the ring connector. The compression side of the ring is determined by the direction of the load and is measured from the center of the ring to the edge of the piece on which the load acts. Note the compression side of the rings for the joint illustrated in Figs. 16–5 (*a*) and (*b*).

A typical five-piece joint is shown in Figs. 16–5 (*d*) and (*e*). Note the compression sides of the rings.

A section through a ring connector joining two pieces of lumber is shown in Fig. 16–5 (*c*). The shaded areas adjacent to the ring indicate the bearing of the ring against the core inside the ring and also the wood outside the core. The latter bearing area is at the compression side of the ring.

16–9. Angle of Axis to Grain. The "angle of axis to grain" is a factor in determining the spacing of connectors. It is the angle formed by a line joining the centers of adjacent connectors (in the same face of a member in a joint) and the longitudinal axis of the member. See Fig. 16–4 (*b*).

16–10. Spacing of Connectors. Spacing is the distance between centers of connectors measured along a line joining their centers. In Fig. 16–6 (*a*) the dimension R is the spacing between the rings

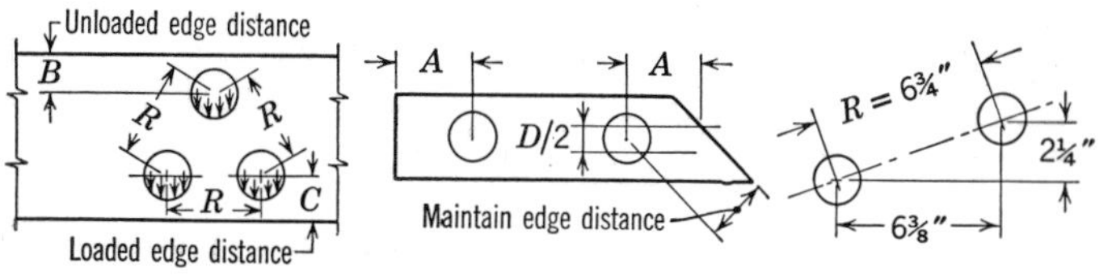

(*a*) Edge Distance and Spacing (*b*) End Distance (*c*) Spacing

FIG. 16–6

shown. Since a connector load is determined by the shearing area of adjacent wood material, connectors not loaded to their full allowable load may be placed with reduced spacings.

Figure 16–7 is a spacing chart for 4-in. Teco split rings showing five parabolic curves representing recommended spacings for full load at the particular angle of load to grain noted on the curve. For intermediate angles of load, straight-line interpolation may be used. If the spacing for full load is desired, select the proper angle of load to grain curve and find where it intersects *the radial lines representing angle of axis to grain.* The distance from that point to the lower left-hand corner, the point 0–0, is the spacing. It is probably more convenient, however, when laying out this spacing to use the parallel-to-grain and perpendicular-to-grain components or measurements of the spacing. The parallel-to-grain component may be read at the bottom of the chart by projecting downward

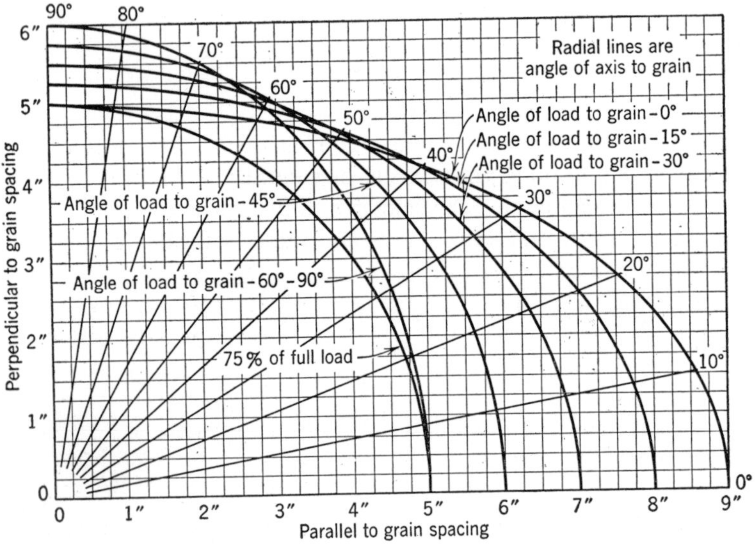

FIG. 16–7. Spacing chart for 4″ Teco split rings. (Reproduced by permission of the Timber Engineering Company.)

from the point on the curve. The perpendicular component of the spacing may be read at the left-hand side of the chart by projecting horizontally from the point on the curve.

As an example, consider 4-in. split-ring connectors in a joint that have a 30° angle of load to grain and a 20° angle of axis to grain. What should be their spacing [dimension R in Fig. 16–6 (*a*)] if the connectors are loaded to their full capacity?

In Fig. 16–7 find the point of intersection of the 30° angle of load to grain curve and the 20° angle of axis to grain radial line. Measure, with a pair of dividers or strip of paper, the *distance* from this point of intersection to point 0–0 at the lower left corner of this chart. Next, from point 0–0 lay off this distance on the bottom horizontal line of the chart. On this line there is a scale of inches (0 to 9″) and the distance measured is $6\frac{3}{4}$ in. This is R, the required spacing when the connectors are loaded to their full capacities. By projecting a vertical line from the point of intersection to the bottom horizontal line we find the parallel to grain spacing; in this instance it is $6\frac{3}{8}$ in. Similarly, by projecting from the point of intersection horizontally to the left side of the chart we find $2\frac{1}{4}$ in., the perpendicular to grain spacing. See Fig. 16–6 (*c*).

The sixth curve on the chart is a quarter-circle. This curve represents the spacing for 75% of full load for any angle of load to grain; it is also the minimum spacing permissible. For percentages between 75 and 100% of full load for an angle of load to grain, interpolate radially on a straight line between the 75% curve and the curve corresponding to the proper angle of load to grain.

In the preceding example we found that the connector spacing for the full load (100%) was $6\frac{3}{4}$ in. Suppose the connectors had been loaded to only 90% of their full capacity, now what would be the spacing?

When the connectors are not loaded to 100% of their full capacity, they may be placed closer together; the spacing may be a shorter distance. Remember that the spacing for 75% of the full load is 5 in. and that 5 in. is also the minimum spacing permitted. Thus if, in this instance, the spacing for 100% of the full load is $6\frac{3}{4}$ in. and 75% of the full load is 5 in., spacing for 90% of the full load will be 5 in. plus a fraction of $(6\frac{3}{4} - 5)$ or $1\frac{3}{4}$ in. Then, by interpolation,

$$5 + \left[\left(\frac{90 - 75}{100 - 75}\right) \times 1.75\right] = 5 + 1.05, \quad \text{say 6 in., the spacing}$$

Problem 16–10–A. The spacing for 4-in. split-ring connectors loaded to 100% of their full load is found to be 9 in. What is the minimum spacing permitted if the connectors are loaded to only 85% of their full capacity?

16–11. Edge Distance. The edge distance is the distance from the edge of the member to the center of the connector closest to the edge of the member measured perpendicular to the edge. The loaded edge distance is the edge distance measured from the edge

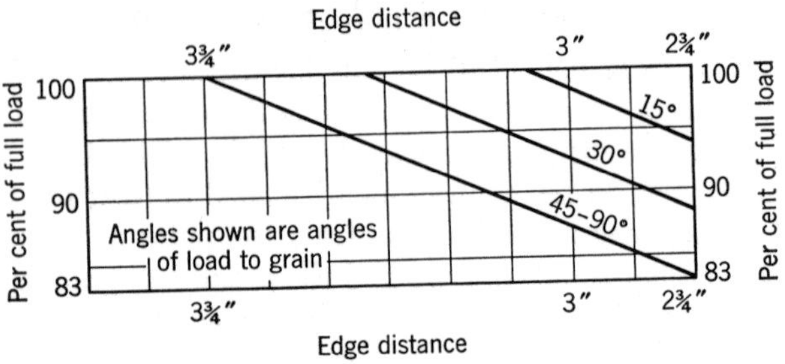

FIG. 16–8. Edge distance chart for 4-in. Teco split rings. (Reproduced by permission of the Timber Engineering Company.)

toward which the load induced by the connector acts. Figure 16–6 (*a*) shows typical measurements of edge distance, *B* being the unloaded edge distance and *C* the loaded edge distance. When bearings are axial on a member, both edges are unloaded or unstressed edges. The edge of a loaded member toward which a connector bears is the loaded edge; the loaded edge may need to be greater than the unloaded edge.

Figure 16–8 is an edge distance chart for 4-in. Teco split rings to be used in determining edge distances. For unloaded edge distance, the standard and minimum edge distance is the dimension at the right-hand edge of the chart. For loaded edge distance there is a variation according to angle of load to grain. After the proper curve for the desired angle of load to grain is selected, a given edge distance projected vertically to the curve and then horizontally to the side will give the percentage of full load allowable. The upper right-hand corner represents the standard and minimum loaded edge distance for 0° angle of load to grain. For intermediate angles, interpolate on a straight line.

16–12. End Distance. The end distance is the distance measured parallel to grain from the center of a connector to the square-cut end of the member. This is distance *A* in Fig. 16–6 (*b*). If the end of the member is not cut square, this figure shows the method of determining the distance from the center of the connector to the end cut on an angle. The distance $\frac{D}{2}$ in the figure is half the diameter of a connector.

Figure 16–9 is an end distance chart for 4-in. Teco split rings for use in determining end distances. The chart is divided into two parts, one for members in tension and one for members in compression. If the member is in tension, find the percentage of full load on the left and from this point project horizontally to the curve. From this intersection project a vertical line and read the end distance on the bottom of the chart.

If the member is in compression, the right-hand portion of the chart is used. The method of determining the proper end distance is similar to that described for tension members, with the exception that the appropriate angle of load to grain must be considered. For intermediate angles interpolate between the curves on a straight line.

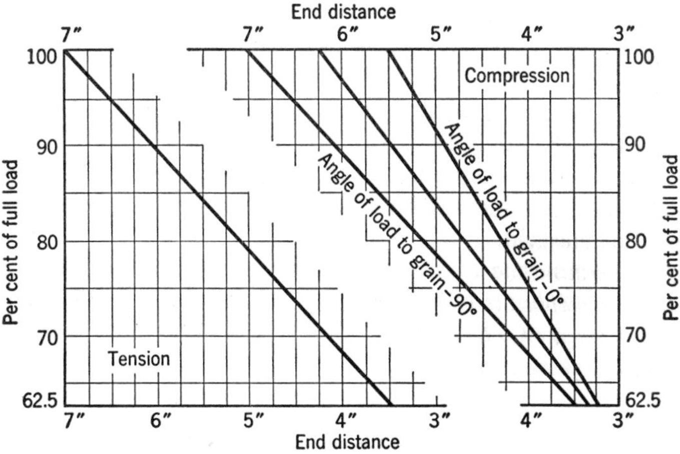

FIG. 16–9. End distance chart for 4-in. Teco split rings. (Reproduced by permission of the Timber Engineering Company.)

16–13. Net Sections. The critical or net section of a timber in a joint, which will generally pass through the center line of a bolt and connector, occurs at the plane of maximum stress. The net cross section at this plane is equal to the gross cross-sectional area of the timber minus the projected area of that portion of the connectors within the member and that portion of the bolt hole, not within the connector projected area, located at this plane.

The cross-sectional area of timbers may be found in Table 3–3, and the projected area of 4-in. split-ring connectors and bolts is given in Table 16–5.

TABLE 16–5. PROJECTED AREA OF SPLIT RING CONNECTORS AND BOLTS FOR USE IN DETERMINING NET SECTIONS

Connectors		Bolt Diameter	Placement of Connectors	Total Projected Area in Square Inches of Connectors and Bolts in Lumber Thickness of				
No.	Size			$1\frac{5}{8}''$	$2\frac{5}{8}''$	$3\frac{5}{8}''$	$5\frac{1}{2}''$	$7\frac{1}{2}''$
2	4″	$\frac{3}{4}''$	One Face	3.15	4.00	4.78	6.30	7.93
	4″	$\frac{3}{4}''$	Two Faces	4.99	5.80	6.61	8.14	9.76

Reproduced by permission of the Timber Engineering Company.

The net section is usually adequate to transmit the full strength of the timber. This is particularly true when the lower stress grades of timber are used. When high stress grades of timber of minimum-sized dimensions are used, the strength of the net section should be checked.

To determine the required net cross-sectional area at the critical section, multiply the total design load in pounds by the appropriate constant given in Table 16–6. The product will be the required net section in square inches.

16–14. Loaded Members. When two or more members are to be connected at a joint, it is first necessary to determine the connector load to be used. As has been explained, the allowable load for a connector depends on the angle at which the connector bears with respect to the direction of the grain of the piece on which it bears. The loaded member is the member on which the bearing of the connector is at an angle to the grain. As an example, consider Figs. 16–5 (*a*) and (*b*) in which two truss members are joined over a support. If the three forces in equilibrium are connected so that the vertical reaction is resisted by pieces A, the bearing of the connectors in piece B is horizontal; the connectors bear axially in piece B and at an angle θ in pieces A. The upper chord (pieces A)

is the loaded member. The angle of load to grain at which a connector bears determines the allowable working value of the connector. In most instances the member loaded at the greatest angle of load to grain is the controlling member.

Figure 16–12 represents a typical five-piece truss joint; the outer two members are the chord, the second and fourth are the diagonal, and the center piece is the vertical web member. In the connector computations the pieces are considered in adjacent pairs. When

TABLE 16–6. CONSTANTS FOR USE IN DETERMINING REQUIRED NET SECTIONS IN SQUARE INCHES

Type of Loading	Thickness of Wood Member in Inches	Constants for Each Connector Load Group		
		Group A	Group B	Group C
Normal	4″ or less	0.00043	0.00050	0.00061
	over 4″	0.00054	0.00063	0.00077
Permanent	4″ or less	0.00048	0.00055	0.00067
	over 4″	0.00059	0.00069	0.00083
Snow	4″ or less	0.00037	0.00044	0.00053
	over 4″	0.00047	0.00054	0.00067
Wind or earthquake	4″ or less	0.00032	0.00038	0.00045
	over 4″	0.00040	0.00047	0.00057

Reproduced by permission of the Timber Engineering Company.

the members are arranged as shown in the figure, the diagonal (the second and fourth pieces) is the loaded member.

16–15. Tension Joints. To illustrate how the number of connectors, their positions in a joint, and also the required cross section of the member are determined, consider the following examples of the design of tension joints.

Example. Let it be required to design a tension lap joint for a member in which the tensile normal loading is 12,000 lb. The connectors will be 4-in. split rings and the lumber will be the dense structural 58 grade of Southern pine. See Fig. 16–10.

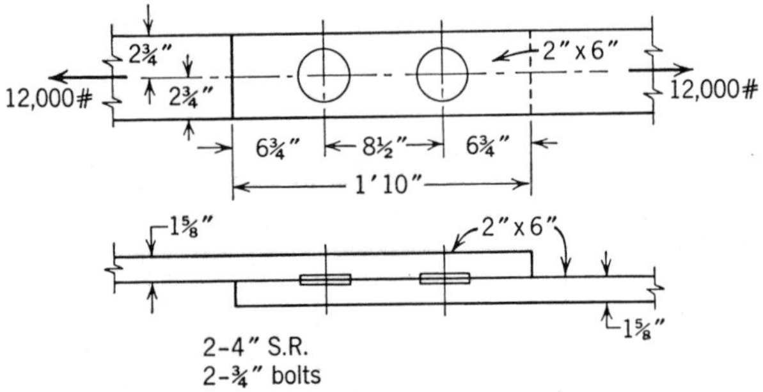

FIG. 16–10

SOLUTION. Table 3–1 shows that t, the allowable tensile unit stress, for this grade of Southern pine is 1600 psi, and in Table 16–2 we see that dense Southern pine is classified in the Group A species. Then 12,000 ÷ 1600 = 7.5 sq in., the required minimum area of one of the tensile members outside the joint. Since 4-in. split rings are to be used, the width of the member must be at least $5\frac{1}{2}$ in.; therefore we shall take a 2 x 6 in. member as a trial section. Its gross area is 1.625 × 5.625 or 9.14 sq in. (Table 3–3).

The projected area of a $\frac{3}{4}$-in. bolt and a 4-in. split ring in one face of a member that has a $1\frac{5}{8}$ in. thickness is 3.15 sq in. (Table 16–5). Then 9.14 − 3.15 = 5.99 sq in., the net area.

Referring to Table 16–6, we see that the constant to be used in determining the required net area is 0.00043. Then 12,000 × 0.00043 = 5.16 sq in., the required net area. Since the actual net area is 5.99 sq in., the 2 x 6 in. member is adequate to resist the tensile stress.

The angle of load to grain is 0°, and Fig. 16–3 gives 6140 lb as the allowable capacity for one 4-in. split ring. Then 12,000 ÷ 6140 = 1.95 and we will use two rings. Thus 1.95 ÷ 2 = 0.975; hence each connector will be loaded to $97\frac{1}{2}\%$ of its full load capacity.

In Fig. 16–7 we see that 9 in. is the connector spacing for 100%

of the full load and that 5 in. is the spacing for 75% of the full load. By interpolation we find that the spacing for $97\frac{1}{2}$% of the full load is $8\frac{1}{2}$ in.

The edge distance is found in Fig. 16–8 to be $2\frac{3}{4}$ in., and Table 16–9 gives the end distance to be $6\frac{3}{4}$ in.

Attention is called to the fact that the spacing, edge distance, and end distances computed above are *minimum* distances; they are shown in Fig. 16–10 and may be increased if it is found to be desirable.

Example. Design a splice joint, with side pieces, for a tensile member to support a normal loading of 30,000 lb. The connectors will be 4-in. split rings and the lumber will be the dense construction grade of Douglas fir.

SOLUTION. From Table 3–1, $t = 1750$ psi, and from Table 16–2 dense Douglas fir is classified in the Group A species.

The required cross-sectional area outside the joint will be $30{,}000 \div 1750$ or 17.15 sq in. For a trial main-member section we will take a 4 x 8 in. member that has a gross cross section of 27.19 sq in. (Table 3–3). For the side members take two 2 x 8 in. splice plates. Two 2 x 8 in. pieces have a gross area of $12.19 \times 2 = 24.38$ sq in.

The projected area of a $\frac{3}{4}$-in. bolt and a 4-in. split ring in two faces of a member with a thickness of $3\frac{5}{8}$ in. is 6.61 sq in. (Table 16–5). Therefore $27.19 - 6.61 = 20.58$ sq in., the net area.

Table 16–6 gives 0.00043 as the constant to be used in determining the required net section. Then $30{,}000 \times 0.00043 = 12.9$ sq in., the required net area. This does not exceed 20.58 sq in.; hence the 4 x 8 in. member is accepted. For the side members, $2 \times (12.19 - 3.15) = 18.08$ sq in., the two 2 x 8's are accepted since 18.08 exceeds 12.9.

The connectors have a bearing angle of zero degrees with the grain, and Fig. 16–3 shows that 6140 lb is the allowable load for one 4-in. split ring. Then $30{,}000 \div 6140 = 4.88$. We shall use six connectors on each side of the joint; $4.88 \div 6 = 0.813$, hence each connector is loaded to 81.3% of its full capacity.

To determine the spacing, we see in Fig. 16–7 that for 100% loading the spacing is 9 in. and for 75% loading it is 5 in. By interpolating, 81.3% loading requires a minimum spacing of 6.01 in., say 6 in.

Figure 16–8 shows the minimum edge distance to be $2\frac{3}{4}$ in., and Fig. 16–9 gives $5\frac{1}{4}$ in. for the minimum end distance. The splice joint is shown in Fig. 16–11.

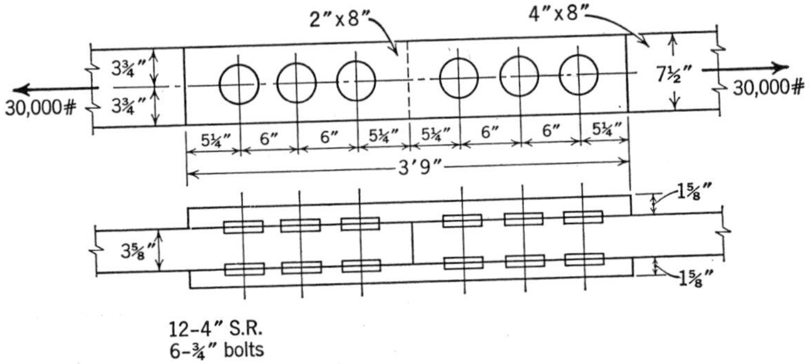

FIG. 16–11

Problem 16–15–A. Design a tension lap joint, as shown in Fig. 16–10, using 4-in. split rings to resist a normal loading of 17,000 lb. The lumber used will be Group B species for which $t = 1600$ psi.

Problem 16–15–B. Design a tension splice joint using 4-in. split rings and side plates as indicated in Fig. 16–11. The joint is subjected to normal loading and the magnitude of the tensile load is 20,000 lb. The lumber is the 1700 f grade of white oak.

Problem 16–15–C. The normal tensile load on a spliced joint is 27,000 lb. The joint consists of a main member and two side plates, as indicated in Fig. 16–11. Design the joint using 4-in. split rings and lumber of Group B species for which $t = 1600$ psi.

16–16. Truss Joints. In the design of a truss joint, using connectors, more than one solution may meet the requirements. In the first of the following examples the chord pieces are placed on the outside, and adjacent to them are the two pieces that constitute the diagonal, as indicated in Fig. 16–12. The center member is the vertical web member. Another arrangement consists in placing the diagonal pieces on the outside, the chord pieces next, and the vertical member in the center. The two arrangements would result in two different solutions. In the arrangement of the pieces shown in Fig. 16–12 the diagonal is the loaded member.

The usual method of design is to assume first the timber thickness and then to determine the number of connectors required, their spacing and edge and end distances. These placement dimensions may determine the widths of the various members. In a truss the members are in compression or tension, and the size of the members must conform to the requirements for these two stresses as well as to the requirements demanded by connector placement

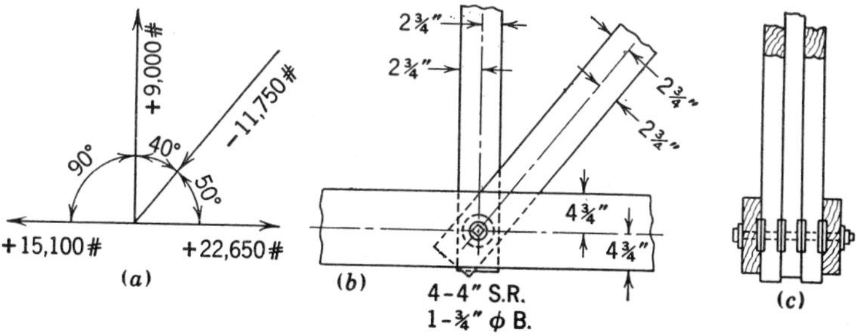

FIG. 16–12

dimensions. The design of tension members is explained in the two examples in Art. 16–15, and members in compression are discussed in Chapter 13. In the two illustrative examples that follow only the connectors and their placement dimensions are determined.

Example. Compute the number of 4-in. split-ring connectors and their placement dimensions for a lower-chord truss joint to resist the loads indicated in Fig. 16–12 (*a*). The vertical web member has a tensile load of 9000 lb, the diagonal web member a compressive load of 11,750 lb, and the chord member tensile loads of 15,100 and 22,650 lb, as shown. The diagonal member has angles of 40 and 50° with the vertical and horizontal members, respectively. Group A species lumber is used, and the loading is normal.

SOLUTION. First we shall consider the connectors between the vertical and diagonal pieces, the vertical being the center piece between the diagonal pieces. See Figs. 16–12 (*b*) and (*c*). The vertical is the loading member, and the diagonal is the loaded member, the angle between them being 40°. Since the vertical is the loading member, the joint load is 9000 lb, and the connectors bear on the diagonal (the loaded member) at an angle of 40° with the grain. We shall assume the thickness of the pieces to be 3 in., actually $2\frac{5}{8}$ in. Therefore, on referring to Fig. 16–3, we find that the working value of one 4-in. split ring in two faces of $2\frac{5}{8}$-in. material bearing at an angle of 40° to the grain is 5120 lb. Then $\frac{9000}{5120} = 1.76$, the theoretical number of connectors required. We shall use two connectors. It is seen that each connector will not be stressed to its full allowable load, and $\frac{1.76}{2} = 88\%$, the percentage of full load carried by each connector.

These two connectors are placed on opposite sides of the vertical member, requiring but one bolt; there is no spacing dimension.

On referring to Fig. 16–8, we find that the minimum edge distance is $2\frac{3}{4}$ in. for both the loaded and unloaded edges.

Figure 16–9 is the end-distance chart. For the vertical, which is the loading member in tension, the chart shows that the end distance for 88% of full load is 6 in. For the diagonal, the loaded member in compression, the end distance is shown on the chart to be $5\frac{1}{4}$ in.

Next let us consider the connectors between the chord pieces and the diagonal pieces. The chord is a through member with a load of 22,650 lb on one side and 15,100 lb on the other; 22,650 − 15,100 = 7550 lb, the tensile load to be transferred by the connectors. For these connectors the chord is the loading member and the diagonal is the loaded member. Thus the joint load is 7550 lb, and the angle of load to grain is 50°. Figure 16–3 shows the working value of one connector to be 4800 lb; $\frac{7550}{4800} = 1.57$, the theoretical number of connectors required. We shall use two connectors; $\frac{1.57}{2} = 78\frac{1}{2}\%$, the percentage of full load carried by each connector. These two connectors are axial with the connectors between the vertical and the diagonal and are held in position by the same bolt; hence there is no spacing dimension.

From Fig. 16–8, the minimum edge distance for both the loaded and unloaded edges is $2\frac{3}{4}$ in.

On referring to Fig. 16–9, the end distance for the loaded member, which is in compression, is $4\frac{1}{2}$ in. The loading member is a through member; hence there is no end dimension.

The 4-in. connector is now drawn at the intersection of the axial lines of the members. The end and edge dimensions computed above are now laid off with respect to the axial lines and connector; thus the minimum dimensions of the members are established. The members must, of course, have dimensions large enough to resist the tensile and compression loads on the members. The placement dimensions computed above are minimum and may be increased if required by the over-all sizes of the members.

Example. Compute the number of 4-in. split-ring connectors and placement dimensions for a truss joint in which the loads in the members are those given in Fig. 16–13 (*a*). The chord pieces

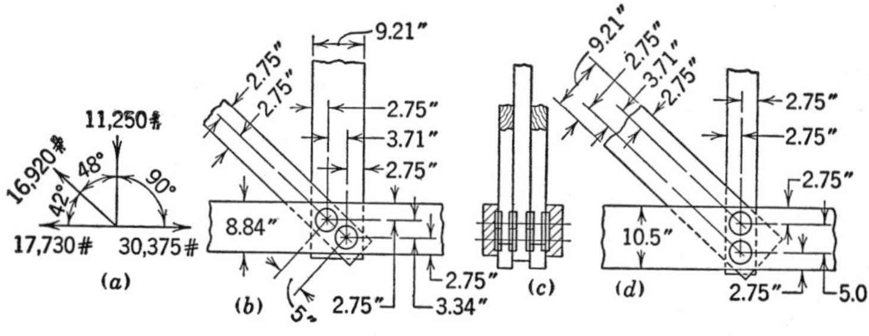

FIG. 16–13

are placed outside, the vertical member in the center, and the diagonal pieces are placed between the vertical and the chord pieces. The diagonal has angles of 42 and 48° with the horizontal and vertical members, respectively. The loading is normal, and the lumber is of a Group A species.

SOLUTION. Let us first consider the connectors between the chord and the diagonal, the chord being the loading member and the diagonal the loaded member. The angle of load to grain is 42°.

Note that the chord is a through member, the stress on one side being 30,375 lb and 17,730 lb on the other. The difference, 30,375 − 17,730 or 12,645 lb, is the load transferred from the chord to the diagonal at a 42° angle of load to grain. To begin, let us assume that all the pieces have a 3-in. thickness—actually $2\frac{5}{8}$ in.

From Fig. 16–3 we find that the allowable load for one 4-in. split-ring connector is 5050 lb. Then 12,645 ÷ 5050 = 2.5, the theoretical number of connectors required. We shall use four 4-in. split rings; hence 2.5 ÷ 4 = $62\frac{1}{2}$%, the percentage of full load carried by each split ring.

Referring to Fig. 16–7, the spacing chart, we see that 5 in. is the minimum required spacing in the diagonal parallel to the grain. Note that the angle of axis to grain is 0° and the angle of load to grain is 42°.

The connector capacity in the diagonal is less than the connector capacity in the chord because the load in the diagonal is at an angle to the grain. For this reason, the required spacing in the diagonal is greater than that in the chord. The minimum 5-in. spacing is accepted.

Figure 16–8 shows the minimum edge distance to be $2\frac{3}{4}$ in., and the end distance in the diagonal, the tension member, is found in Fig. 16–9 to be $3\frac{1}{2}$ in.

Now consider the connectors between the vertical member and the diagonal. The vertical is the loading member, the load is 11,250 lb, and the angle of load to grain is 48°. The diagonal is the loaded member.

The allowable connector load for one 4-in. split ring at 48° in two faces of $2\frac{5}{8}$-in. material in the diagonal is 4850 lb. Thus 11,250 ÷ 4850 = 2.32, the theoretical number of connectors required. We shall use four 4-in. split rings. Hence 2.32 ÷ 4 = 58%, the percentage of full load carried by each connector. Figure 16–7 shows that 75% of full load requires a 5-in. spacing, and this is the minimum spacing permitted. Note that this is the same spacing used for the connectors between the chord and diagonal pieces. This 5-in. dimension will determine the widths of the members.

The edge distance in both the diagonal and the chord is $2\frac{3}{4}$ in. for both edges. The end distance for the diagonal member is $3\frac{1}{2}$ in.

The axis lines of the members are now drawn, and the two 4-in. connectors are laid off on the diagonal with a 5-in. spacing. Note that this is the spacing dimension required for both chord-to-diagonal and vertical-to-diagonal computations. If these spacings had been unequal, the greater dimension would have been accepted. Next we lay off the edge and end distances, as computed above, and thus determine the minimum widths of the members to meet the connector requirements.

When more than one bolt and their accompanying connectors are used at a truss joint, the designer has a choice of arrangements. In this particular problem one arrangement places the connectors on the axis of the diagonal member, as shown in Fig. 16–13 (*b*).

To find the vertical and horizontal distances between the two connectors with a 5-in. spacing, the connectors being on a line that makes a 42° angle with the horizontal, we can use trigonometry or we can find the distances graphically, as shown in Fig. 16–14. First, draw a horizontal line and from any point, *B*, draw a line (with the aid of a protractor) to make an angle of 42° with the horizontal. From point *B* measure a distance of 5 in. and call this point *A*. This is the spacing dimension of the connectors. From *A* draw a vertical line; call *C* the point at which it intersects the horizontal line. Then *AC* and *BC* are the vertical and horizontal projections of *AB*, which is 5 in. By scaling these distances, $AC = 3.34$ in. and $BC = 3.71$ in.

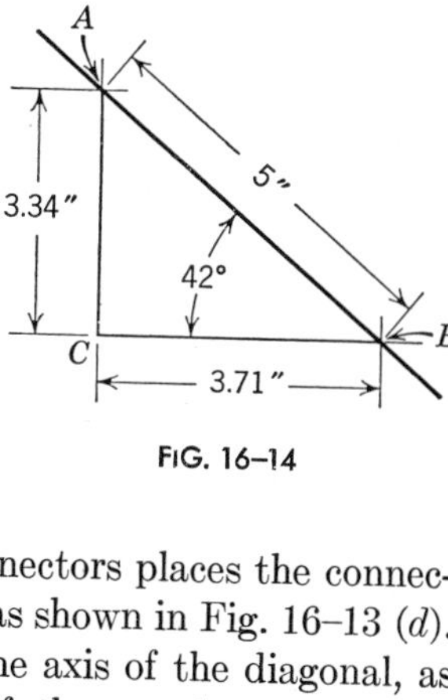

FIG. 16–14

The alternate arrangement of the connectors places the connectors on the axis of the vertical member, as shown in Fig. 16–13 (*d*).

When the connectors are placed on the axis of the diagonal, as shown in Fig. 16–13 (*b*), the widths of the members are computed thus:

Width of diagonal $= 2.75 + 2.75 = 5.5$ in. use $5\frac{1}{2}$ in.

Width of vertical $= 2.75 + 3.71 + 2.75 = 9.21$ in. use $9\frac{1}{2}$ in.

Width of chord $= 2.75 + 3.34 + 2.75 = 8.84$ in. use $9\frac{1}{2}$ in.

If the connectors are placed on the axis of the vertical member, the minimum dimensions are as shown in Fig. 16–13 (*d*).

Width of diagonal $= 2.75 + 3.71 + 2.75 = 9.21$ in. use $9\frac{1}{2}$ in.

Width of vertical $= 2.75 + 2.75 = 5.5$ in. use $5\frac{1}{2}$ in.

Width of chord $= 2.75 + 5 + 2.75 = 10.5$ in. use $11\frac{1}{2}$ in.

The minimum dimensions of the members having been determined in accordance with connector requirements, the various members are investigated to see that they are large enough to resist tensile and compressive stresses. Members resisting compressive stresses are, of course, designed as columns.

CHAPTER 17

STRESSES IN TRUSSES

17–1. Timber Trusses. The use of timber connectors enables the designer to design timber trusses that far surpass in efficiency the timber truss in which notches, bolts, and rods are employed for making connections at the joints. Formerly, the cross-sectional areas of the members, in order to provide joints strong enough to resist the loads, had to be much larger than required by the stresses within them. Whereas the individual members were long and had large cross sections, the metal connector permits the use of short lengths of much smaller cross sections. Timber trusses in the past frequently employed metal rods for certain tension members. Today we can build timber trusses in which all the members are of wood, the joints and splices being made by connectors and their accompanying bolts. Furthermore, connectors now enable us to construct all types of trusses, some of which could have been constructed only by employing steel members.

17–2. Truss Loads. The type of truss to be used having been determined, the first step is to compute the loads the truss will be required to support. The dead load consists of the roofing materials, planking, rafters, purlins, suspended loads, and the weight of the truss. Weights of roofing materials are given in Table 17–1, and Table 17–2 gives approximate weights of timber trusses. The live loads are snow and wind loads; the designer is generally required to use the live loads given in his local building code. If there are no code requirements, Tables 17–3 and 17–4 may be used to determine the live loads.

Because of the many factors to be considered, the design of a truss with timber connectors requires the attention of an experienced designer. Space, here, does not permit an example that would include the design of the tension and compression mem-

TABLE 17–1. WEIGHTS OF ROOFING MATERIALS

Roofing Material	Weight, in Pounds per Square Foot
Shingles	
Wood	3.0
Asbestos	5.0– 6.0
Asphalt, slate-covered	2.0
Slate	
3/16″ thick	7.0
1/4″ thick	10.0
3/8″ thick	12.0–14.0
Tile, clay	
Flat	12.0–16.0
Spanish	10.0–14.0
Built-up roofing	
4-ply felt	4.0– 5.0
5-ply felt	6.0– 8.0
Corrugated iron	
20-gage	2.0
18-gage	3.0
Tin plate	1.0
Copper, sheets	1.0
Lead, sheets	7.0
Sheathing, wood	
Spruce and hemlock, 1″ thick	3.0
Yellow pine, 1″ thick	4.0
Nailing concrete, per inch of thickness	8.0
Concrete slab, cinder, per inch of thickness	9.0
Gypsum slab, per inch of thickness	8.0
Plaster ceiling	10.0

TABLE 17–2. APPROXIMATE WEIGHTS OF TIMBER TRUSSES, IN POUNDS PER SQUARE FOOT OF ROOF SURFACE

Span, in Feet	1/2 Pitch	1/3 Pitch	1/4 Pitch	Flat
Up to 36	3	3 1/2	3 3/4	4
36 to 50	3 1/4	3 3/4	4	4 1/2
50 to 60	3 1/2	4	4 1/2	4 3/4
60 to 70	3 3/4	4 1/2	4 3/4	5 1/4
70 to 80	4 1/4	5	5 1/2	6

TABLE 17–3. SNOW LOADS FOR ROOF TRUSSES, IN POUNDS PER SQUARE FOOT OF ROOF SURFACE

Locality	Slope of Roof				
	45°	30°	25°	20°	Flat
Northwestern and New England States	10–15	15–20	25–30	35	40
Western and Central States	5–10	10–15	20–25	25–30	35
Southern and Pacific States	0– 5	5–10	5–10	5–10	10

TABLE 17–4. WIND PRESSURE ON ROOF SURFACES

Pitch of Roof, in Degrees	Normal Pressure, in Pounds per Square Foot
10	10
15	15
20	18
25	22
30	24
35	26
40	27
45	28
50	29
55	29
60	30
For pitches over 60° use 30#	

bers as well as the detailed connector placement dimensions of the joints. The following discussion illustrates the method of determining the stresses in truss members.

Example. Determine the stresses in the members of a timber parallel-chord Pratt truss for a span of 33 ft 0 in.; the truss spacing is 12 ft 0 in. on centers, and the live load (snow load) is 30 psf. The roof construction consists of 4-ply built-up roofing laid on planking. The planking is supported by purlins extending from truss to truss at the panel points. See Fig. 17–1. The lumber is to be the dense

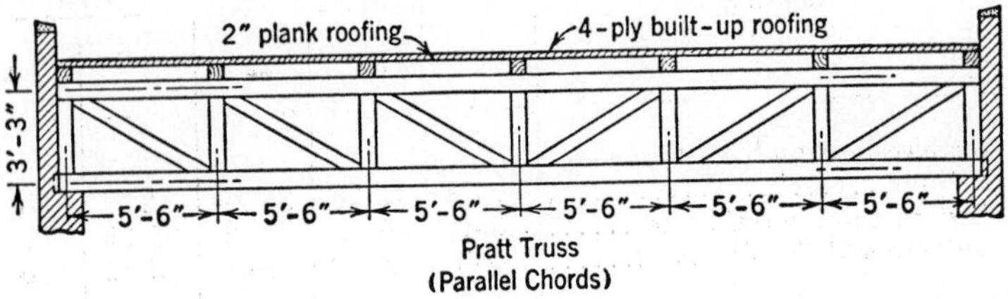

FIG. 17–1

construction grade of Douglas fir, a Group A species for which

t = 1750 psi, the allowable tensile stress
c = 1200 psi, the allowable compressive stress parallel to the grain
E = 1,760,000 psi, the modulus of elasticity (Table 3–1)

SOLUTION. Referring to Table 12–2, we see that 2-in. planking is adequate for the span of 5 ft 6 in. For the purpose of computing the dead load on the truss we shall assume the purlins to be 3 x 12 in.

Dead Load

Built-up roofing	5.0	(Table 17–1)
2-in. planking	5.4	(Table 12–1)
Weight of truss	4.0	(Table 17–2)
Total	14.4 psf, not including the weight of the purlins	

Live Load

Snow load 30.0 psf

Dead load + live load = 14.4 + 30.0 = 44.4 psf.
Since each panel point of the truss supports a roof area of

12×5.5 or 66 sq ft, $66 \times 44.4 = 2930.4$ lb, the panel loads exclusive of the weight of the purlins.

The weight of a 3 x 12 in. is 8.8 lb per lin ft; hence the purlin weight at each panel point is 8.8×12 or 105.6 lb.

Then $2930.4 + 105.6 = 3036$ lb, say 3040 lb, the sum of the live and dead loads at each panel point of the truss, excepting the end loads, which are each $\frac{1}{2} \times 3040$ or 1520 lb.

Now let us determine the size of the purlins, using a timber for which $f = 1200$ psi. The panel point load, 3040 lb, includes the weight of the truss, which, of course, is not a load on the purlin. The estimated weight of the truss at each panel point is 66×4 or 264 lb. Then $3040 - 264 = 2776$ lb, the uniformly distributed load on each purlin, the span of which is 12 ft 0 in.

$$M = \frac{Wl}{8} = \frac{2776 \times 12 \times 12}{8} = 49{,}968 \text{ in-lb}$$

(Case II, Fig. 5–17)

$$S = \frac{M}{f} = \frac{49{,}968}{1200} = 41.6 \text{ in.}^3, \text{ the required section modulus}$$

Table 3–3 shows the section modulus of a 3 x 12 in. to be 57.86 in.^{3}, and therefore it is acceptable.

Further computations show that a 3 x 12 in. is also acceptable for shear and deflection.

It should be noted that there are no wind loads on this truss because the roof surface is flat. For triangular and curved trusses the dead, live, and wind loads must all be given consideration. In designing the various truss members the two combinations of loads to consider are

(*a*) dead load plus live load;
(*b*) dead load plus live load plus wind load.

Reference to Art. 16–5 shows that working stresses may be increased for loads that are not of permanent duration; the percentages of increase are given in Table 16–3. In this particular instance the live load, or snow load, is more than twice the magnitude of the dead load; hence the design is based on a 15% increase in the allowable unit stresses. This combination of loads with the permitted increased design stress will require larger members than the dead load alone (permanent loading) when no increase in design stress is allowed. For trusses subjected to wind loads the two combinations noted above are tested, and the combination requiring the larger section or the greater number of connectors is accepted. For this example a 15% increased stress is taken; thus

$$t = 1750 \times 1.15 = 2010 \text{ psi}$$

$$c = 1200 \times 1.15 = 1380 \text{ psi}$$

$$E = 1{,}760{,}000 \text{ psi} \quad \text{(no increase)}$$

17–3. Determining the Stresses in Truss Members. Probably the most convenient method of determining the magnitude and character of stresses in the members of a truss is to construct a stress

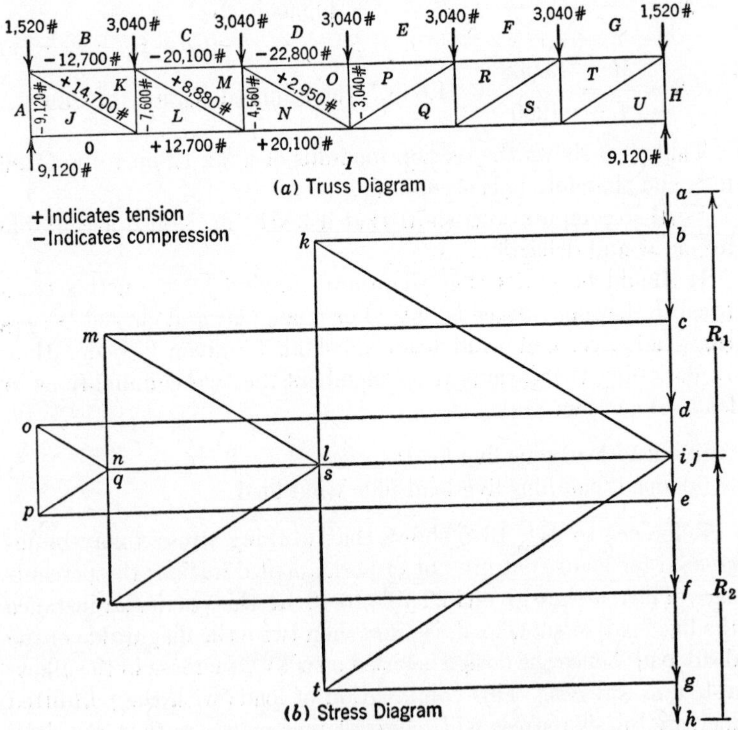

FIG. 17–2

diagram.* This graphic analysis requires a system of lettering, such as is shown in Fig. 17–2 (*a*), by the aid of which the stress diagram is drawn. See Fig. 17–2 (*b*). The lengths of the lines in the stress diagram represent the magnitudes of the stresses in the members; hence they are scaled and tabulated. See Table 17–5. We note that the upper chord and verticals are in compression and that the lower chord and diagonal web members are in tension. There are no stresses in the lower-chord members adjacent to the supports.

TABLE 17–5. STRESSES IN TRUSS MEMBERS

Member	Character of Stress	Magnitude of Stress, in Pounds
BK	Compression	12,700
CM	Compression	20,100
DO	Compression	22,800
AJ	Compression	9,120
KL	Compression	7,600
MN	Compression	4,560
OP	Compression	3,040
JK	Tension	14,700
LM	Tension	8,880
NO	Tension	2,950
LI	Tension	12,700
NI	Tension	20,100
JI	No stress	No stress

In Fig. 17–2 (*a*) the members with the minus sign, before the magnitude of stress, are members in compression. The members with plus signs are in tension.

17–4. Design of Truss Members. The stresses to be used in the design of the various members of a truss are given in Table 17–5. Note that some members are in compression and that others are in tension. In member *JI* there is no stress. The members in compression are designed as columns, as explained in Chapter 13.

* For a review of the construction of a stress diagram see Chapter 8 of *Simplified Design of Roof Trusses for Architects and Builders*, Second Edition, by Harry Parker, John Wiley and Sons, New York, 1953.

Remember that in designing compression members their length is an important factor, whereas the length of members in tension has no significance. When timber connectors are to be used, the members often consist of two or more individual pieces, and consequently such compression members are designed as spaced columns, as explained in Art. 13–10. Members resisting tensile stresses are discussed in Art. 16–15.

When truss members meet at a joint, it is important to know the angle between them. These angles may be determined by trigonometry or by graphical construction with the aid of a protractor. For example, the diagonal member KJ in Fig. 17–2 (a) makes an angle of approximately 31° with the upper chord BK and 59° with the vertical member JA.

In the example given in Art. 17–2 the loading includes snow. Bear this in mind in determining the allowable connector loads. As an example, let us suppose that the angle between two members at a joint is 59° and that the connectors are placed in two faces of Group A species $2\frac{5}{8}$-in. material. What is the allowable connector load? In the load chart (Fig. 16–3) we see that the load for one 4-in. connector is 4580 lb. However, in Table 16–3 we find that the allowable load may be increased 15% for snow loading. Thus $4580 \times 1.15 = 5260$ lb, the allowable connector load.

Because of the length of the truss shown in Fig. 17–1, it would be necessary to have splices in both the upper and lower chords.

CHAPTER 18

TRUSSED RAFTERS AND FRAMING ANCHORS

18–1. Split-Ring Trussed Rafters. The use of split-ring connectors permits a trussed-rafter type of roof construction that is frequently used in residential and similar types of light framing construction. A trussed rafter is a wood truss in which the material is commonly 2 x 4's and 2 x 6's, with a truss spacing not exceeding 24 in. The joints in these lightweight trusses are made with $2\frac{1}{2}$-in. split rings and their accompanying $\frac{1}{2}$-in. bolts, as indicated in Fig. 18–1.

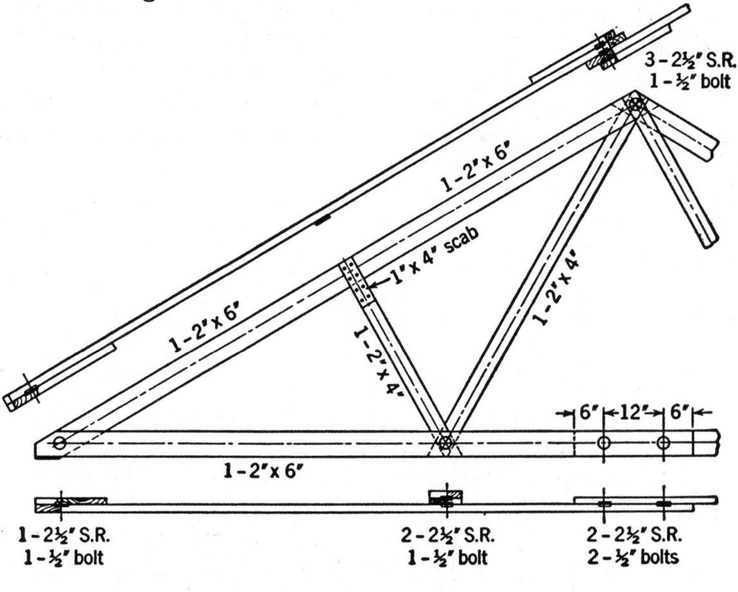

FIG. 18–1

Trussed rafters provide clear spans from wall to wall and *eliminate the need for interior load-bearing partitions.* The trusses are shop assembled. For housing and small industrial buildings the use of trussed rafters can result in a saving of labor and material when compared with the conventional type of roof and ceiling framing.

18–2. Teco Plate Trussed Rafters. A more recent method of constructing a trussed rafter employs Teco truss plates, shown in Fig. 18–2 (*a*). They are rectangular prepunched plates, manufac-

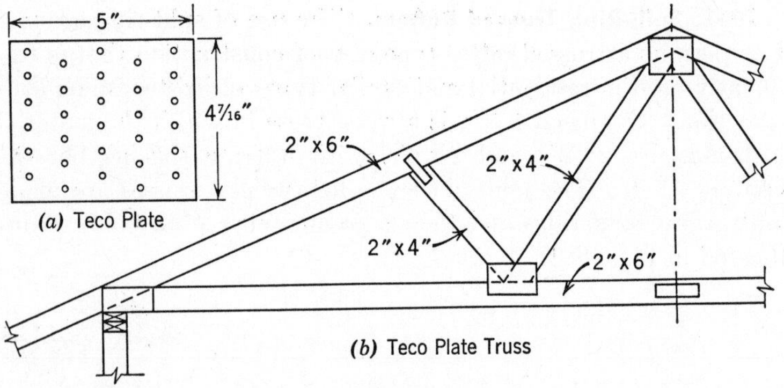

FIG. 18–2

tured from 20 gage, galvanized sheet steel, placed on both sides over the intersecting wood members at the joints and secured with 8d, $1\frac{1}{2}$-in. nails. See Fig. 18–2 (*b*). These truss plates are used in single-plane trussed rafters and, like the split rings, afford an economical and efficient clear span framing system with no need of load-bearing partitions. The truss spacing should not exceed 24 in., center to center.

Typical designs for truss-plate trusses range from 16 to 32 ft with slopes of $2\frac{1}{2}$ in 12 to 7 in 12. For spans in excess of 32 ft and slopes greater than 7 in 12 in., it is recommended that a split-ring truss be used.

Designs for trussed rafters employing both split rings and truss plates are furnished by TECO, the Timber Engineering Company. In any truss accurate fabrication and assembly is important.

Trusses should be shop assembled in jigs so that wood members will have full bearings, particularly at the peak and heel joints. Truss plates should be placed exactly as indicated on the design drawings, and plates on opposite sides of a joint should be offset $\frac{1}{4}$ in. with respect to each other. Design drawings for trusses of various spans and slopes show the exact camber to be introduced into bottom chord panel points. Care should be taken to provide this camber during fabrication.

18–3. Framing Anchors. Framing anchors are widely used where simple joints that are stronger than those provided by nails alone are needed. They are used in light frame construction and are ideally suited for fastening rafters, joists, studs, or headers. Teco Trip-L-Grip anchors are manufactured from 18 gage, zinc-coated, corrosion-resistant sheet steel. They are made in three basic types, *A*, *B*, and *C*, with right- and left-hand bends for the usual joints with dimension lumber 2 to 4 in. in thickness. See Fig. 18–3.

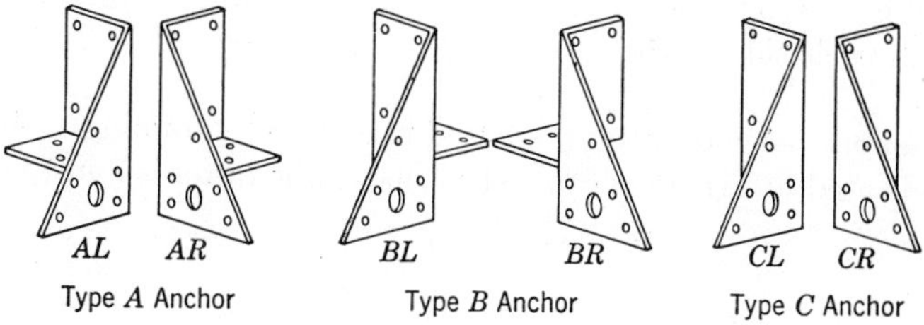

FIG. 18–3

Each anchor is $4\frac{7}{8}$ in. high; the rectangular flange is $1\frac{5}{8}$ in. wide; the triangular flange is $2\frac{3}{8}$ in. wide, and the bent portions on the *A* and *B* types are $1\frac{5}{8}$ in. long. Special nails, approximately equal in strength to 8d common nails, are furnished with the anchors. The nails fit snugly in the holes punched in the framing anchors. One of the advantages of using the framing anchors is that the nails are always loaded laterally, the most efficient direction with respect to strength.

Tests of load capacities of framing anchors have been made and allowable working loads for different directions and duration of loading, based on these tests, are tabulated in Fig. 18–4.

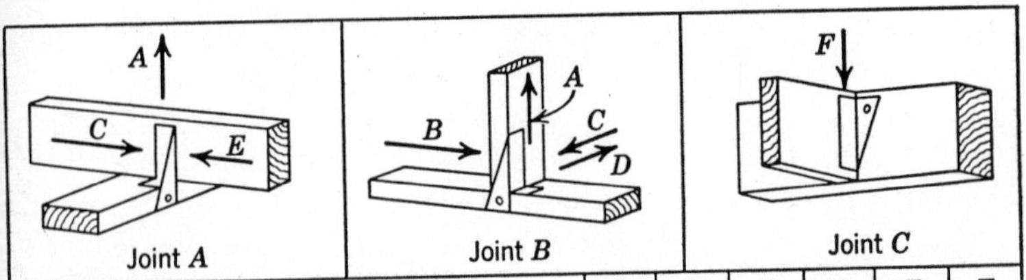

Direction of load (joints A–B–C)	A	B	C	D	E	F
Short term loading—wind or earthquake	450	825	420	300	450	675
Long term loading—live loads and dead loads	300	530	290	200	300	450

FIG. 18–4

Example. The total live and dead load on a floor joist is 1600 lb. The joist is secured to a header by Type C framing anchors. See Fig. 18–4, Joint C. How many anchors are required?

SOLUTION. The total load on one joist is 1600 lb; therefore the load transferred to the header is 1600 ÷ 2 or 800 lb. In Fig. 18–4 we see that the allowable live and dead load for one Type C anchor is 450 lb. Hence 800 ÷ 450 = 1.77, and we will use two anchors, one on each side of the joist.

Example. A roof rafter is secured to a plate by framing anchors as indicated in Fig. 18–5 (a). The slope of the rafter is 8 in 12 and

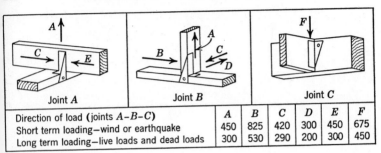

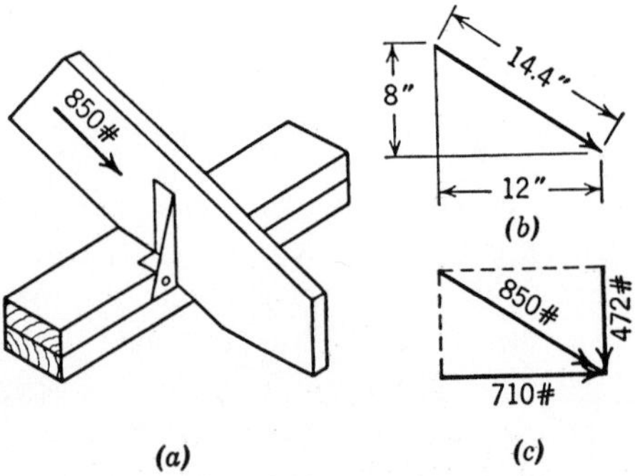

FIG. 18–5

the magnitude of the thrust is 850 lb. This load is "short-term loading." How many anchors are required?

SOLUTION. For a right triangle with a base of 12 units and a height of 8, the hypotenuse is the square root of $(8^2 + 12^2)$. Thus $8^2 + 12^2 = 208$ and $\sqrt{208} = 14.4$. See Fig. 18–5 (*b*). We will assume that the vertical component of the 850 lb thrust is resisted by the plate and that the framing anchors resist the horizontal component. Referring to Fig. 18–5 (*b*), let V be the vertical component of the 850-lb thrust. Then $\frac{8}{14.4} = \frac{V}{850}$ and $V = 472$ lb. Similarly, H, the horizontal component, is found by the equation $\frac{12}{14.4} = \frac{H}{850}$ and $H = 710$ lb. See Fig. 18–5 (*c*). Minute accuracy is unnecessary in computing these two components, and, if preferred, a triangle with a slope of 8 in 12 may be drawn with a hypotenuse with a length of 850 lb drawn at some convenient scale. The two components of the thrust are found by scaling the lengths of V and H.

The anchor shown in Fig. 18–5 (*a*) is Type A, and Fig. 18–4 shows the allowable horizontal load C to be 420 lb. Then $710 \div 420 = 1.69$. Thus, we shall use two anchors, one on each side of the rafter.

Note that the anchors might have been placed on the inside of the stud wall instead of the outside, as shown in Fig. 18–5 (*a*). In this case the allowable load on one anchor is found in Fig. 18–4 to be E, 450 lb.

CHAPTER 19

TRUSSED BEAMS

19–1. Trussed Beams. Because structural steel beams are readily obtainable in most sections of the country, trussed timber beams are used infrequently. The four usual types of trussed beams are shown in Fig. 19–1. For the types illustrated in Figs.

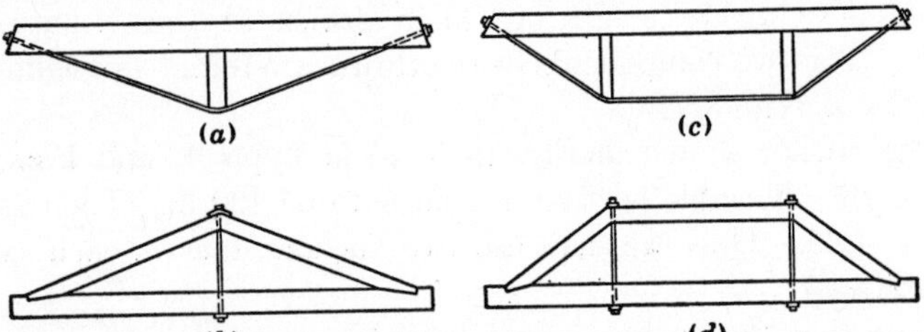

FIG. 19–1

19–1 (*a*) and (*c*) the tension members below the beam are steel or wrought-iron rods. The struts, the vertical members, are usually of timber. For the types shown in Figs. 19–1 (*b*) and (*d*), in which the members are above the beam, the vertical members are in tension and rods are employed. In reality such structural elements may be designed as trusses, but the beams, the horizontal members, should always be in one continuous length for the entire span. When the loads and over-all dimensions of the trussed beams have been determined, the stresses in the component parts may be found by graphical methods or by the formulas given in handbooks on structural design.

19–2. Design of a Trussed Beam. The following example is given to illustrate the application of the design principles discussed previously. Whereas examples of trussed beams are frequently found in existing buildings, their use in modern construction has been supplanted by structural steel.

Example. Design a trussed beam with the over-all dimensions shown in Fig. 19–2. The span of the beam is 20 ft 0 in., the total

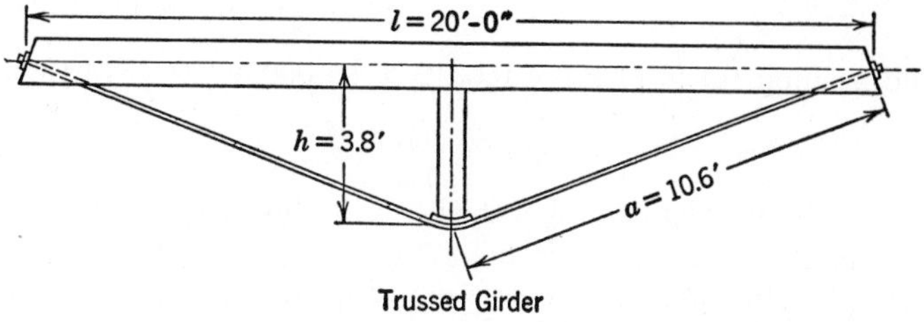

FIG. 19–2

uniformly distributed load W is 21,000 lb, the wood is Southern pine dense structural 58 grade, and the allowable working stresses are

allowable extreme fiber stress	= 1600 psi
allowable compressive stress parallel to grain	= 1300 psi
allowable compressive stress perpendicular to grain	= 455 psi
modulus of elasticity of timber	= 1,760,000 psi
allowable tensile stress of steel	= 20,000 psi

SOLUTION. When the dimensions l, h, and a, as shown in Fig. 19–2, are in feet, the stresses in the members of this trussed beam are

tension in tie rod $= 0.312 \dfrac{Wa}{h}$ lb

compression in strut $= 0.625W$ pounds lb

compression in beam $= 0.156 \dfrac{Wl}{h}$ lb

bending moment in beam $= 0.0312Wl$ ft-lb

Thus

$$\text{tension in tie rod} = \frac{0.312 \times 21{,}000 \times 10.6}{3.8} = 18{,}300 \text{ lb}$$

$$\text{compression in strut} = 0.625 \times 21{,}000 = 13{,}125 \text{ lb}$$

$$\text{compression in beam} = \frac{0.156 \times 21{,}000 \times 20}{3.8} = 17{,}300 \text{ lb}$$

$$\text{bending moment in beam} = 0.0312 \times 21{,}000 \times 20 = 13{,}100 \text{ ft-lb}$$

$$= 157{,}200 \text{ in-lb}$$

To begin, first let us design the beam. This member is subjected to an axial compressive stress of 17,300 lb and also to a distributed load producing a bending moment of 157,200 in-lb. The design of a member thus loaded is discussed in Art. 14–1. We shall assume that the beam is an 8 x 12 in. with the long axis vertical and test it to see that the quantity $\left(\frac{P/A}{c} + \frac{M/S}{f}\right)$ does not exceed 1.

The actual dimensions of an 8 x 12 in. are $7\frac{1}{2}$ x $11\frac{1}{2}$ in., the cross-sectional-area is 86.25 sq in., and the section modulus S is 165.31 in.^{3} (Table 3–3).

We begin by computing the value of $\frac{P/A}{c}$. Assuming that the beam is not braced laterally, its length is 20 ft and $\frac{l}{d} = \frac{20 \times 12}{7.5}$ or 32. Substituting in the column formula given in Art. 13–3,

$$\frac{P}{A} = \frac{0.3 \times E}{(l/d)^2} = \frac{0.3 \times 1{,}760{,}000}{32 \times 32} = 515 \text{ psi}$$

This is the magnitude of c, the allowable compressive unit stress that would be permitted in a column if only axial stress existed. Thus $\frac{P/A}{c} = \frac{17{,}300/86.25}{515} = 0.389$.

$M = 157{,}200$ in-lb, $S = 165.31$ in.^{3} and $f = 1600$ psi. Substituting in the quantity $\frac{M/S}{f}$, $\frac{157{,}200/165.31}{1600} = 0.594$.

Then $\frac{P/A}{c} + \frac{M/S}{f} = 0.389 + 0.594 = 0.983$. Since this quantity does not exceed 1, the 8 x 12 in. beam is accepted.

The tensile stress in the tie rod is 18,300 lb, and, since the allowable tensile stress of the steel rod is 20,000 psi, 18,300 ÷ 20,000 = 0.915 sq in., the minimum cross-sectional area of the rod. Referring to Table 19–1, we see that a $1\frac{3}{8}$-in. rod has a net area at the root of the thread of 1.057 sq in. and is acceptable. The proper rod diameter might have been selected directly from the table, for we see that a $1\frac{3}{8}$-in. rod has an allowable tensile load of 21,140 lb and the actual stress in the rod is only 18,300 lb.

TABLE 19–1. SAFE LOADS FOR STEEL RODS

(BASED ON AN ALLOWABLE TENSILE STRESS OF 20,000 PSI)

Diameter, in Inches	Net Area at Base of Thread, in Square Inches		Safe Load, in Pounds	
	Not upset	Upset	Not upset	Upset
¾	0.302	0.551	6,040	8,840
⅞	0.420	0.890	8,400	12,020
1	0.550	1.054	11,000	15,700
1⅛	0.694	1.294	13,880	19,880
1¼	0.893	1.515	17,860	24,540
1⅜	1.057	1.744	21,140	29,700
1½	1.295	2.300	25,900	35,340
1⅝	1.515	2.649	30,300	41,480
1¾	1.746	3.021	34,920	48,100

The vertical strut resists a compressive stress of 13,125 lb. Since the beam has a nominal width of 8 in., the strut that frames into it will also have an 8-in. width. The strut exerts a compressive stress perpendicular to the grain of the beam and this bearing area may determine the size of the strut.

Assume that the strut is a 4 x 8 in. member. By data, the allowable compressive stress perpendicular to the grain is 455 psi, but, in accordance with Art. 7–1 this stress may be increased by the factor $\frac{(l + \frac{3}{8})}{l}$. Table 3–3 shows the dressed dimensions of a 4 x 8 in. member to be 3.625 × 7.5 in. and the area to be 27.19 sq in. Then $\frac{3.625 + 0.375}{3.625} = 1.1$ and $455 \times 1.1 = 500$ psi, the allowable compressive unit stress on the beam perpendicular to the grain. As the cross-sectional area is 27.19 sq in., 27.19 × 500 = 13,595 lb, the allowable compressive stress of the 4 x 8. This allowable stress exceeds the 13,125-lb stress in the strut and, consequently, the 4 x 8 in. member is accepted. This compression member is actually a short post with a length of 3.8 ft. Its slenderness ratio, $\frac{l}{d}$, is $\frac{44}{3.625}$ or 12.1. By use of the column formula for solid wood columns we find that the quantity $\frac{P}{A} = 3600$ psi. This stress exceeds the allowable; hence the cross-sectional dimensions of the strut are determined by the bearing stress perpendicular to the grain.

The next step is to determine the area of the washer or plate on the ends of the beam. These plates exert compressive stresses on the wood fibers that result from the tensile load of 18,300 lb in the tie rod.

The angle between the direction of the load and the direction of the grain in the beam may be found either graphically or by trigonometry. For the dimensions given in Fig. 19–2 the angle is approximately 20°. Our problem is to find the allowable compressive stress on the inclined surface. To accomplish this we use the formula given in Art. 3–6.

$$N = \frac{PQ}{P \sin^2 \theta + Q \cos^2 \theta}$$

and, by use of Table 3–2, we write

$$N = \frac{1300 \times 455}{(1300 \times 0.11698) + (455 \times 0.88302)} = 1070 \text{ psi}$$

Then $\frac{18{,}300}{1070} = 17.1$ sq in., the minimum required number of square inches in bearing. If the rod diameter is $1\frac{3}{8}$ in., the hole in the plate or washer will be $1\frac{1}{2}$ in. in diameter, an area of 1.77 sq in. Thus 17.1 + 1.77 = 18.87 sq in., the minimum required plate area including the hole. Accept a $\frac{3}{4}$ x 5 x 5 in. flat plate washer.

CHAPTER 20

TIMBER PURLINS

20–1. Timber Purlins. A roof purlin is the beam that spans from truss to truss and transfers the roof loads to the truss. For convenience in framing, the purlins are often placed on, or framed into, the truss in such a manner that one of the major axes of the purlin is parallel to the slope of the roof. This arrangement results in the vertical roof load not being parallel to either of the two major axes of the purlin.

In Fig. 20–1 (*a*) the line *L* represents a vertical roof load sup-

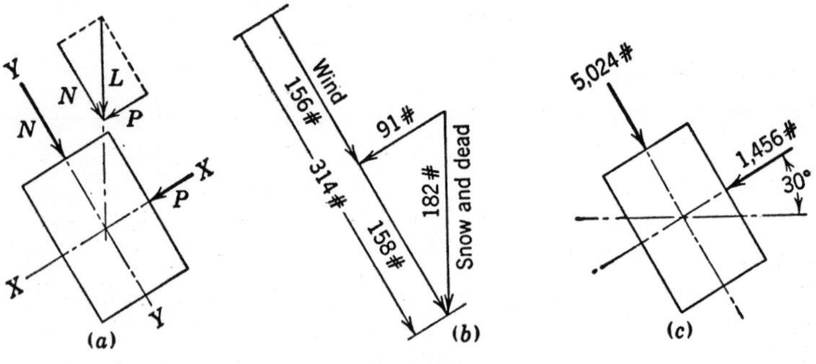

FIG. 20–1

ported by a purlin whose major axes are parallel and normal to the pitch of the roof. The two components of *L* are *N* and *P*, found graphically. *N* is the component normal to the roof surface and parallel to the *Y–Y* axis of the purlin. The component *P* is parallel to the slope of the roof. If the roof construction, planking for example, prevents the purlin from bending in the direction of *P*, the design of the purlin is accomplished by considering the force *N* as producing bending with respect to the *X–X* axis of the purlin.

20–2. Design of Timber Purlins. When there is no lateral restraint, the purlin may be designed as explained in the following example.

Example. Roof trusses are placed 16 ft 0 in. on centers and the timber purlins are 6 ft 0 in. apart. The roof has a pitch of 30° with the horizontal, and the roof loads, per square foot of roof surface, are rafters, 2 lb; sheathing, 3 lb; slate roofing, 12 lb; snow, 10 lb; wind, 26 lb. Design the purlin with respect to bending, assuming that the timber has an allowable extreme fiber stress of 1500 psi.

SOLUTION. The first step is to compute the vertical loads.

Rafters	=	2
Sheathing	=	3
Slate roofing	=	12
Snow	=	10
Total	=	27 psf

As the distance between purlins is 6 ft 0 in., 6 × 27 = 162 lb. If we assume that the purlin weighs 20 lb per lin ft, 162 + 20 = 182 lb, the load on the purlin per linear foot of length. Note that this is a *vertical* load.

The next step is to find the two components of this load, the components being parallel to the two major axes of the purlin. To accomplish this, lay off, at some suitable scale, a vertical line equivalent to 182 lb and complete the parallelogram of forces.* See Fig. 20–1 (*b*). Scaling the length of these two components, we find them to be 158 and 91 lb, the former being normal to the roof surface and the latter parallel to it.

The wind load is considered to be normal to the roof surface; hence 26 × 6 = 156 lb, the wind load on the purlin per linear foot of length. Therefore 156 + 158 = 314 lb per lin ft, the total load on the purlin parallel to the Y–Y axis of the purlin. See Fig. 20–1 (*b*).

* See Chapter 2 of *Simplified Mechanics and Strength of Materials*, Second Edition, by Harry Parker, John Wiley and Sons, New York, 1961.

The total load on the purlin parallel to the Y–Y axis is 314 × 16 = 5024 lb, and the bending moment it produces is

$$M = \frac{Wl}{8} \quad \text{or} \quad \frac{5024 \times 16 \times 12}{8} = 120{,}500 \text{ in-lb}$$

The load on the purlin parallel to axis X–X is 91 × 16 or 1456 lb. It produces a bending moment of $\frac{1456 \times 16 \times 12}{8} = 34{,}944$ in-lb.

The design of the purlin is accomplished by the trial method. As a trial, let us assume that the purlin is an 8 x 10 in. Referring to Table 3–3, we find $S_{X-X} = 112.81$ in.^{3} and $S_{Y-Y} = 89.06$ in.^{3}

$$f = \frac{M}{S}$$

Hence

$$f = \frac{120{,}500}{112.81} = 1070 \text{ psi}$$

$$f = \frac{34{,}944}{89.06} = 392 \text{ psi}$$

These two unit stresses are the stresses on the fibers at the extreme top and bottom fibers of the purlin. Their sum is 1070 + 392 or 1462 psi, the maximum fiber stress. As this stress is within 1500 psi, the allowable, the 8 x 10 in. purlin is approved for strength in bending.

$$\frac{7.5 \times 9.5}{144} \times 40 = 19.8 \text{ lb}$$

the weight of the 8 x 10 in. purlin per linear foot, if it is assumed that the timber weighs 40 lb per cu ft. As the weight assumed was 20 lb, the 8 x 10 in. purlin is acceptable.

Problem 20–2–A. Design a roof purlin having a span of 15 ft 0 in. and a spacing of 5 ft 0 in. The roof has a pitch of 35° and the following loads per square foot of roof surface: slate roofing, 12 lb; planking, 6 lb; snow, 10 lb; wind, 27 lb. The allowable extreme fiber stress of the timber is 1400 psi.

CHAPTER 21

COMPOUND BEAMS

21–1. Built-Up Beams. It frequently happens that timbers of large dimensions are unobtainable, and a built-up beam is constructed by fastening together a number of smaller beams side by side with their long axes vertical. The individual beams are held together by bolts, lag screws, or spikes. A built-up beam thus constructed has a strength equal to the sum of the strengths of the individual pieces. As an example, a 3 x 14 in. beam with a span length of 16 ft 0 in. and an allowable extreme fiber stress of 1400 psi will support a uniformly distributed load of 4650 lb. If four 3 x 14's are bolted together side by side, the built-up beam will support a uniformly distributed load of 4 × 4650 or 18,600 lb.

Example. It is desired to construct a built-up beam having a span of 14 ft 0 in. and a uniformly distributed load of 8000 lb. If 2 x 12 in. joists with an allowable extreme fiber stress of 1200 psi are available, how many are required?

SOLUTION. First let us determine the allowable distributed load for one 2 x 12 in.

$$M = \frac{W \times l}{8} = \frac{W \times 14 \times 12}{8} = 21W \text{ in-lb}$$

the maximum bending moment. The section modulus of a 2 x 12 in. is 35.82 in.^{3} (Table 3–3).

$$\frac{M}{f} = S$$

$$21W = 1200 \times 35.82$$

$$W = 2047 \text{ lb}$$

Since one 2 x 12 in. will support a uniformly distributed load of 2047 lb, $\frac{8000}{2047} = 3.9$, the number of 2 x 12's required to support a distributed load of 8000 lb. Therefore, we shall use four 2 x 12 in. joists.

Problem 21–1–A. A built-up beam composed of 3 x 12's, bolted together, side by side, is to be used for a span of 15 ft 0 in. How many individual pieces should be used if the total uniformly distributed load is 14,000 lb, the allowable extreme fiber stress of the timber is 1400 psi, and E = 1,760,000 psi?

Problem 21–1–B. Six 2 x 14's are to be used as a built-up beam for a span of 17 ft 0 in. and a uniformly distributed load of 15,000 lb. If the allowable extreme fiber stress is 1300 psi and E = 1,760,000 psi, is six the proper number of individual pieces?

21–2. Keyed Beams. Since structural steel is generally available, compound beams, with the exception of the type referred to in the preceding article, are not commonly constructed today. Compound beams were used when a solid timber of proper dimensions was unobtainable.

The beams referred to in Art. 21–1 are formed by placing the individual pieces side by side, the long axes being vertical. In another method the pieces are placed one above the other. For instance, one 8 x 8 in. could be placed *above* a timber of the same dimensions, thus forming an 8 x 16 in. section. Regardless of the method used to hold the two pieces together, a compound beam thus constructed is never so efficient as a solid timber of the same dimensions. In this type of construction the particular stress to guard against is horizontal shear, described in Art. 6–2. For rectangular beams these stresses are maximum at the neutral surface. If the beam is built up of two pieces, as referred to above, the greatest horizontal shearing stresses will occur at the plane of contact between the two pieces.

To prevent this tendency to slide horizontally, several methods have been employed. Vertical bolts have been used, and wood or metal keys have been inserted and wedged tight in grooves at the plane of contact. Because of the inherent tendency of timber to shrink, keyed beams should not be employed unless there is access to the bolts for tightening. Not only are keyed beams less efficient, with respect to strength, than solid timbers, but their deflection is greater. If compound beams are to be constructed by placing the pieces one above the other, the most effective method of securing them in position is to use bolts and split-ring connectors.

21–3. Flitched Beams. A flitched beam is constructed by bolting together timber beams and steel sections, side by side. Although they were common in the past, their use has been eliminated by readily obtainable structural steel beams. This brief discussion of flitched beams is presented to illustrate the use of two materials having different moduli of elasticity and used as a unit. Timber and steel thus combined do not afford an efficient construction because the timber cannot be stressed up to its full allowable extreme fiber stress. A timber beam reinforced with steel plates forms a compound beam in which the deformations in the fibers of the steel and timber are equal.

Consider a simple beam in bending made up of a rectangular timber cross section with steel plates bolted to its sides, the plates and the timber having equal depths. See Fig. 21–1 (*b*).

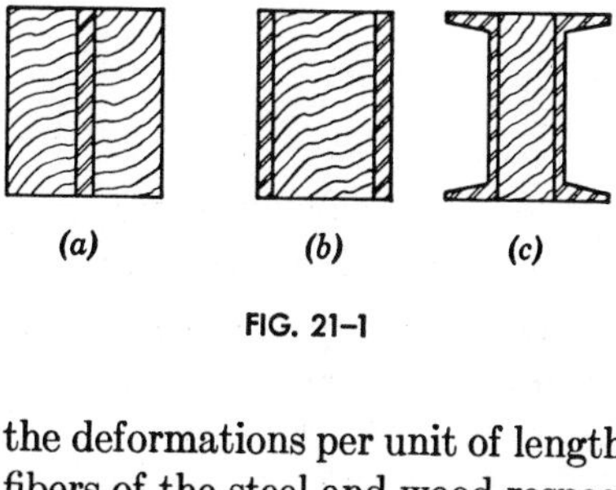

(*a*) (*b*) (*c*)

FIG. 21–1

Let

Δ_s and Δ_w = the deformations per unit of length on the extreme fibers of the steel and wood respectively, in inches

f_s and f_w = the extreme fiber unit stresses of the steel and wood respectively, in pounds per square inch

E_s and E_w = the moduli of elasticity of the steel and wood respectively, in pounds per square inch

By definition, the modulus of elasticity of a material is equal to the unit stress divided by the unit deformation. Therefore

$$E_s = \frac{f_s}{\Delta_s} \quad \text{and} \quad E_w = \frac{f_w}{\Delta_w}$$

or

$$\Delta_s = \frac{f_s}{E_s} \quad \text{and} \quad \Delta_w = \frac{f_w}{E_w}$$

Since the unit deformations of the steel and wood must be equal,

$$\frac{f_s}{E_s} = \frac{f_w}{E_w} \quad \text{and} \quad f_w = f_s \times \frac{E_w}{E_s}$$

If we assume that $f_s = 20{,}000$ psi, $E_w = 1{,}760{,}000$ psi, and $E_s = 29{,}000{,}000$ psi,

$$f_w = 20{,}000 \times \frac{1{,}760{,}000}{29{,}000{,}000}$$

$$f_w = 1213 \text{ psi}$$

the extreme fiber stress in the wood when $f = 20{,}000$ psi in the steel.

Both Douglas fir and Southern pine have a modulus of elasticity of 1,760,000 psi; they are two of our strongest woods. However, regardless of the grade or allowable extreme fiber stress, when used with steel in flitched beams their maximum extreme fiber stress is only 1213 psi when the steel is stressed to 20,000 psi.

Example. A simple beam has a span of 18 ft 0 in. It is made up of a 10 x 14 in. Southern pine timber of dense structural 58 grade, with $\frac{1}{2}$ x $13\frac{1}{2}$ in. steel plates bolted to its sides, as shown in Fig. 21–1 (*b*). Compute the allowable uniformly distributed load this flitched beam will support.

SOLUTION. In accordance with the foregoing discussion, we accept 20,000 psi and 1213 psi as the extreme fiber stresses of the steel and timber, respectively. The section modulus, S, of a 10 x 14 in. wood beam is 288.56 in.^{3}; it is found in Table 3–3.

The section modulus of a rectangular section is given in Art. 4–6 to be $\frac{bh^2}{6}$. Therefore for the section modulus of *two* $\frac{1}{2}$ x $13\frac{1}{2}$ in. steel plates

$$S = 2 \times \frac{0.5 \times 13.5 \times 13.5}{6} = 30.37 \text{ in.}^3$$

First, let us compute the distributed load that will be carried by the timber beam.

$$M = \frac{Wl}{8} = \frac{W \times 18 \times 12}{8} = 27W \text{ in-lb}$$

the maximum bending moment. The flexure formula is $M = f \times S$, Art. 9–3. Hence $27W = 1213 \times 288.56$ and $W = 12{,}900$ lb, the load carried by the 10 x 14 in. wood beam.

Next, we compute the distributed load that will be supported by the two steel plates. As before,

$$M = \frac{Wl}{8} = \frac{W \times 18 \times 12}{8} = 27W \text{ in-lb}$$

the maximum bending moment $M = f \times S$. Hence $27W = 20{,}000 \times 30.37$ and $W = 22{,}500$ lb, the load carried by the two steel plates.

Adding the loads carried by the timber and the steel plates, $12{,}900 + 22{,}500 = 35{,}400$ lb, the uniformly distributed load that may be carried by the flitched beam.

Problem 21–3–A. A flitched beam is composed of two 6 x 12 in. Douglas fir, select structural grade beams bolted to the sides of a 1 x $11\frac{1}{2}$ in. steel plate, as shown in Fig. 21–1 (*a*). It is used as a simple beam with a span of 16 ft 0 in. Compute the uniformly distributed load that this flitched beam will support.

Problem 21–3–B. Assume that the two 6 x 12 in. wood beams in Problem 21–3–A is of the dense structural grade of redwood instead of Douglas fir. What uniformly distributed load will this flitched beam carry?

CHAPTER 22

STUD WALLS

22–1. Stud Walls. The stud bearing walls commonly used in light frame construction are invariably strong enough to support their imposed loads. When, however, an unusual condition occurs, it is well to compute the loads and to determine both the size of the studs and their spacing. When the loads have been established, as well as the species and allowable compressive stress of the lumber parallel to the grain, the proper stud sizes and spacing may be found by referring to Table 22–1. The loads in this table are for normal duration and are based on the column formula and recommendations of the National Lumber Manufacturers Association. The loads given are loads *per linear foot of wall* on studs surfaced on four sides and *spaced 16 in. on centers*, the strength of the stud column being determined by the wider of the two cross-sectional dimensions of the studs. It is assumed that the studs have ample lateral bracing parallel to the wall. Thus in the column formula the ratio $\frac{l}{d}$ is the stud length, in inches, divided by the wider dimension of the stud, also in inches. See Fig. 22–1.

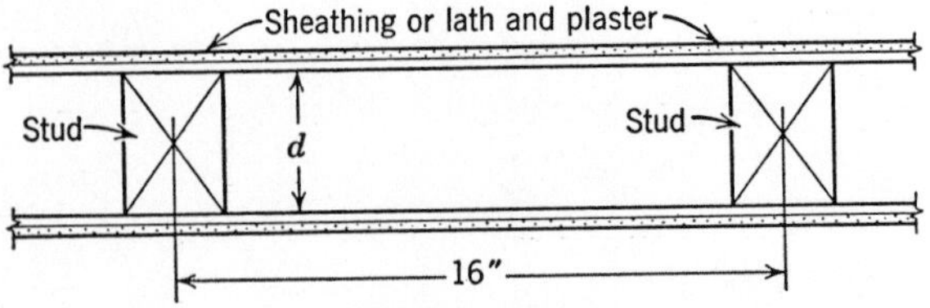

FIG. 22–1

22–2. Lateral Support of Studs. In the construction of stud walls sheathing, lath, and plaster or bridging generally provide ample

TABLE 22–1. SAFE AXIAL LOADS FOR STUD WALLS

In Loads Per Linear Foot of Wall When Studs Are Spaced 16 in. on Centers

Note. $\frac{P}{A}$ must not exceed c, the allowable compressive stress parallel to the grain

E	2 x 3		2 x 4		3 x 4		4 x 4		2 x 6		3 x 6		2 x 8	
	$\frac{P}{A}$	w	$\frac{P}{A}$	w	$\frac{P}{A}$	w	$\frac{P}{A}$	w	$\frac{P}{A}$	w	$\frac{P}{A}$	w	$\frac{P}{A}$	w
	Length = 7′ 0″													
1,000,000	293	938	557	2,461	557	3,978	557	5,491	1,351	9,263	1,351	14,969	2,392	21,874
1,100,000	322	1,032	613	2,709	613	4,378	613	6,043	1,486	10,189	1,486	16,465	2,632	24,069
1,210,000	354	1,134	674	2,978	674	4,814	674	6,644	1,635	11,211	1,635	18,116	2,895	26,474
1,320,000	387	1,240	736	3,252	736	5,256	736	7,255	1,784	12,232	1,784	19,767	3,157	28,870
1,430,000	419	1,342	797	3,522	797	5,692	797	7,856	1,932	13,247	1,932	21,407	3,421	31,284
1,540,000	451	1,445	858	3,791	858	6,128	858	8,458	2,081	14,269	2,081	23,058	3,684	33,689
1,650,000	483	1,547	920	4,065	920	6,570	920	9,069	2,230	15,290	2,230	24,709	3,947	36,094
1,760,000	516	1,653	981	4,335	981	7,006	981	9,670	2,378	16,305	2,378	26,349	4,211	38,509
1,980,000	580	1,858	1,104	4,878	1,104	7,885	1,104	10,883	2,676	18,349	2,676	29,651	4,737	43,319
	Length = 8′ 0″													
E	2 x 3		2 x 4		3 x 4		4 x 4		2 x 6		3 x 6		2 x 8	
	$\frac{P}{A}$	w	$\frac{P}{A}$	w	$\frac{P}{A}$	w	$\frac{P}{A}$	w	$\frac{P}{A}$	w	$\frac{P}{A}$	w	$\frac{P}{A}$	w
1,000,000	224	717	427	1,887	427	3,050	427	4,209	1,026	7,035	1,026	11,368	1,832	16,753
1,100,000	246	788	470	2,077	470	3,356	470	4,633	1,129	7,741	1,129	12,509	2,015	18,427
1,210,000	271	868	517	2,284	517	3,692	517	5,096	1,241	8,509	1,241	13,751	2,216	20,265
1,320,000	296	948	564	2,492	564	4,028	564	5,560	1,354	9,284	1,354	15,003	2,418	22,112
1,430,000	320	1,025	611	2,700	611	4,364	611	6,023	1,467	10,059	1,467	16,255	2,619	23,950
1,540,000	345	1,105	658	2,907	658	4,699	658	6,486	1,580	10,834	1,580	17,507	2,821	25,798
1,650,000	369	1,182	705	3,115	705	5,035	705	6,950	1,693	11,608	1,693	18,759	3,022	27,635
1,760,000	394	1,262	752	3,323	752	5,371	752	7,413	1,806	12,383	1,806	20,011	3,223	29,473
1,980,000	443	1,419	846	3,738	846	6,042	846	8,339	2,031	13,926	2,031	22,504	3,626	33,159

TABLE 22–1. SAFE AXIAL LOADS FOR STUD WALLS (Continued)

Length = 9′ 0″

E	2 x 3		2 x 4		3 x 4		4 x 4		2 x 6		3 x 6		2 x 8	
	$\frac{P}{A}$	w	$\frac{P}{A}$	w	$\frac{P}{A}$	w	$\frac{P}{A}$	w	$\frac{P}{A}$	w	$\frac{P}{A}$	w	$\frac{P}{A}$	w
1,000,000	178	570	338	1,494	338	2,414	338	3,332	814	5,581	814	9,020	1,446	13,223
1,100,000	195	625	372	1,644	372	2,656	372	3,667	895	6,137	895	9,917	1,591	14,549
1,210,000	215	689	409	1,807	409	2,921	409	4,032	985	6,754	985	10,914	1,750	16,004
1,320,000	234	749	446	1,971	446	3,185	446	4,396	1,074	7,364	1,074	11,900	1,909	17,458
1,430,000	254	814	483	2,134	483	3,450	483	4,761	1,164	7,981	1,164	12,897	2,068	18,911
1,540,000	274	878	520	2,298	520	3,714	520	5,126	1,253	8,591	1,253	13,884	2,228	20,374
1,650,000	293	939	557	2,461	557	3,978	557	5,491	1,343	9,209	1,343	14,881	2,387	21,829
1,760,000	313	1,003	595	2,629	595	4,249	595	5,865	1,432	9,818	1,432	15,867	2,546	23,282
1,980,000	352	1,128	669	2,956	669	4,778	669	6,595	1,612	11,053	1,612	17,861	2,864	26,191

Length = 10′ 0″

E	2 x 3		2 x 4		3 x 4		4 x 4		2 x 6		3 x 6		2 x 8	
	$\frac{P}{A}$	w	$\frac{P}{A}$	w	$\frac{P}{A}$	w	$\frac{P}{A}$	w	$\frac{P}{A}$	w	$\frac{P}{A}$	w	$\frac{P}{A}$	w
1,000,000	144	461	274	1,211	274	1,957	274	2,701	661	4,532	661	7,324	1,172	10,718
1,100,000	158	506	301	1,330	301	2,149	301	2,967	727	4,985	727	8,055	1,289	11,788
1,210,000	174	557	331	1,460	331	2,364	331	3,263	800	5,485	800	8,864	1,418	12,967
1,320,000	190	608	361	1,595	361	2,578	361	3,559	873	5,986	873	9,673	1,547	14,147
1,430,000	205	656	391	1,728	391	2,792	391	3,854	946	6,486	946	10,482	1,676	15,326
1,540,000	221	708	422	1,865	422	3,014	422	4,160	1,018	6,980	1,018	11,280	1,805	16,506
1,650,000	237	759	452	1,997	452	3,228	452	4,455	1,091	7,481	1,091	12,089	1,934	17,686
1,760,000	253	810	482	2,130	482	3,443	482	4,751	1,164	7,981	1,164	12,897	2,063	18,866
1,980,000	284	910	542	2,395	542	3,871	542	5,343	1,309	8,975	1,309	14,504	2,320	21,216

E	Length = 11′ 0″													
	2 x 3		2 x 4		3 x 4		4 x 4		2 x 6		3 x 6		2 x 8	
	$\frac{P}{A}$	w	$\frac{P}{A}$	w	$\frac{P}{A}$	w	$\frac{P}{A}$	w	$\frac{P}{A}$	w	$\frac{P}{A}$	w	$\frac{P}{A}$	w
1,000,000	119	381	226	999	226	1,614	226	2,228	543	3,723	543	6,017	968	8,852
1,100,000	130	416	249	1,100	249	1,778	249	2,455	598	4,100	598	6,626	1,065	9,739
1,210,000	143	458	274	1,211	274	1,956	274	2,701	657	4,505	657	7,280	1,172	10,718
1,320,000	157	503	299	1,321	299	2,135	299	2,947	717	4,916	717	7,945	1,278	11,687
1,430,000	170	545	324	1,431	324	2,314	324	3,194	777	5,327	777	8,609	1,385	12,665
1,540,000	183	586	349	1,542	349	2,492	349	3,440	837	5,739	837	9,274	1,491	13,635
1,650,000	196	628	374	1,653	374	2,671	374	3,686	896	6,143	896	9,928	1,598	14,614
1,760,000	209	669	398	1,758	398	2,842	398	3,923	956	6,555	956	10,593	1,704	15,583
1,980,000	235	752	448	1,980	448	3,200	448	4,416	1,076	7,378	1,076	11,923	1,917	17,530

E	Length = 12′ 0″													
	2 x 3		2 x 4		3 x 4		4 x 4		2 x 6		3 x 6		2 x 8	
	$\frac{P}{A}$	w	$\frac{P}{A}$	w	$\frac{P}{A}$	w	$\frac{P}{A}$	w	$\frac{P}{A}$	w	$\frac{P}{A}$	w	$\frac{P}{A}$	w
1,000,000	100	320	190	840	190	1,357	190	1,873	458	3,140	458	5,075	814	7,525
1,100,000	109	349	209	923	209	1,493	209	2,060	504	3,456	504	5,584	895	8,274
1,210,000	120	384	230	1,017	230	1,643	230	2,267	554	3,799	554	6,139	985	9,008
1,320,000	131	419	251	1,109	251	1,793	251	2,474	604	4,142	604	6,692	1,074	9,821
1,430,000	142	455	272	1,202	272	1,942	272	2,681	655	4,491	655	7,257	1,164	10,644
1,540,000	153	490	293	1,295	293	2,092	293	2,888	705	4,834	705	7,812	1,253	11,458
1,650,000	164	525	314	1,387	314	2,242	314	3,095	755	5,177	755	8,365	1,343	12,281
1,760,000	175	560	335	1,480	335	2,392	335	3,302	806	5,527	806	8,931	1,432	13,095
1,980,000	197	631	377	1,666	377	2,692	377	3,716	906	6,212	906	10,039	1,612	14,741

Reproduced by permission of the National Lumber Manufacturers Association.

lateral support in a direction parallel to the wall. If, however, a stud wall depends on bridging (between studs) alone for lateral support, the maximum vertical spacing in inches between rows of

TABLE 22–2. SPACING FACTORS FOR STUD BRIDGING

Nominal size, in inches	2 x 3	2 x 4	3 x 4	4 x 4	2 x 6	3 x 6	2 x 8
Spacing factor for bridging	0.70	0.45	0.72	1.00	0.29	0.47	0.22

Reproduced by permission of the National Lumber Manufacturers Association.

bridging may be obtained by multiplying the length of the stud in inches by the appropriate spacing factor given in Table 22–2. See Fig. 22–2.

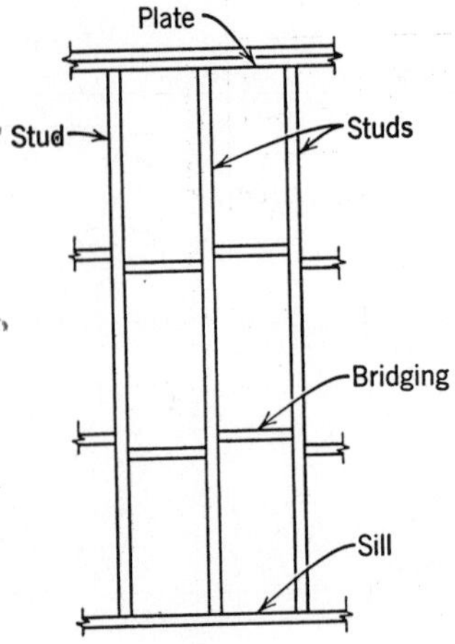

FIG. 22–2

Example. A stud wall 9 ft 6 in. in height, composed of 3 x 4 in. studs spaced 16 in. on centers, depends on bridging alone for lateral support. What is the maximum permissible vertical spacing of the bridging?

SOLUTION. The height of the stud wall in inches is $(9 \times 12) + 6$ or 114 in. In Table 22–2 we find the spacing factor for 3 x 4 in. studs to be 0.72. Therefore $114 \times 0.72 = 82$ in., the maximum allowable bridging spacing. Consequently one row of bridging at the midheight will be adequate.

In this example the studs are 3 x 4s. What should be the vertical spacing of the bridging if 2 x 4 in. studs are used?

The height of the stud wall, as before, is 114 in. Referring to

Table 22–2, we see that the spacing factor for 2 x 4 in. studs is 0.45. Then, $114 \times 0.45 = 51.3$ in., the maximum spacing between rows of bridging. In this instance two rows of bridging will be required in the 9 ft 6 in. height, as indicated in Fig. 22–2.

22–3. Safe-Load Table for Stud Walls. Table 22–1 gives allowable loads of normal duration on stud walls. The most common spacing of studs is 16 in. on centers, and the loads, in pounds per linear foot of wall, in this table are computed for a 16-in. stud spacing. These loads are computed in accordance with the formula for solid wood columns given in Art. 13–3. In the table $\frac{P}{A}$ is the allowable unit stress on the studs and w is the safe load in pounds per linear foot of wall.

To show how the loads in the table are determined, consider the following example.

Example. A stud wall 9 ft 0 in. in height is composed of 3 x 4 in. studs spaced 16 in. on centers, well braced by sheathing in a direction parallel to the length of the wall. The studs are of Eastern hemlock, utility structural grade. Compute the load, in pounds per linear foot of wall, that this stud wall will support.

SOLUTION. Referring to Table 3–1, we find that E, the modulus of elasticity of Eastern hemlock, is 1,210,000 psi, and for the utility structural grade c the allowable compressive stress parallel to the grain is 600 psi. The dressed dimensions of a 3 x 4 given in Table 3–3 are $2\frac{5}{8} \times 3\frac{5}{8}$ in. and the cross-sectional area is 9.52 sq in.

As noted previously d, used in determining the slenderness ratio, is the wider dimension of the stud. Then $\frac{l}{d} = \frac{9 \times 12}{3.625} = 29.8.$ Substituting in the column formula,

$$\frac{P}{A} = \frac{0.3 \times E}{(l/d)^2}, \qquad \frac{P}{A} = \frac{0.3 \times 1{,}210{,}000}{29.8 \times 29.8} = 409 \text{ psi}$$

the allowable compressive unit stress.

Now refer to Table 22–1. In the section marked "length = 9 ft 0 in." opposite $E = 1{,}210{,}000$ psi and under $\frac{P}{A}$ in the 3 x 4 section, we find $\frac{P}{A} = 409$ psi, the same allowable compressive unit stress found by our computations.

The cross-sectional area of a 3 x 4 is 9.52 sq in. Therefore $9.52 \times 409 = 3894$ lb, the allowable load on the 3 x 4 in. stud wall per linear foot of wall *if the stud spacing is 12 in. on centers.* Hence, $3894 \times \frac{12}{16} = 2921$ lb, the allowable load per linear foot of wall *if the studs are spaced 16 in. on centers.* Note that this is the load given in the table under the letter w.

In this example the value of $\frac{P}{A}$ was found to be 409 psi. In using the column formula, the value of $\frac{P}{A}$ must not exceed c, the allowable compressive stress parallel to the grain. For the species and grade given as data in this example $c = 600$ psi. Thus, since 409 is less than 600, 409 psi is the allowable compressive unit stress and w, the allowable load per linear foot of wall, is 2921 lb.

Consequently, to find the allowable load per linear foot for stud walls with a 16-in. spacing of studs, first refer to Table 3–3 and find c and E for the species and grade of wood to be used. In Table 22–1 find the section giving the length (height) of the studs. Then, opposite the appropriate E and in the column marked w for the specific stud size, find the allowable load per linear foot. Be certain that the value of $\frac{P}{A}$, in the table, does not exceed the allowable c.

Example. By use of Table 22–1, determine the allowable load on a stud partition, 10 ft 0 in. in height, constructed of 2 x 4s, 16 in. on centers. The studs are of the common structural grade of Eastern hemlock.

SOLUTION. For this species and grade of wood $E = 1{,}210{,}000$ psi and $c = 650$ psi. See Table 3–1. Referring to Table 22–1, we find that $\frac{P}{A} = 331$ psi. Since this stress is less than c (650 psi) w, given in the table, is 1460 lb, the allowable load per linear foot of wall for a 16-in. stud spacing.

Example. If the studs in the foregoing example are 2 x 6s instead of 2 x 4s, compute the allowable load on the stud partition.

SOLUTION. By use of Table 22–1 we see that $\frac{P}{A} = 800$ psi. Since this value exceeds c (650 psi), the allowable compressive stress is only 650 psi. The area of a 2 x 6 is 9.14 sq in.; hence $9.14 \times 650 = 5940$ lb, the allowable load per linear foot of wall if the studs have 12-in. spacing. Therefore $5940 \times \frac{12}{16} = 4450$ lb per lin ft of wall for a 16-in. stud spacing.

Problem 22–3–A. A stud wall is 10 ft 0 in. in height and is composed of 3 x 4 in. studs, 16 in. on centers. The wood is the 1200 f grade of Eastern spruce. What is the allowable load on the partition in pounds per linear foot?

Problem 22–3–B. A stud wall has a height of 11 ft 0 in. and a load of 1900 lb per lin ft. If the studs are of the common structural grade of Eastern hemlock, what should be their size if they are spaced 16 in. on centers?

22–4. Spacing of Studs. The most common spacing of studs in stud walls is 16 in. on centers, as shown in Fig. 22–1. The loads per linear foot of wall, given in Table 22–1, are based on a 16-in. stud centering. Excessive loads might require a 12-in. spacing, or some other spacing might be advantageous. To find the allowable load per linear foot of wall with other than 16-in. spacing, multiply the loads given in Table 22–1 by the appropriate load factor given in Table 22–3.

TABLE 22–3. SAFE LOAD SPACING FACTORS FOR STUD WALLS

Stud spacing	12″	20″	24″	32″	36″	42″	48″
Load factor	1.33	0.80	0.67	0.50	0.44	0.38	0.33

Reproduced by permission of the National Lumber Manufacturers Association.

Example. The No. 2 SR grade of Southern pine is used for 3 x 4 in. studs in a wall that has a height of 10 ft 0 in. What load per linear foot will the wall support if the studs are spaced 12 in. on centers?

SOLUTION. Referring to Table 3–1, we see for this grade and species of wood that $E = 1{,}760{,}000$ psi and $c = 900$ psi. Table 22–1 shows that the allowable load per linear foot is 3443 lb if the stud spacing is 16 in. The conversion factor for 12-in. spacing, given in Table 22–3, is 1.33. Therefore $3443 \times 1.33 = 4579$ lb, the allowable load per linear foot for a 12-in. stud spacing.

Problem 22–4–A. For the studs described in the previous example, compute the allowable load per linear foot of wall if the stud spacing is 20 in. on centers.

Problem 22–4–B. A stud partition 10 ft 0 in. in height is composed of 3 x 4 in. studs of the utility structural grade of Eastern hemlock. What load per linear foot of wall will the partition support if the studs are spaced 24 in. on centers?

CHAPTER 23

LAMINATED LUMBER

23–1. Glued Laminated Structural Members. Structural glued laminated lumber is composed of an assembly of wood laminations in which the grain of all the laminations is approximately parallel longitudinally. The laminations are bonded by adhesives. One of the great advantages of laminated lumber lies in the fact that it may be fabricated to straight and curved shapes and to unusually large cross sections and great lengths. The use of seasoned lumber and the dispersion of defects results in higher allowable unit stresses than can be employed in solid sawn lumber.

Structural glued laminated lumber should conform in design and fabrication to the provisions of the *National Design Specification for Stress-Grade Lumber and Its Fastenings* recommended by the National Lumber Manufacturers Association.

23–2. Advantages and Limitations. Some of the advantages claimed for the use of glued laminated lumber are the following:

1. Members may be built to almost any desired cross section or length.

2. Small sizes of the lower grades of lumber can be utilized in the construction of large structural members.

3. The lumber of higher stress grades may be placed in those parts of the built-up member in which the stresses are greatest, the low-grade material being used where the stresses are lowest.

4. A laminated member of large cross section is more fire resistant than a type of construction in which small individual pieces are exposed.

5. Because 1-in. and 2-in. material is readily seasoned, glued laminated members seasoned throughout are obtainable.

6. Curved shapes with varying cross sections may be constructed.

7. Laminated beams may be cambered during their construction to eliminate the sag that frequently accompanies the seasoning of a straight solid beam.

8. Proper gluing enables the laminations to act as a unit more effectively than is possible with nails, bolts, or other mechanical devices.

9. Because thoroughly cured lumber, free from defects, may be used in the laminations, higher unit stresses may be allowed in the design of laminated beams and arches than in solid pieces of timber.

Although a laminated beam offers certain advantages, the cost of preparation usually exceeds that of a solid green member. If green lumber is acceptable, it can probably be obtained in less time than that required for a laminated member. Laminated members must be fabricated in a plant equipped for the purpose, and the size of the members may be limited by transportation facilities. The laminating process requires special equipment, plant facilities, and fabricating skills that are not required for the production of solid green timbers.

23–3. The Laminating Process. Fabrication of laminated members consists in gluing together kiln-dried laminations 2 in. or less in thickness. Straight beams are usually constructed with $1\frac{5}{8}$-in. (2-in. nominal) laminations and curved beams with 1 or 2 in. nominal thicknesses. When curved members are used, the thickness of the laminations is controlled by the radius of curvature.

The moisture content of the lumber should not exceed 15% during the period of fabrication. In general the structural glue types are water-resistive for interior members and waterproof for exterior exposures. Before gluing, the laminations should be machined to a uniform thickness. It is important that the glued surface be a smooth plane surface and that the pressure be uniformly distributed during the setting period.

Because of the size of the members, the individual laminations must be joined end to end. The most efficient joints are the plain scarf joints shown in Fig. 23–1 (*a*). Before laminating horizontally, the individual boards should be end-glued at the scarf joints

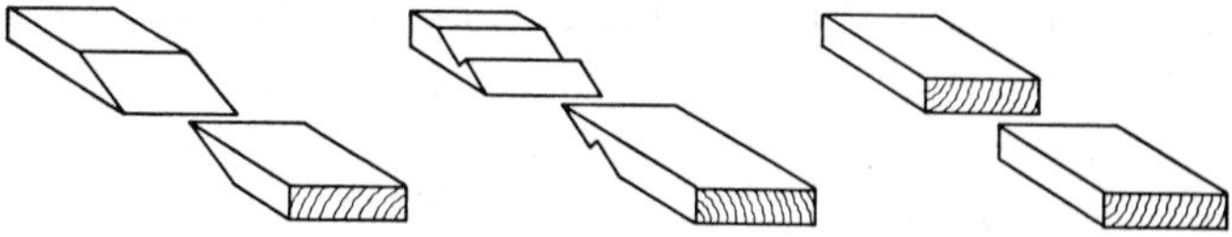

(*a*) Plain Scarf (*b*) Hooked Scarf (*c*) End Butt

FIG. 23–1

and resurfaced to ensure a uniform thickness of the lamination. This pregluing and surfacing is essential for high quality work. The stepped or hooked scarf joint [Fig. 23–1 (*b*)] is assumed to have the same strength as the plain scarf. Butt joints [Fig. 23–1 (*c*)] can resist no tension and should not be used in tension members.

23–4. Stresses in Laminated Members. Laminations may be completely dried before fabrication. Also, they may be selected free of checks or other defects found in large one-piece members. Because of this a laminated member has greater strength than a solid member of the same grade of lumber. Greater allowable unit stresses may be used in design. Softwoods, Douglas fir and Southern pine, two of our strongest woods, are commonly used for laminated structural members. Allowable stresses for glued laminated structural members may be found in the *National Design Specification for Stress-Grade Lumber and Its Fastenings.* In laminated members bent to a curve the induced stresses vary with the radius of curvature. For the curved portion of members the allowable unit stress in bending should be modified by multiplying by the following curvature factor:

$$1 - 2000\left(\frac{t}{R}\right)^2$$

in which t = thickness of the lamination, in inches
R = radius of curvature of a lamination, in inches

The ratio $\frac{t}{R}$ should not exceed $\frac{1}{125}$ for softwoods or $\frac{1}{100}$ for hardwoods. For softwoods the recommended minimum radii of curvature for $\frac{25}{32}$-in. (1-in. nominal) and $1\frac{5}{8}$-in. (2-in. nominal) laminations are 7 ft 0 in. and 15 ft 0 in., respectively.

TABLE 23–1. PROPERTIES OF SECTIONS OF GLUED LAMINATED STRUCTURAL LUMBER

1 ⅝ Inch Laminations Only

Sections arranged in order of ascending section modulus

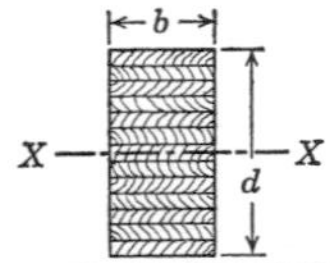

Nominal Width in Inches	Number of 1⅝″ Laminations	Net Finished Size in Inches b ▽ d ▽	Area of Section in Square Inches	Moment of Inertia $I = \frac{bd^3}{12}$	Section Modulus $S = \frac{bd^2}{6}$	Bd Ft per Lin Ft	Weight per Lin Ft Lb	Nominal Width in Inches	Number of 1⅝″ Laminations	Net Finished Size in Inches b ▽ d ▽	Area of Section in Square Inches	Moment of Inertia $I = \frac{bd^3}{12}$	Section Modulus $S = \frac{bd^2}{6}$	Bd Ft per Lin Ft	Weight per Lin Ft Lb
3	4	2¼ x 6½	14.6	51.5	15.8	2.00	3.65	6	14	5¼ x 22¾	119	5,151	453	14.00	29.75
4	4	3¼ x 6½	21.1	74.4	22.9	2.67	5.27	10	11	9 x 17⅞	161	4,284	479	18.33	40.25
3	5	2¼ x 8⅛	18.3	101	24.8	2.50	4.58	12	10	11 x 16¼	179	3,933	484	20.00	44.75
5	4	4¼ x 6½	27.6	97.3	29.9	3.33	6.90	6	15	5 x 24⅜	122	6,034	495	15.00	30.50
6	4	5 x 6½	32.5	114	35.2	4.00	8.13	16	9	14½ x 14⅝	212	3,780	517	24.00	53.00
3	6	2¼ x 9¾	21.9	174	35.7	3.00	5.48	6	15	5¼ x 24⅜	128	6,336	520	15.00	32.00
4	5	3¼ x 8⅛	26.4	145	35.8	3.33	6.60	8	13	7 x 21⅛	148	5,499	521	17.33	37.00
6	4	5¼ x 6½	34.1	120	37.0	4.00	8.52	14	10	12½ x 16¼	203	4,470	550	23.33	50.75
5	5	4¼ x 8⅛	34.5	190	46.8	4.17	8.63	6	16	5 x 26	130	7,323	563	16.00	32.50
3	7	2¼ x 11⅜	25.6	276	48.5	3.50	6.40	10	12	9 x 19½	176	5,561	570	20.00	44.00
4	6	3¼ x 9¾	31.7	251	51.5	4.00	7.92	12	11	11 x 17⅞	197	5,235	586	22.00	49.25
6	5	5 x 8⅛	40.6	223	55.0	5.00	10.15	6	16	5¼ x 26	137	7,690	592	16.00	34.25
6	5	5¼ x 8⅛	42.7	235	57.8	5.00	10.67	8	14	7 x 22¾	159	6,868	604	18.66	39.75
5	6	4¼ x 9¾	41.4	328	67.3	5.00	10.35	16	10	14½ x 16¼	236	5,185	638	26.67	59.00
4	7	3¼ x 11⅜	37.0	399	70.1	4.67	9.25	14	11	12½ x 17⅞	223	5,949	666	25.67	55.75
8	5	7 x 8⅛	56.9	313	77.0	6.67	14.22	10	13	9 x 21⅛	190	7,071	669	21.67	47.50
6	6	5 x 9¾	48.8	386	79.2	6.00	12.20	8	15	7 x 24⅜	171	8,448	693	20.00	42.75
6	6	5¼ x 9¾	51.2	406	83.2	6.00	12.80	12	12	11 x 19½	215	6,797	697	24.00	53.75
4	8	3¼ x 13	42.3	595	91.6	5.33	10.58	16	11	14½ x 17⅞	259	6,901	772	29.33	64.75
5	7	4¼ x 11⅜	48.3	521	91.7	5.83	12.07	10	14	9 x 22¾	205	8,831	776	23.33	51.25
6	7	5 x 11⅜	56.9	613	108	7.00	14.22	8	16	7 x 26	182	10,250	789	21.33	45.50
8	6	7 x 9¾	68.3	541	111	8.00	17.07	14	12	12½ x 19½	244	7,724	792	28.00	61.00
6	7	5¼ x 11⅜	59.7	644	113	7.00	14.93	12	13	11 x 21⅛	232	8,642	818	26.00	58.00
4	9	3¼ x 14⅝	47.5	847	116	6.00	11.88	8	17	7 x 27⅝	193	12,300	890	21.67	48.25

5	8	4¼ x 13	55.3	778	120	6.67	13.82	10	15	9 x 24⅜	219	10,860	891	25.00	54.75
6	8	5 x 13	65.0	915	141	8.00	16.25	16	12	14½ x 19½	283	8,960	919	32.00	70.75
4	10	3¼ x 16¼	52.8	1,162	143	6.67	13.20	14	13	12½ x 21⅛	264	9,820	930	30.33	66.00
10	6	9 x 9¾	87.8	695	143	10.00	21.95	12	14	11 x 22¾	250	10,790	949	28.00	62.50
6	8	5¼ x 13	68.3	961	148	8.00	17.07	8	18	7 x 29¼	205	14,600	998	24.00	51.25
8	7	7 x 11⅜	79.6	859	151	9.33	19.90	10	16	9 x 26	234	13,180	1,014	26.67	58.50
5	9	4¼ x 14⅝	62.2	1,108	152	7.50	15.55	14	14	12½ x 22¾	284	12,270	1,078	32.67	71.00
6	9	5 x 14⅝	73.1	1,303	178	9.00	18.27	16	13	14½ x 21⅛	306	11,390	1,078	34.67	76.50
5	10	4¼ x 16¼	69.1	1,520	187	8.33	17.28	12	15	11 x 24⅜	268	13,280	1,089	30.00	67.00
6	9	5¼ x 14⅝	76.8	1,369	187	9.00	19.20	8	19	7 x 30⅞	216	17,170	1,112	25.33	54.00
10	7	9 x 11⅜	102	1,104	194	11.67	25.50	10	17	9 x 27⅝	249	15,810	1,145	28.33	62.25
8	8	7 x 13	91.0	1,282	197	10.67	22.75	8	20	7 x 32½	228	20,030	1,232	26.67	57.00
6	10	5 x 16¼	81.3	1,788	220	10.00	20.33	14	15	12½ x 24⅜	305	15,090	1,238	35.00	76.25
5	11	4¼ x 17⅞	76.0	2,023	226	9.17	19.00	12	16	11 x 26	286	16,110	1,239	32.00	71.50
6	10	5¼ x 16¼	85.3	1,877	231	10.00	21.33	16	14	14½ x 22¾	330	14,230	1,251	37.33	82.50
12	7	11 x 11⅜	125	1,349	237	14.00	31.25	10	18	9 x 29¼	263	18,770	1,283	30.00	65.75
8	9	7 x 14⅝	102	1,825	250	12.00	25.50	8	21	7 x 34⅛	239	23,180	1,359	28.00	59.75
10	8	9 x 13	117	1,648	254	13.33	29.25	12	17	11 x 27⅝	304	19,320	1,399	34.00	76.00
6	11	5 x 17⅞	89.4	2,380	266	11.00	22.35	14	16	12½ x 26	325	18,310	1,408	37.33	81.25
5	12	4¼ x 19½	82.9	2,626	269	10.00	20.73	10	19	9 x 30⅞	278	22,070	1,430	31.67	69.50
6	11	5¼ x 17⅞	93.8	2,499	280	11.00	23.45	16	15	14½ x 24⅜	353	17,500	1,436	40.00	88.25
8	10	7 x 16¼	114	2,503	308	13.33	28.50	8	22	7 x 35¾	250	26,650	1,491	29.33	62.50
12	8	11 x 13	143	2,014	310	16.00	35.75	12	18	11 x 29¼	322	22,940	1,569	36.00	80.50
5	13	4¼ x 21⅛	89.8	3,339	316	10.83	22.45	10	20	9 x 32½	293	25,750	1,584	33.33	73.25
6	12	5 x 19½	97.5	3,090	317	12.00	24.38	14	17	12½ x 27⅝	345	21,960	1,590	39.67	86.25
10	9	9 x 14⅝	132	2,346	321	15.00	33.00	16	16	14½ x 26	377	21,240	1,634	42.67	94.25
6	12	5¼ x 19½	102	3,244	333	12.00	25.50	10	21	9 x 34⅛	307	29,800	1,747	35.00	76.75
14	8	12½ x 13	163	2,289	352	18.67	40.75	12	19	11 x 30⅞	340	26,980	1,748	38.00	85.00
6	13	5 x 21⅛	106	3,928	372	13.00	26.50	14	18	12½ x 29¼	366	26,070	1,782	42.00	91.50
8	11	7 x 17⅞	125	3,332	373	14.67	31.25	16	17	14½ x 27⅝	401	25,470	1,844	45.33	100.25
6	13	5¼ x 21⅛	111	4,124	390	13.00	27.75	10	22	9 x 35¾	322	34,270	1,917	36.67	80.50
12	9	11 x 14⅝	161	2,867	392	18.00	40.25	12	20	11 x 32½	358	31,470	1,936	40.00	89.50
10	10	9 x 16¼	146	3,218	396	16.67	36.50	14	19	12½ x 30⅞	386	30,660	1,986	44.33	96.50
6	14	5 x 22¾	114	4,906	431	14.00	28.50	16	18	14½ x 29¼	424	30,240	2,068	48.00	106.00
8	12	7 x 19½	137	4,325	444	16.00	34.25	10	23	9 x 37⅜	336	39,160	2,095	38.33	84.00
14	9	12½ x 14⅝	183	3,258	446	21.00	45.75	12	21	11 x 34⅛	375	36,430	2,135	42.00	93.75

TABLE 23–1. PROPERTIES OF SECTIONS OF GLUED LAMINATED STRUCTURAL LUMBER (Continued)

Nominal Width in Inches	Number of $1\frac{5}{8}''$ Laminations	Net Finished Size in Inches b ▽ d ▽	Area of Section in Square Inches	Moment of Inertia $I = \frac{bd^3}{12}$	Section Modulus $S = \frac{bd^2}{6}$	Bd Ft per Lin Ft	Weight per Lin Ft Lb	Nominal Width in Inches	Number of $1\frac{5}{8}''$ Laminations	Net Finished Size in Inches b ▽ d ▽	Area of Section in Square Inches	Moment of Inertia $I = \frac{bd^3}{12}$	Section Modulus $S = \frac{bd^2}{6}$	Bd Ft per Lin Ft	Weight per Lin Ft Lb
14	20	$12\frac{1}{2}$ x $32\frac{1}{2}$	406	35,760	2,201	46.67	101.50	14	25	$12\frac{1}{2}$ x $40\frac{5}{8}$	508	69,840	3,438	58.33	127.00
10	24	9 x 39	351	44,490	2,282	40.00	87.75	12	27	11 x $43\frac{7}{8}$	483	77,420	3,529	54.00	120.75
16	19	$14\frac{1}{2}$ x $30\frac{7}{8}$	448	35,560	2,304	50.67	112.00	16	24	$14\frac{1}{2}$ x 39	566	71,680	3,676	64.00	141.50
12	22	11 x $35\frac{3}{4}$	393	41,880	2,343	44.00	98.25	14	26	$12\frac{1}{2}$ x $42\frac{1}{4}$	528	78,560	3,719	60.67	132.00
14	21	$12\frac{1}{2}$ x $34\frac{1}{8}$	427	41,390	2,426	49.00	106.75	12	28	11 x $45\frac{1}{2}$	501	86,350	3,795	56.00	125.25
10	25	9 x $40\frac{5}{8}$	366	50,290	2,476	41.67	91.50	16	25	$14\frac{1}{2}$ x $40\frac{5}{8}$	589	81,020	3,988	66.67	147.25
16	20	$14\frac{1}{2}$ x $32\frac{1}{2}$	471	41,480	2,553	52.33	117.75	14	27	$12\frac{1}{2}$ x $43\frac{7}{8}$	548	87,980	4,010	63.00	137.00
12	23	11 x $37\frac{3}{8}$	411	47,860	2,561	46.00	102.75	12	29	11 x $47\frac{1}{8}$	518	95,930	4,071	58.00	129.50
14	22	$12\frac{1}{2}$ x $35\frac{3}{4}$	447	47,590	2,663	51.33	111.75	14	28	$12\frac{1}{2}$ x $45\frac{1}{2}$	569	98,120	4,313	65.33	142.25
10	26	9 x $42\frac{1}{4}$	380	56,560	2,678	43.33	95.00	16	26	$14\frac{1}{2}$ x $42\frac{1}{4}$	613	91,130	4,314	69.33	153.25
12	24	11 x 39	429	54,380	2,789	48.00	107.25	12	30	11 x $48\frac{3}{4}$	536	106,200	4,357	60.00	134.00
16	21	$14\frac{1}{2}$ x $34\frac{1}{8}$	495	48,020	2,814	56.00	123.75	14	29	$12\frac{1}{2}$ x $47\frac{1}{8}$	589	109,010	4,627	67.67	147.25
10	27	9 x $43\frac{7}{8}$	395	63,350	2,888	45.00	98.75	12	31	11 x $50\frac{3}{8}$	554	117,180	4,652	62.00	138.50
14	23	$12\frac{1}{2}$ x $37\frac{3}{8}$	467	54,380	2,910	53.67	116.75	16	27	$14\frac{1}{2}$ x $43\frac{7}{8}$	636	102,060	4,652	72.00	159.00
12	25	11 x $40\frac{5}{8}$	447	61,460	3,026	50.00	111.75	14	30	$12\frac{1}{2}$ x $48\frac{3}{4}$	609	120,680	4,951	70.00	152.25
16	22	$14\frac{1}{2}$ x $35\frac{3}{4}$	518	55,210	3,089	58.67	129.50	16	28	$14\frac{1}{2}$ x $45\frac{1}{2}$	660	113,820	5,003	74.67	165.00
10	28	9 x $45\frac{1}{2}$	410	70,650	3,105	46.67	102.50	14	31	$12\frac{1}{2}$ x $50\frac{3}{8}$	630	133,160	5,287	72.33	157.50
14	24	$12\frac{1}{2}$ x 39	488	61,790	3,169	56.00	122.00	16	29	$14\frac{1}{2}$ x $47\frac{1}{8}$	683	126,460	5,367	77.33	170.75
12	26	11 x $42\frac{1}{4}$	465	69,130	3,273	52.00	116.25	16	30	$14\frac{1}{2}$ x $48\frac{3}{4}$	707	139,990	5,743	80.00	176.75
16	23	$14\frac{1}{2}$ x $37\frac{3}{8}$	542	63,090	3,376	61.33	135.50	16	31	$14\frac{1}{2}$ x $50\frac{3}{8}$	730	154,470	6,133	82.67	182.50

Compiled by permission from data furnished by the West Coast Lumbermen's Association.

23–5. Properties of Laminated Beams. Glued laminated members may be constructed in an infinite number of sizes and shapes, but it is economical to use laminations of standard widths and thicknesses. Multiples of these dimensions for rectangular cross sections, are shown in Table 23–1. Straight beams are usually built up of $1\frac{5}{8}$-in. (2-in. nominal) laminations, and the table is based on this thickness of material. Curved beams are fabricated of either 1-in. or 2-in. material. The actual thickness of 1-in. material is $\frac{25}{32}$ in.

The nominal widths and standard finished widths of glued laminated beams are given in Table 23–2. Many additional sizes may

TABLE 23–2. NOMINAL AND FINISHED WIDTHS OF LAMINATED BEAMS

Nominal width	3″	4″	5″	6″	8″	10″	12″	14″	16″
Standard finished widths	$2\frac{1}{4}$″	$3\frac{1}{4}$″	$4\frac{1}{4}$″	$5\frac{1}{4}$ or 5″	7″	9″	11″	$12\frac{1}{2}$″	$14\frac{1}{2}$″

be obtained, but the sizes given in the table provide the greatest economy.

In addition to the standard dimensions, the section modulus and moment of inertia of rectangular sections are also given in Table 23–1. These properties are helpful in the design of beams as is indicated in Art. 23–8. The weights of the beams listed in Table 23–1 are based on the weight of 36 lb per cu ft.

23–6. Types of Laminated Beams. Although numerous shapes of glued laminated beams may be fabricated, the three basic types are straight, tapered, and curved, as shown in Fig. 23–2. The pur-

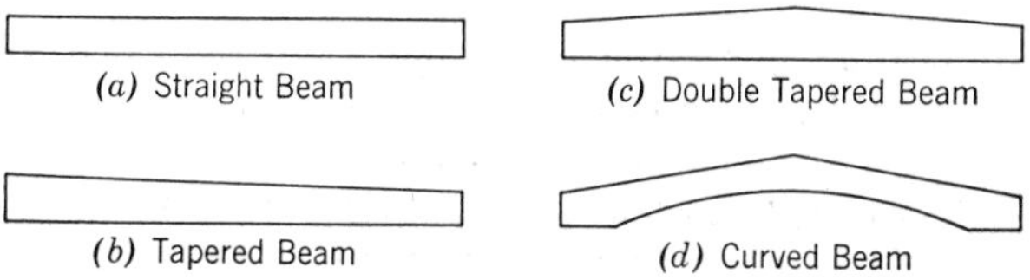

FIG. 23–2

pose of a tapered beam is to provide a sloping roof surface for drainage. These beams may slope in one direction only or be symmetrically tapered from the center of the span as shown in Figs. 23–2 (*b*) and (*c*). Straight and tapered beams are usually built with a slight camber. In computing the deflection, engineers often consider only the live load on the assumption that the deflection resulting from the dead load will be accounted for by the camber.

23–7. Laminated Arches. The two general classifications of laminated arches are the haunched (also called gothic or boomerang) and the constant radius. Both types usually employ three-hinged construction. The names commonly given to describe a V arch (Fig. 23–3) are as follows: A = span, back to back; B =

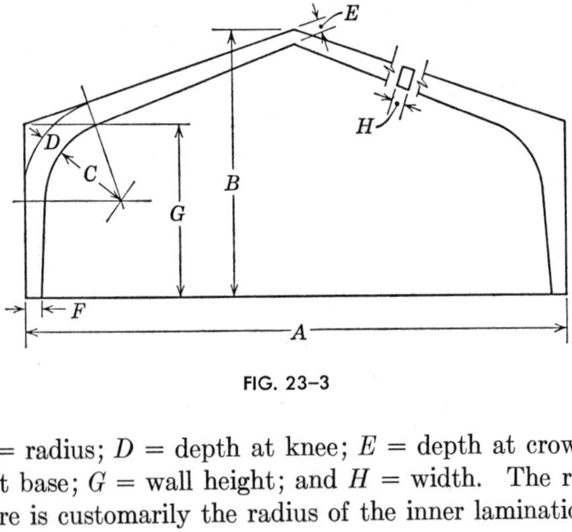

FIG. 23–3

rise; C = radius; D = depth at knee; E = depth at crown; F = depth at base; G = wall height; and H = width. The radius of curvature is customarily the radius of the inner laminations.

23–8. Design of a Laminated Beam. The following example illustrates the general procedure to be used in the design of a glued laminated beam. For given conditions more than one solution may be acceptable. In a tapered beam the depth varies throughout its length but the width is a constant. In the design of a straight beam the dimensions of the cross section are determined by the required section modulus at the point of maximum bending. Referring to Table 23–1, we find that a number of beam sizes are available. It is best to select a section having a depth-to-width ratio of about 4, accepting, of course, the section containing the smallest cross-sectional area.

Example. Design a symmetrically double-tapered glued laminated beam to support a live load of 30 psf for a span of 32 ft 0 in., the beams being spaced 8 ft 0 in. on centers. The shape of this beam is shown in Fig. 23–2 (*c*). The design will conform with the following unit stresses:

f = 2400 psi, the allowable extreme fiber stress
c = 2000 psi, the allowable compressive stress parallel to the grain
$c\perp$ = 385 psi, the allowable compressive stress perpendicular to the grain
H = 200 psi, the allowable horizontal shearing stress
E = 1,800,000 psi, the modulus of elasticity

SOLUTION. The first step is to compute the loads. We assume that roof planking extends from beam to beam; consequently the beam will support a uniformly distributed load.

Live load	= 30 psf
Planking	= 7 psf
5-ply roofing	= 6 psf
Total	= 43 psf on the roof surface

The beams are 8 ft 0 in. apart; therefore $8 \times 43 = 344$ lb, the load per linear foot of beam not including its own weight. Then, assuming the average weight of the beam to be 20 lb per lin ft, $344 + 20 = 364$ lb. This is w, the load per linear foot of beam. Since the beam has a span of 32 ft, $364 \times 32 = 11{,}650$ lb, W, the total uniformly distributed load on the beam. Each reaction = $\frac{1}{2} \times 11{,}650 = 5825$ lb. This is V, the magnitude of the maximum vertical shear. The beam loading is shown in Fig. 23–4.

The maximum bending moment is at the center of the span, as indicated in Fig. 5–17, Case II.

$$M = \frac{Wl}{8} \quad \text{or} \quad M = \frac{11{,}650 \times 32 \times 12}{8} = 560{,}000 \text{ in-lb}$$

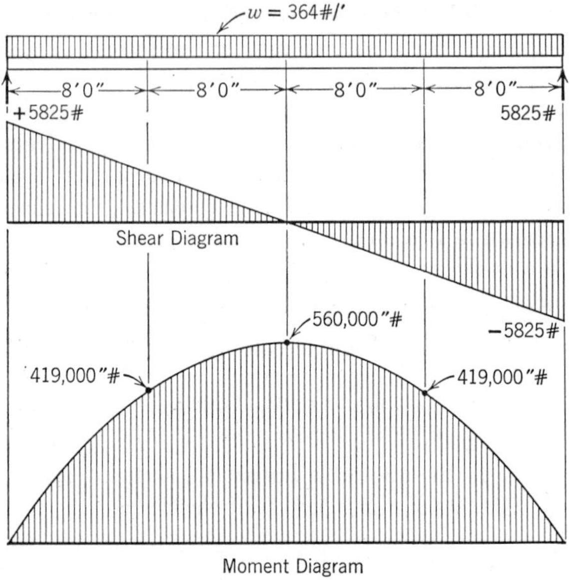

FIG. 23–4

the maximum bending moment. The shear and moment diagrams are constructed in the usual manner; they are shown in Fig. 23–4.

The flexure formula (Art. 9–3) is

$$S = \frac{M}{f} \quad \text{or} \quad S = \frac{560{,}000}{2400} = 233 \text{ in.}^3$$

the required section modulus at the center of the span.

Referring to Table 23–1, we select a beam built-up of eleven $1\frac{5}{8}$-in. laminations. The cross section, then, will be 5 in. in width and $17\frac{7}{8}$ in. deep *at the center* of the 32-ft span. This section has a section modulus of 266 in.^{3} and a cross-sectional area of 89.4 sq in.

We know that the bending moment curve for a distributed load on a simple beam is a parabola, as shown in Fig. 23–4. This beam is tapered, and any section in its length must have a section modulus equal to or greater than that required by the bending moment at that point.

Let us compute the bending moment at the quarter point of

span, $x = 8$. Then $M_{(x=8)} = [(5825 \times 8) - (364 \times 8 \times 4)] \times 12 = 419{,}000$ in-lb. $S = \dfrac{M}{f}$ or $S = \dfrac{419{,}000}{2400} = 175$ in.^{3}, the required section modulus at 8 ft from the support.

Because we have accepted a 5-in. width of beam, we shall now select a 5 x $14\frac{5}{8}$ in. section at 8 ft from the left end of the beam. This selection was made by referring to Table 23–1, in which we find S for this cross section to be 178 in.^{3} and only 175 in.^{3} is required.

Assuming the bottom of the beam to be level, the depth at the center of the span is $17\frac{7}{8}$ in. and at 8 ft to the left (or right) of the center the depth is $14\frac{5}{8}$ in. This determines the slope of the top of the beam and, by computations, the depth of the beam at the ends in $11\frac{3}{8}$ in. See Fig. 23–5.

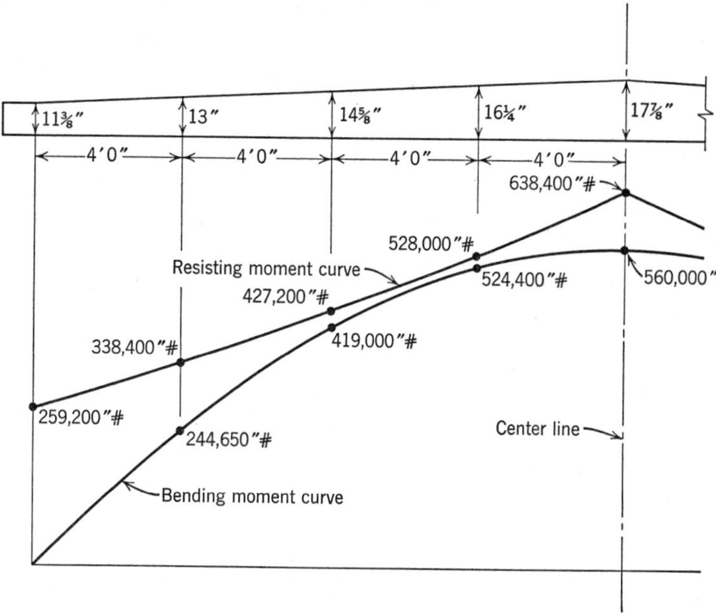

FIG. 23–5

Now let us investigate the horizontal shear at the ends of the beam. Here the area is 5 x $11\frac{3}{8}$ in. or 56.9 sq in. In accordance with Art. 6–2, $q = \frac{3}{2} \times \frac{V}{bh}$ or $q = \frac{3}{2} \times \frac{5825}{56.9}$ and $q = 154$ psi, the horizontal shearing unit stress. Since this stress is less than the allowable, 200 psi, the dimensions just computed are accepted. The beam is $17\frac{7}{8}$ in. deep at the center of the span and tapers uniformly, on each side, to an $11\frac{3}{8}$-in. depth at the ends. Its finished width is 5 in. By computations it is found that the bending moments at 4 and 8 ft from the left end of the beam are 244,650 in.-lb and 419,000 in.-lb, respectively. These moments are shown in the moment curve, a parabola, shown in Fig. 23–5.

In Art. 9–3 it was shown that at any section in the length of a beam the resisting moment must be equal to or greater than the bending moment, $M = f \times S$. Then, since the resisting moment is $f \times S$, we can compute its value at any section. For instance, the section modulus at the center of the span is 266 in.^{3}; consequently $266 \times 2400 = 638{,}400$ in.-lb, the resisting moment. At a section 8 ft from the left end of the beam $f \times S = 178 \times 2400$ or 427,200 in.-lb. Because the depth of the beam varies throughout its length, the resisting moment also varies in magnitude.

In Fig. 23–5 we show the bending moment curve, a parabola, and at the same scale we have plotted a curve for the resisting moment. The resisting moment must always be equal to or greater than the bending moment.

In laminated beams and arches the cross-sectional areas of the members may vary throughout their lengths. The basic principle in designing laminated members is to provide ample material throughout the length of the members so that at every section the resisting moment is at least equal to the bending moment. In addition to bending stresses, there must be sufficient material at the various sections to resist shear.

CHAPTER 24

PLYWOOD CONSTRUCTION

24–1. Plywood. The term *plywood* is used to designate glued wood panels made up of layers, or plies, with the grain of one or more layers at an angle (usually 90°) with the grain of adjacent plies. The outside layers are called *faces*, or *face* and *back*, and the inside layer or layers are called the *core*. The plies immediately below and at right angles to the face plies are called *crossbands*. The number of combinations of plies and core materials is almost unlimited. The plies in plywood normally used in building construction extend from $\frac{1}{24}$ to $\frac{7}{32}$ in. in thickness and the total thicknesses range from $\frac{1}{8}$ to $\frac{13}{16}$ in. The different plies vary in number, thickness, and species of wood. There is always an odd number of plies, three, five, or seven. The crossbands and their arrangement largely govern the warping characteristics.

Cross laminating of the plies adds strength to plywood in all directions. The greater the number of plies for a given thickness, the more nearly equal are the strength and shrinkage properties and the greater resistance to splitting.

24–2. Douglas Fir Plywood. In general, two classes of plywood are available, *hardwood* and *softwood plywood*. Plywoods used for furniture and flush-type doors are usually made from the hardwoods. Much of the softwood plywood is made of Douglas fir, but many other species are used as well. The *grade* is determined by the quality of the veneer and the *type* by the moisture resistance of the glue joints.

Two types of Douglas fir plywood are listed as interior and exterior. The interior type is expected to retain its form and nearly all its strength when occasionally subjected to a thorough wetting and subsequent normal drying. It is commonly bonded with soybean glue or an extended resin glue of the phenol type. The exterior type plywood is expected to retain its form and strength when repeatedly wet and dried and to be suitable for permanent exterior use. It is usually bonded with hot-press phenol resin glue.

There are several grades in each type, the grades being established by the veneer on the faces of the panel. In descending order of quality, the veneer is designated as *A*, *B*, *C*, or *D*. Grade *A–A* plywood, for example, has grade *A* veneer on both faces, grade *A–D* plywood has grade *A* veneer on one face and grade *D* on the other. In general, grade *C* is used for the inner plies of the exterior type and grade *D* for the inner plies of the interior type.

24–3. Strength of Plywood. Because of the numerous combinations of ply thickness, species, number of plies, and direction of grain in the plies, it is impractical to establish allowable working stresses by tests alone. Formulas relating to the strength of plywood have been developed mathematically and checked by tests to verify their validity. These formulas are available for the design of plywood structural members, but they are too involved to be appropriate in this text for the design of the usual structural elements in buildings. Two valuable references are *Technical Data on Plywood*, published by the Douglas Fir Plywood Association, and the Forest Products Laboratory Report 1630, *Approximate Methods of Calculating the Strength of Plywood.* Because of the many factors involved, structural problems relating to the strength of plywood are beyond the scope of this book.

24–4. Stressed-Skin Construction. Plywood is used extensively in building construction for subfloors, wall and roof sheathing, lining for concrete forms, paneling, cabinets, counters, etc. In recent years plywood has been used in the construction of structural panels that serve somewhat as slabs.

Stressed-skin construction is a development of the plywood industry. A stressed-skin panel consists of plywood sheets placed above and below relatively small wood blocks or joists, the sheets and the blocks being securely glued together as indicated in Fig. 24–1. When this assembly is used as a floor panel, it acts as a structural unit; the upper sheet resists compressive stresses and the bottom sheet resists the tensile stresses. When plywood is

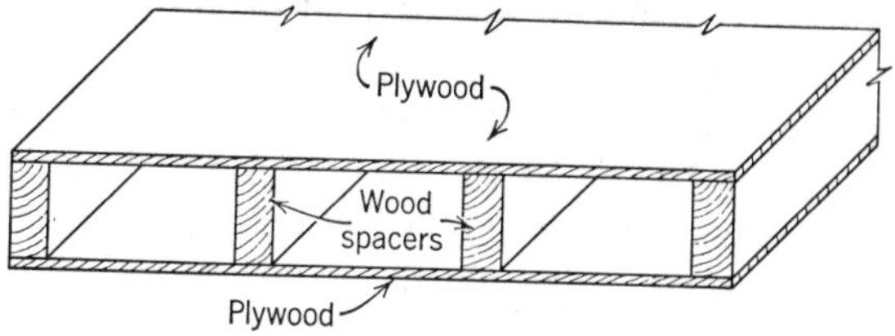

FIG. 24-1

used in this manner, the unit acts as a slab and the tensile and compressive stresses that result from bending are resisted by the plywood sheets. Such built-up members are economical with respect to material, but this saving may be offset by the cost of fabrication. These panels must be fabricated in a shop equipped for the purpose.

24-5. Built-Up Plywood Beams. Glued structural built-up beams in the form of a box beam, I-beam or double I-beam may be designed as shown in Fig. 24-2. In these beams the web mem-

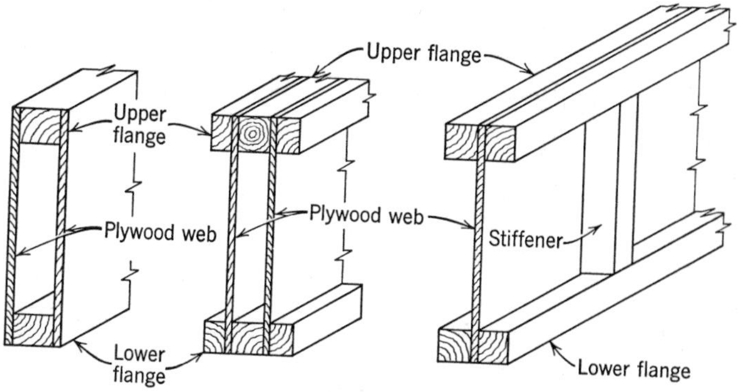

(a) Box Beam *(b)* Double I-Beam *(c)* I-Beam

FIG. 24-2

bers are of plywood; the flanges may be of solid pieces or laminated. These built-up beams afford the opportunity of placing selected material where the stresses are greatest. Although the cost of fabrication is an important item in constructing such beams, there s a considerable saving in material when compared with solid members designed for the same loads and spans.

As in the design of steel-plate girders, the flanges (upper and lower) are designed to resist the compression and tensile stresses that result from bending. The plywood webs are designed to resist the shearing stresses. The glued joints between the web and flanges must be designed with care because they transfer stresses between the web and the flanges. Figure 24–2 (*c*) shows stiffeners used to limit the length of unsupported web panels and to aid in distributing concentrated loads as well as the reactions at supports. The design procedure of these built-up beams is similar to that of steel-plate girders. A trial section is investigated to determine the actual stresses in the component parts of the beam, making adjustments that may be necessary.

24–6. Plywood Gussets. Another use of plywood in building construction is in gusset plates between studs and roof rafters and also in trusses constructed of lightweight material. See Fig. 24–3.

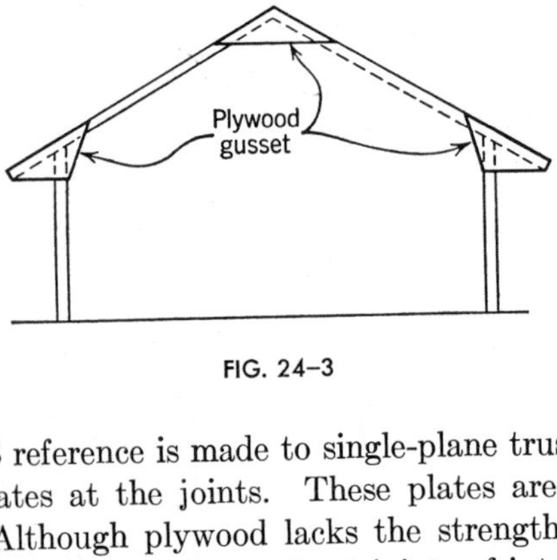

FIG. 24–3

In Chapter 18 reference is made to single-plane trusses employing Teco truss plates at the joints. These plates are of galvanized sheet steel. Although plywood lacks the strength, size for size, of the steel plates, plywood gussets at joints of intersecting members serve the same purpose and result in an economical construction.

INDEX

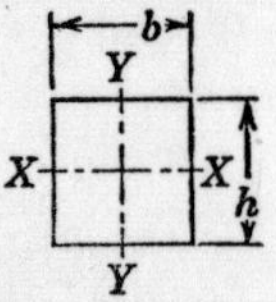

TABLE 3–3. PROPERTIES OF AMERICAN STANDARD SIZES OF YARD LUMBER AND TIMBERS *

Nominal Size, in Inches	American Standard Dressed Size (S4S), in Inches	Area of Section, in Inches²	Moment of Inertia, in Inches⁴		Section Modulus, in Inches³	
			$I_{X-X} = bh^3/12$	$I_{Y-Y} = b^3h/12$	$S_{X-X} = bh^2/6$	$S_{Y-Y} = b^2h/6$
b h	b h	$A = b \times h$				
2 x 4	1⅝ x 3⅝	5.89	6.45	1.30	3.56	1.60
2 x 6	1⅝ x 5⅝	9.14	24.10	2.01	8.57	2.48
2 x 8	1⅝ x 7½	12.19	57.13	2.68	15.23	3.30
2 x 10	1⅝ x 9½	15.44	116.10	3.40	24.44	4.18
2 x 12	1⅝ x 11½	18.69	205.95	4.11	35.82	5.06
2 x 14	1⅝ x 13½	21.94	333.18	4.83	49.36	5.94
2 x 16	1⅝ x 15½	25.19	504.27	5.54	65.07	6.82
2 x 18	1⅝ x 17½	28.44	725.75	6.25	82.94	7.70
3 x 4	2⅝ x 3⅝	9.52	10.42	5.46	5.75	4.16
3 x 6	2⅝ x 5⅝	14.77	38.93	8.48	13.84	6.46
3 x 8	2⅝ x 7½	19.69	92.29	11.30	24.61	8.61
3 x 10	2⅝ x 9½	24.94	187.55	14.32	39.48	10.91
3 x 12	2⅝ x 11½	30.19	332.69	17.33	57.86	13.21
3 x 14	2⅝ x 13½	35.44	538.21	20.35	79.73	15.50
3 x 16	2⅝ x 15½	40.69	814.60	23.36	105.11	17.80
3 x 18	2⅝ x 17½	45.94	1,172.36	26.38	133.98	20.10
4 x 4	3⅝ x 3⅝	13.14	14.39	14.39	7.94	7.94
4 x 6	3⅝ x 5⅝	20.39	53.76	22.33	19.12	12.32
4 x 8	3⅝ x 7½	27.19	127.44	29.77	33.98	16.43
4 x 10	3⅝ x 9½	34.44	259.00	37.71	54.53	20.81
4 x 12	3⅝ x 11½	41.69	459.43	45.65	79.90	25.19
4 x 14	3⅝ x 13½	48.94	743.24	53.59	110.11	29.57
4 x 16	3⅝ x 15½	56.19	1,124.92	61.53	145.15	33.95
4 x 18	3⅝ x 17½	63.44	1,618.98	69.47	185.03	38.33
6 x 6	5½ x 5½	30.25	76.26	76.26	27.73	27.73
6 x 8	5½ x 7½	41.25	193.36	103.98	51.56	37.81
6 x 10	5½ x 9½	52.25	392.96	131.71	82.73	47.90
6 x 12	5½ x 11½	63.25	697.07	159.44	121.23	57.98
6 x 14	5½ x 13½	74.25	1,127.67	187.17	167.06	68.06
6 x 16	5½ x 15½	85.25	1,706.78	214.90	220.23	78.15
6 x 18	5½ x 17½	96.25	2,456.38	242.63	280.73	88.23
8 x 8	7½ x 7½	56.25	263.67	263.67	70.31	70.31
8 x 10	7½ x 9½	71.25	535.86	333.98	112.81	89.06
8 x 12	7½ x 11½	86.25	950.55	404.30	165.31	107.81

*** Reproduced by permission of the Timber Engineering Company.**